SMALL ARMS

1914 – PRESENT

SMALL ARMS

1914 – PRESENT

THE WORLD'S GREATEST WEAPONS

MARTIN J. DOUGHERTY & MICHAEL E. HASKEW

METRO BOOKS

New York

METRO BOOKS
New York

An Imprint of Sterling Publishing
387 Park Avenue South
New York, NY 10016

Editorial and design by
Amber Books Ltd
74–77 White Lion Street
London N1 9PF
www.amberbooks.co.uk

The material in this book has previously appeared in the books
The Essential Weapons Identification Guide: Small Arms 1914–45 and
The Essential Weapons Identification Guide: Small Arms 1945–Present.

ISBN: 978-1-4351-4652-5

For information about custom editions, special sales, and premium and corporate purchases,
please contact Sterling Special Sales at 800-805-5489 or specialsales@sterlingpublishing.com.

Manufactured in China

2 4 6 8 10 9 7 5 3 1

www.sterlingpublishing.com

PICTURE CREDITS
Amber Books: 100
Art-Tech/Aerospace: 10, 12, 70, 87, 93, 109, 136
Art-Tech/MARS: 8, 28, 68, 81, 124, 177, 210, 230, 236, 237, 256, 257, 288, 296, 344
Cody Images: 6/7, 14, 16, 51, 62, 66, 88, 113, 120, 140, 162, 195, 206, 208, 209, 214, 220, 227, 234
Corbis: 251 (Sygma/Patrick Robert), 254 (Bettmann), 260 (Sygma/Patrick Chauvel), 342
(Reuters/Kimberly White), 363 (Reuters/Chico Sanchez), 369 (Military Picture Library/Eric Micheletti)
Nik Cornish/Stavka: 55
Mary Evans Picture Library: 48
Getty Images: 71, 76, 286 (Gamma), 289, 291, 312 (Gamma), 314 (Time & Life Pictures), 345
(Hulton/Alex Bowie), 346 (Hulton/Alex Bowie)
Krigsarkivet: 32, 46
Library of Congress: 9
Photos.com: 49
Ukrainian State Archive: 138, 139, 156, 158
U.S. Department of Defense: 11, 15, 41, 84, 86 102, 164, 167, 180, 186, 188/189, 190, 191, 192, 194, 203, 276, 304, 306, 307, 327, 332
United States Marine Corps: 329

All artworks courtesy of Art-Tech

Contents

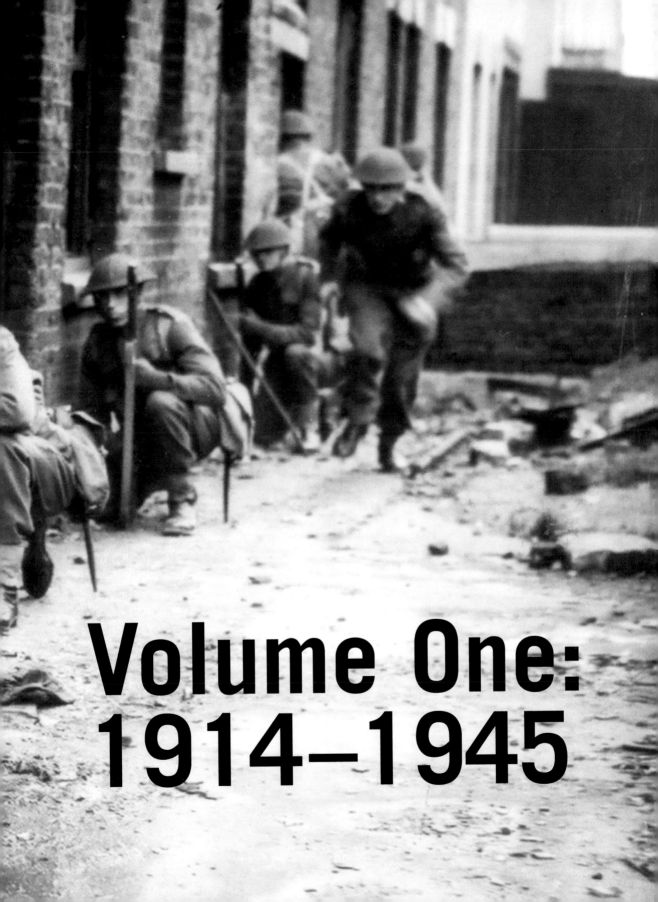

Volume One:
1914–1945

Introduction

The two world wars prosecuted during the first half of the twentieth century and the interwar years of the 1920s and 1930s were heavily influenced by advancing small-arms technology.

AS THE GREAT POWERS fought for preeminence in Europe and Asia and indeed around the globe from 1914 to 1918 and again from 1939 to 1945, the rifle or the submachine gun in the hands of the individual soldier often meant the difference between victory and defeat. The great plans of military strategists were regularly reduced to the outcome of single combat between soldiers loading and firing their weapons to the best of their ability.

From the turn of the century forward, modern military men were becoming increasingly aware of the advancing technology that confronted them on land and sea and in the air. Nowhere was the profound effect of man's ingenuity more dramatically proved than on the battlefield. The repeating rifle had given way to the improved bolt-action shoulder arms of Mauser, Lee-Enfield, Springfield and others, and in turn the semiautomatic rifle had emerged in the mid-1930s with the introduction of the M1 Garand. By 1944, US general George S. Patton Jr. (1885–1945) had commented that the Garand was the 'greatest battle implement ever devised'.

Without doubt, the generation of firearms designers that altered, improved and generally revised the rifles of the years prior to World War I were influenced by a legion of innovators and designers who had gone before them. The Mauser line can claim descendants around the world, for example, and many of the rifles that were fielded by armies of World War II trace their components to the Mauser Gewehr 98, the forerunner of the Karabiner 98k standard issue rifle of the *Wehrmacht* from the 1930s until the end of World War II. More than 14 million examples of the K98k were manufactured in the decade from 1935 to 1945.

Accuracy, endurance and firepower were the three pillars on which a successful rifle was built, and the crucible of war provided a proving ground for design innovation. The US M1 Garand, a semiautomatic weapon, was followed by Germany's Sturmgewehr 44, an awesome innovation that could truly be called the first assault rifle to see major

◀ **Prisoner round-up**

This rare colour photograph shows French infantry rounding up German prisoners. The sky blue tunic, conspicuous red trousers and black leather gaiters indicate that this was early in World War I, before the French Army adopted the more practical 'horizon blue' uniform in 1915.

deployment in the history of warfare. Thus between 1939 and 1945, the bolt-action rifle of a half-century earlier was fighting alongside the semiautomatic and fully automatic rifles that would dominate the battlefield into the twenty-first century. From the Sturmgewehr 44 rose the iconic Kalashnikov AK-47 assault rifle, the US-made M16 and other such weapons that shaped the future of warfare.

Machine-gun menace

Perhaps no other infantry-level weapon has illustrated the tragic failure of military tactics to keep pace with advancing technology more than the machine gun, which proliferated during World War I. Reaping a harvest of death like no other small arms in history, machine guns fired from entrenched positions killed infantrymen with reckless abandon during the war of attrition in the trenches. The British Vickers and German Maschinengewehr designs were both influenced heavily by the work of Hiram Maxim (1840–1916), an American-born inventor who

emigrated to Britain and revolutionized modern warfare with an automatic weapon that produced an incredibly high sustained rate of fire.

In the summer of 1916, British sergeant Charles Quinnell faced German machine guns on the Western Front and lived to tell of his horrifying ordeal. 'The first wave were down,' he remembered. 'Two machine guns played on them and they were completely wiped out. Everybody was either killed or wounded. We went through. We got halfway across [no-man's-land] and then the machine guns found us and they played on us like spraying with a hose. At the finish I was the only one standing.'

During the interwar years, the battlefield prowess of the machine gun was further refined as capacity and calibre were increased. The landmark German machine gun of the 1930s, the MG 34, was a precision-built weapon with a substantial rate of fire. It was a primary support weapon of World War II and respected by all who opposed it; however, the need for increased production and the scarcity of raw materials

▼ **Ottoman Maxim Gun**
Turkish infantry undergo training with tripod-mounted Maxim Maschinengewehr 08 heavy machine guns, supplied by their German allies.

▲ **Bayonet charge**
Bayonets fixed to Lee-Enfield No. 1 Mk III SMLE rifles, Commonwealth infantry advance across open ground during the Battle of El Alamein, October 1942.

began to take precedence over the precise tolerances and machining process that went into the manufacture of the individual weapon. With the MG 42, an outstanding machine gun in its own right, some of the fit and finish of the MG 34 was lost, although the lethal weapon was respected as the 'Buzzsaw' by Allied troops and its rate of fire was astonishing.

From the Vickers to the Bren, British machine guns were either reliable, updated versions of World War I-era weapons or the product of research and development undertaken during the 1930s. The Vickers Mk I and its successors served the British Army from 1912 through to the late 1960s, and the weapon gained a tremendous reputation for reliability and ruggedness in prolonged combat. The story of the famous Bren began in 1931 with the British military establishment in search of a light machine gun. A Czechoslovakian design was chosen and modified to British specifications, resulting in one of the best known automatic weapons of World War II.

In the United States, the influence of John Browning (1855–1926) was widespread. His Model 1911 11.4mm (.45in) pistol remains an icon of form and function to this day, while the Browning Automatic Rifle (BAR), primarily a 7.62mm (.3in) weapon, resonates with veterans from all theatres of World War II. The Model 1919 7.62mm (.3in) infantry machine gun and the M2 12.7mm (.5in) heavy machine gun have earned distinctive places in the history of modern firearms.

Soviet automatic weapons such as the PPSh-41 7.62mm (.3in) submachine gun were produced in huge quantities during World War II and gave rise to a reconsideration of infantry firepower. A squad of Red Army soldiers, each of them armed with an automatic weapon, was a formidable adversary indeed. When the *Wehrmacht* tide began to recede on the Eastern Front, it was the Red Army that showed the world the awesome potential of the submachine gun issued to large formations of foot soldiers.

Along with the rifle, machine gun and assault rifle, the anti-tank weapon developed during the interwar years and rapidly matured in World War II. As the anti-tank rifle was generally discarded in favour of rocket- or spring-propelled bombs or hollow-charge projectiles, the tank-killer team armed with the Bazooka, Panzerfaust or PIAT foreshadowed a generation of smart, fire-and-forget weapons designed to thwart the advantage of armour today.

Terrible technology

Although small-arms technology steadily advanced prior to World War I, its pace quickened substantially with the onset of global conflict, subsiding only slightly during the years between the wars due primarily to budget constraints from the high cost of the war of 1914–18. The coming of World War II brought innovation and even deadlier small arms to the battlefield as mass production churned out semiautomatic and automatic weapons at tremendous rates to augment the efficiency of the click-and-fire bolt-action rifles still in use.

Building on proven systems and working with innovations of their own, small-arms designers of the twentieth century further validated that the more some weapons change the more they do indeed remain the same. The refinement of one man's ability to dispatch another efficiently and economically is the continuing key to victory on the battlefield. But then, of course, the weapon itself is only as productive in its understood mission as the soldier who carries it.

▲ **Island battle**
A US Marine cradles his Browning Model 1919 7.62mm (.3in) machine gun, while he and his buddy take time out for a cigarette during mopping-up operations on Peleliu Island, September 1944.

Chapter 1

World War I: Western Front and Dardanelles

The global conflagration of World War I brought about destruction and loss of life on an unprecedented scale as the war of attrition in the trenches of the Western Front and the abortive Allied campaign in the Dardanelles demonstrated the devastating firepower of modern small arms. During the latter half of the nineteenth century, improvements in weapons technology, including the deadly accuracy of shoulder arms and the enhanced operational effectiveness of the machine gun, reaped a ghastly harvest of dead and wounded. Unfortunately, battlefield tactics often did not take into account the newly realized lethality of such weapons. Soldiers of both the Allied and Central Powers were sacrificed before the muzzles of modern weapons, the victims of outmoded tactics.

◀ **Dardanelles stalemate**
ANZAC infantrymen wait in their trenches during one of the many lulls in the fighting on the Gallipoli peninsula, 1915. All are armed with the Lee-Enfield SMLE bolt-action rifle.

Introduction

Rapid movement soon gave way to the stalemate of the trenches on the Western Front, as both sides experienced heavy losses before fortified positions.

NEITHER THE ALLIES nor the Central Powers had real reason to expect a costly, protracted war on the Western Front as World War I began. However, the continuing modernization of armies was to accelerate appreciably during the four long years of the Great War. Fuelled by the French obsession with regaining the provinces of Alsace and Lorraine lost in the humiliating defeat of the Franco-Prussian War of 1870–71, the German desire for eminence among the nations of Europe through achieving its 'place in the sun', a complex tangle of treaties and alliances, and the burgeoning arms race that had continued unabated for decades, world war broke out in August 1914, sparked by the assassination of Archduke Franz Ferdinand of Austria-Hungary at the end of June.

Terrifying technology

At war's outbreak, the armies of the belligerent nations were undergoing substantial reorganization while such innovations as the aeroplane, the submarine and the armoured fighting vehicle were evaluated as to their roles in modern warfare. Artillery had been divided into field and heavy categories, with the famed French 75mm (2.9in) M1897 setting the standard for mobile, sustained fire support. Heavy siege guns were the order of the day as well, with mammoth mortars and howitzers such as the improvised British Mark I, initially fashioned from rebored naval weapons, reaching calibres of 200–400mm (7.9-15.7in) and heavier. The Mark I fired a 91kg (200lb) shell a distance of 9600m (10,500 yards).

The role of the anachronistic cavalry was changing as well. Unlike during its glory days, cavalry was recognized as a reconnaissance, screening or pursuit arm with very limited capabilities to exploit a breakthrough in enemy lines, rather than as a weapon of lightning quick 'shock and awe'. Further, even the scouting role of the cavalry was coming into question as visionary military thinkers such as British

▲ **Moving up**
French infantry rest on their way to the front in the Verdun sector, 1916. The French Army sustained over 300,000 casualties at Verdun – roughly the same number as the German forces.

▲ **Bayonet charge**
Australian infantry charge across no-man's-land towards Turkish trenches, Gallipoli, Dardanelles 1915. In this case, the Turkish positions had been evacuated and the trench was uncontested.

Major-General J.F.C. Fuller (1878–1966) and Sir Basil Liddell Hart (1895–1970) pondered the role of the tank and armoured vehicle in modern warfare and the aeroplane assumed a more prominent role in reconnaissance and, later, in aerial combat.

Despite the pronounced evolution of weapons and, though lagging behind substantially, the development of tactical doctrine to employ them effectively, the infantry remained the backbone of the armies of 1914. Although its size varied from nation to nation, the combat infantry division might well reach a strength of more than 16,000 riflemen. The primary shoulder arm of the infantryman was the bolt-action, magazine-fed rifle. Depending upon the design of his weapon and the degree of training he had undergone, the skilled rifleman could deliver a devastating rate of fire upon the advancing enemy. Improved ammunition was employed as well, particularly the aerodynamic jacketed bullet. The ubiquitous bayonet remained a standard issue item among infantrymen.

In terms of small arms, the most devastating innovation of the late nineteenth century was the machine gun. French use of the Reffye *mitrailleuse* during the Franco-Prussian War had proved disappointing; however, recent improvements, particularly those of American-born inventor Hiram Maxim (1840–1916), were to prove deadly. Along with the substantial killing capacity of the artillery, the proliferation of the machine gun on the Western Front was responsible for soaring casualty rates in World War I. Beyond the obvious consequences of these modern weapons, the experience of combat often took on a more impersonal nature.

While the rifle had been intended as the principal infantry weapon in the twentieth century and its role was not appreciably diminished, the machine gun added a new and horrifying dimension to the battlefield. Troops going over the top and into no-man's-land often instinctively turned their shoulders to the enemy as if walking into a strong wind. In reality, there was little defence against a hail of bullets.

Belgian Army
1914–15

Severely outnumbered and under-equipped, the Belgian Army of King Albert I (1875–1934) disrupted the German timetable and held its ground at Liège and Namur.

WHEN THE GERMAN ARMY crossed into Belgium on its trek to attack its arch-enemy, France, it did so with little regard for the tiny nation's field army of fewer than 120,000 soldiers. The Belgians had already initiated a reorganization plan which was intended to be completed over the course of several years; however, this effort was barely a year old when war came.

Only 102 machine guns were available to equip the six field army divisions, each of which consisted of up to four mixed brigades, including single regiments of infantry, cavalry and artillery, an engineer battalion, transport unit and telegraph section. The relatively few machine guns available were primarily variants of the Maxim Gun, and these were often mounted on sleds that were hauled by teams of dogs.

To their own detriment, the Germans underestimated the Belgian will to fight and had completely discounted the stubborn fortress defences of Liège and Namur. At both locations, Belgian forces disrupted German progress and delayed the advance against the French Army and the British Expeditionary Force for up to two weeks. Near the Channel coast, the Belgians refused to yield a defensive salient along the Yser River and held out during four years of trench fighting.

The Belgian soldier was typically equipped with a variant of the German Mauser rifle designated the Fusil FN-Mauser Mle 1889. This weapon had been

▲ **In retreat**
Belgian infantry retreat along a road, 1914. The Belgian Army used dogs to tow machine guns and light guns. Many European armies used dogs to pull small carts carrying ammunition, supplies and provisions.

manufactured by the Fabrique Nationale d'Armes de Guerre, a company formed in 1889 to produce the rifle for the Belgian government. The first rifles produced by Mauser had been the 1871 series, and the development of the Model 1889 was begun in the early 1880s. It was introduced with a five-round vertical magazine, heavier wooden stock and a barrel shroud.

Although it had initially been hoped that the rifle would be sold to the German government, Mauser was not completely successful in competing with another excellent design produced by Mannlicher. Nevertheless, the Belgian attaché had seen the rifle in action during the Bavarian Arms Trials of 1884, and subsequently the Fabrique Nationale was formed to produce the Model 1889 in Belgium. When FN's production capacity at Herstal, near Liège, was deemed inadequate, a contract was concluded with a British firm to manufacture the Model 1889

and combined production figures reached approximately 250,000.

An officer variant of the Chamelot Delvigne Mle 1873 revolver, the Mle 1874, was widely used by both the Belgian and French Armies in the early years of World War I, and more than 35,000 were manufactured. Although it was eventually replaced by the Mle 1892, it remained in service for more than half a century and was issued to Belgian officers and soldiers as late as 1940. The Mle 1874 differed from the standard issue 1873 in having a darker finish and lighter weight. Both revolvers fired a light 10.4mm (.41in) round, which at times provided insufficient knockdown power at even close range. Among other sidearms issued to Belgian troops in 1914 were a variant of the Browning Model 1899 pistol designated the Model 1900 and the Colt Model 1903 pistol. These fired an interchangeable 8.1mm (.32in) Colt round.

◀ Chamelot Delvigne Mle 1874
Belgian Army / 11 Régiment de Ligne, 1914

Firing an understrength 10.4mm (.41in) bullet, the Chamelot Delvigne revolver was nevertheless considered a heavy and solidly built sidearm. The Modèle 1874 was the officer variant and essentially the same weapon as the Modèle 1873.

Specifications

Country of Origin: Belgium	Overall Length: 284mm (11.18in)
Date: 1874	Barrel Length: 159mm (6.25in)
Calibre: 10.4mm (.41in)	Muzzle Velocity: 190m/sec (625ft/sec)
Operation: Revolver	Feed/Magazine: 6-round cylinder
Weight: 1.13kg (2.5lb)	Range: 6m (20ft)

▲ Fusil FN-Mauser Mle 1889
Belgian Army / 31 Régiment de Ligne, 1914

Manufactured under licence from the German Mauser firm, the Modèle 1889 incorporated a robust wooden stock and a barrel shroud. It was produced both in Belgium and Great Britain.

Specifications

Country of Origin: Belgium	Overall Length: 1295mm (51in)
Date: 1889	Barrel Length: 780mm (30.6in)
Calibre: 7.65mm (.301in)	Muzzle Velocity: 610m/sec (2000ft/sec)
Operation: Bolt action	Feed/Magazine: 5-round box magazine
Weight: 4.1kg (8.8lb)	Range: 1000m (3280ft)

French Army
1914–15

Although it had suffered a tremendous blow to its prestige during the Franco-Prussian War, the French Army was still regarded as the most formidable land force in Western Europe.

IN THE SUMMER OF 1914, the French Army stood 750,000 strong and could be mobilized with reserves up to a strength of more than 1.1 million men. In theory, the French high command stressed a doctrine of the offensive, maintaining the initiative in combat wherever and whenever possible; however, in practice such tactics proved costly in the face of improved weaponry fielded by the German Army. A typical French division consisted of two brigades formed of 12 battalions and populated by approximately 12,000 riflemen.

The standard issue French rifle of 1914–15 was the 8mm (.314in) Lebel design of 1886 which had been subsequently modified a decade later. The Lebel entered service in the spring of 1887 and quickly became noticeable for a shortcoming with its magazine. Although the magazine held a generous eight rounds, the reloading process was time consuming and accomplished by feeding the bullets end to end through a tube bored into the forward end of the weapon. The rifle faced the criticism that it became increasingly inaccurate as the magazine was emptied, due to a changing centre of gravity.

Although it was the first rifle to use smokeless powder, the Model 1886 was functionally obsolescent by 1915 and was replaced by the lighter

Models 1902 and 1907 Lebel Berthier rifles, which were never produced in large numbers but offered a three-round clip and wider sights. However, the Model 1886 rifle remained the primary infantry shoulder arm for French forces throughout World War I. Following the introduction of the Berthier models, the Lebel remained in service not only as a primary weapon but also as a sniper rifle when equipped with high-powered sights. From 1887 to 1920, a total of 2,880,000 examples of the Model 1886 and variants were produced, and it was issued to French troops as late as 1940. A relative few examples were known to have been used by the Germans. Although it was considered a highly serviceable weapon, the Lebel Berthier rifle was deemed less than adequate by some simply because of its paltry three-round clip. During heated combat, such a short supply of ammunition and the necessity to reload often proved problematic. By the summer of 1918, the Fusil Mle 1907/15-M16 with a five-round clip had reached the front in limited numbers.

Colonial carbine

The 1907 Berthier carbine was originally introduced as a replacement for the ageing Mle 1874 Gras single-shot carbine but also proved superior to the Model

▲ **Lebel Berthier Mle 1907/15 carbine**

French Army / 43rd Territorial Infantry Regiment, 1914

Although it proved unpopular with some troops and equipped primarily the colonial troops of the French Army, the Berthier 1907/15 carbine provided some improvement over the slow-loading Lebel rifle.

Specifications	
Country of Origin: France	Overall Length: 945mm (37.2in)
Date: 1907	Barrel Length: 455mm (17.9in)
Calibre: 8mm (.314in)	Muzzle Velocity: 725m/sec (2379ft/sec)
Operation: Bolt action	Feed/Magazine: 5-round box magazine
Weight: 3.2kg (7.056lb)	(from 1915)
	Range: 500m (1640ft)

1886 in that it incorporated a single-piece stock and a three- or five-round clip rather than the cumbersome tubular magazine. By 1916, a shortage of Model 1886 rifles had resulted in the issue of the Mle 1907/15 Berthier rifle to French regular army troops, while colonial soldiers and those of the Foreign Legion had been issued the weapon somewhat earlier. During World War I, nearly 440,000 examples of the Fusil Mle 1907/15 were produced. This weapon employed a three-round clip.

Used as late as the 1960s by French police officers, the Lebel Mle 1892 revolver was the standard sidearm of French Army officers during World War I. Firing an 8mm (.314in) cartridge from a six-chambered cylinder, the Modèle 1892 was a popular weapon but lacked power in comparison with other revolvers of the day. It was manufactured by the state-owned and state-operated Manufacture d'armes de Saint-Etienne from 1892 to 1924, and more than 350,000 examples were produced.

Another well-known French sidearm of World War I was the Pistolet Automatique de 7 millim.65 genre, popularly known as the Ruby pistol and similar in construction to the Browning M1903. Noted for its ease of operation, even among those with little experience of handling firearms, the Ruby pistol was manufactured in Spain and Belgium and fired a 7.65mm (.301in) bullet from a detachable nine-round magazine. More than 750,000 were produced in over 50 variants.

▲ **Lebel Mle 1892**

French Army / 50th Line Infantry Regiment, 1914

The standard issue French sidearm of World War I, the Modèle 1892 revolver was produced by the state-run Manufacture d'armes de Saint-Etienne and remained a popular weapon among the military and civilian law enforcement agencies for decades.

Specifications

Country of Origin: France	Overall Length: 240mm (9.44in)
Date: 1892	Barrel Length: 117mm (4.60in)
Calibre: 8mm (.314in)	Muzzle Velocity: 213m/sec (698ft/sec)
Operation: Revolver	Feed/Magazine: 6-round cylinder
Weight: .94kg (2.1lb)	Range: 20m (66ft)

FRENCH INFANTRY COMPANY, 1914		
Unit	**Officers**	**Men**
Company HQ	5	15
1st Section	2	
1st Half-section	1	
1st Squad (riflemen)	1	14
2nd Squad (riflemen)	1	13
2nd Half-section	1	
3rd Squad (riflemen)	1	14
4th Squad (riflemen)	1	13
2nd Section	2	
1st Half-section	1	
1st Squad (riflemen)	1	14
2nd Squad (riflemen)	1	13
2nd Half-section	1	
3rd Squad (riflemen)	1	14
4th Squad (riflemen)	1	13
3rd Section	2	
1st Half-section	1	
1st Squad (riflemen)	1	14
2nd Squad (riflemen)	1	13
2nd Half-section	1	
3rd Squad (riflemen)	1	14
4th Squad (riflemen)	1	13
4th Section	2	
1st Half-section	1	
1st Squad (riflemen)	1	14
2nd Squad (riflemen)	1	13
2nd Half-section	1	
3rd Squad (riflemen)	1	14
4th Squad (riflemen)	1	13
Total Strength	37	231

2nd Ypres: British II and V Corps
APRIL–MAY 1915

Canadian troops gained a measure of national identity as a machine-gun crew stemmed the enemy tide, while German forces deployed poison gas on a grand scale.

IN THE SPRING OF 1915, the Allied defensive positions in the northern sector of the Western Front included a definitive bulge or salient around the Belgian town of Ypres. A tenacious enclave of Belgian troops clung to the line north of the salient, while French and colonial Algerian soldiers along with the men of the British II and V Corps defended the perimeter of the salient to the north and east. As German forces attempted to reduce the salient, which threatened their positions on its flanks, four separate engagements erupted in April and May. By the time the fighting ended, the Allied lines had held, but the size of the salient had been reduced.

During the opening phase of what came to be collectively known as the Second Battle of Ypres, the Germans released chlorine gas from thousands of cylinders into the positions manned by French and colonial troops. Within minutes, the defenders were withdrawing in disarray as thousands were killed or incapacitated by the gas. As the Germans advanced, troops of the Canadian 1st Division counterattacked to stabilize the situation, culminating their assault in the area of Kitchener's Wood with a bayonet charge.

Meanwhile, near the village of St. Julien, Lance-Corporal Frederick Fisher of the Canadian 13th Battalion machine-gun detachment led a small group of soldiers in an attempt to prevent the Germans from outflanking the Canadian line. Manning a Colt machine gun, Fisher demonstrated the battlefield capabilities of the weapon, thwarting the German advance and preventing the collapse of the Canadian forward positions. For his heroism, Lance-Corporal Fisher was awarded the Victoria Cross. Unfortunately, he was killed the following day during a similar defensive action.

The 7.7mm (.303in) Colt machine gun fired by Fisher was among the first successful gas-operated machine guns to see action. Designated the Colt-Browning M1895 and nicknamed the Potato Digger because of its mechanics, the weapon was patented in 1892. Canadian troops took it into battle in 1914; however, it was replaced by the Vickers machine gun in a relatively short period of time.

Nevertheless, the Colt-Browning M1895 proved remarkably adept on the battlefield, with a cyclic rate of fire of 450 rounds per minute. Although this was slightly lower than other guns of the period, its air-cooled feature kept the barrel in action for a longer period of time without overheating. Further, it was of simpler design than its water-cooled contemporaries, much lighter in weight and therefore more portable. The weapon itself weighed about 16kg (35.25lb), while its tripod and gunner's seat added another 25.4kg (56lb).

◀ **Webley Bulldog**
British Expeditionary Force / 2nd Battalion East Yorkshire Regiment, 1915
The Webley Bulldog was shorter and lighter than other Webley revolvers of the period. Although it was cheap to produce, it proved a robust weapon.

Specifications

Country of Origin: United Kingdom	Overall Length: 140mm (5.5in)
Date: 1878	Barrel Length: 53mm (2.1in)
Calibre: 8.1mm (.32in)	Muzzle Velocity: 190m/sec (625ft/sec)
Operation: Revolver	Feed/Magazine: 5-round cylinder
Weight: .31kg (.7lb)	Range: 15m (49ft)

Specifications

Country of Origin: United Kingdom

Date: 1912

Calibre: 7.7mm (.303in)

Operation: Recoil, water cooled

Weight: 18kg (40lb)

Overall Length: 1155mm (40.5in)

Barrel Length: 725mm (28.5in)

Muzzle Velocity: 600m/sec (1970ft/sec)

Feed/Magazine: Belt fed

Cyclic Rate: 600rpm

Range: 2000m (6560ft) + ; later 3000m (9842ft)

Vickers volume

The most famous British machine gun of World War I, the Vickers Mk I was based upon the design popularized by American-born inventor Hiram Maxim, who lived in Great Britain for many years. Maxim was credited with producing the earliest self-powered machine gun during the mid-1880s. The Maxim Gun was first demonstrated in the autumn of 1884 and later was deployed with British troops in Central Africa. A larger model saw action during the Boer War at the turn of the twentieth century. The British Army officially adopted the Vickers machine gun in the autumn of 1912, and updated variants of the weapon remained in service with the British armed forces until the late 1960s.

The Vickers Mk I differed from the Maxim Gun in that it was considerably lighter due to an inverted

▲ **Vickers Mk I**

British Expeditionary Force / 2nd Battalion Seaforth Highlanders, 1915

An improvement of the Maxim Gun, the Vicker Mk I machine gun entered service with the British Army in 1912 and was later designated a heavy weapon following the introduction of the light Lewis Gun. Its durability and versatility extended its service life into the 1960s.

BATTALION MACHINE-GUN SECTION (VICKERS HMG), 1915	
Unit	Strength
Lieutenant	1
Sergeant	1
Corporal	1
Driver	2
Batman	1
Privates	24

▼ British Battalion Machine-Gun Section, 1915

The British battalion machine-gun section was capable of producing a combined cyclic rate of fire of 2400 rounds per minute with each of its four Vickers heavy machine guns. Originally, the machine-gun section contained only two guns, but this was increased in February 1915. Such formations were transferred to the Machine Gun Corps in October of that year in an effort to improve the efficiency of machine guns deployed on the Western Front.

Section (4 x Vickers HMG)

toggle lock that moved upwards rather than downwards and allowed the receiver to be considerably smaller. Additionally, the Vickers machine gun was noted for its durability. The gun had a cyclic rate of fire of about 450 rounds per minute and the water-cooled barrel was routinely changed every 10,000 rounds. However, it has been recorded that during periods of intense combat the Vickers gun fired as many as 100,000 rounds before the barrel was changed. In one remarkable engagement, the 100th Company of the British Machine Gun Corps was reported to have fired its 10 Vickers guns for 12 hours continuously, each gun changing barrels 10 times. A total of one million rounds of 7.7mm (.303in) ammunition were fired without any of the guns failing.

Following the introduction of the light Lewis Gun, the Vickers was redesignated as a heavy machine gun.

Numerous variants were introduced in succeeding decades, and during World War I the weapon was also used aboard aircraft.

Other weapons in action at Second Ypres included the Webley Bulldog and Fosbury revolvers. These sidearms were from a family of break-top or self-extracting handguns that were produced from 1887 to 1963. The best known of the Webley revolvers is probably the Mark VI, introduced in 1915 and in service during World War I. The smaller Bulldog fired an 8.1mm (.32in) bullet and was effective to about 15m (49ft), while the Fosbury is easily recognized due to the distinctive zig-zag pattern on the cylinder. It fired an 11.55mm (.455in) round.

▶ Webley Fosbury

British Expeditionary Force / 3rd Battalion King's Royal Rifle Corps, 1915
The operation of the Webley Fosbury revolver utilized recoil energy rather than a standard mechanism and was responsible for the term 'automatic revolver'. Production of the weapon was discontinued in 1915 after repeated breakdowns.

Specifications

Country of Origin: United Kingdom	Overall Length: 292mm (11.5in)
Date: 1915	Barrel Length: 190mm (7.5in)
Calibre: 11.55mm (.455in)	Muzzle Velocity: 198m/sec (650ft/sec)
Operation: Automatic revolver	Feed/Magazine: 6-round cylinder
Weight: 1.08kg (2.4lb)	Range: 20m (66ft)

▲ Pattern 1914 Enfield

British Expeditionary Force / 5th Battalion Durham Light Infantry, 1915
Although it was originally configured to fire a high-powered round, the Pattern 1914 Enfield was eventually adapted to the 7.7mm (.303in) ammunition generally in use. It never reached the front in great numbers.

Specifications

Country of Origin: United Kingdom/United States	Overall Length: 1175mm (46.2in)
Date: 1914	Barrel Length: 660mm (26in)
Calibre: 7.7mm (.303in)	Muzzle Velocity: 762m/sec (2500ft/sec)
Operation: Bolt action	Feed/Magazine: 5-round box magazine
Weight: 4.35kg (9.6lb)	Range: 500m (1640ft)

▶ **Webley & Scott Mk IV**

British Expeditionary Force / 5th (Royal Irish) Lancers Regiment, 1915

The Webley & Scott Mk IV was introduced in 1899 and soon became known as the Boer War Model. Like other Webley & Scott designs, it was a break-top revolver. At the outbreak of World War I, it was in the possession of many British officers.

Specifications

Country of Origin: United Kingdom	Overall Length: 279mm (11in)
Date: 1899	Barrel Length: 152mm (6in)
Calibre: 11.55mm (.455in)	Muzzle Velocity: 198m/sec (650ft/sec)
Operation: Revolver	Feed/Magazine: 6-round cylinder
Weight: 1.5kg (3.3lb)	Range: 20m (66ft)

2nd Ypres: German Fourth Army
APRIL–MAY 1915

Carrying out the assault against the Ypres salient, the German Fourth Army had been in the vanguard of the early 1914 advance, defeating Belgian and French troops in the attempt to capture Paris. Eventually, it settled into the trenches of Flanders.

ON THE AFTERNOON OF 22 APRIL 1915, German forces launched a massive poison gas attack against French positions in the Ypres salient. The troops who followed this curtain of lethal vapour into action were veterans of the Fourth Army, which had rushed towards Paris the previous year and raced the Allies to the Channel coast.

These soldiers were armed with one of the iconic shoulder arms in military history, the Mauser Gewehr 98 rifle. Designed by the Mauser brothers and manufactured by the arsenals of Imperial Germany and numerous private contractors, the weapon replaced the Gewehr 1888 and was the standard German shoulder arm of World War I. During a 20-year period from 1898 to 1918, an estimated five million were produced. The weapon was withdrawn in 1935 in favor of the Karabiner 98k but reintroduced with home defence forces during the later years of World War II.

At the Belgian village of Bleid in August 1914, with the 6th Württemberg Infantry Regiment, young Lieutenant Erwin Rommel, who would rise to the rank of field marshal and earn the nickname of the Desert Fox during World War II, carried a Mauser

into combat. 'I quickly informed my men of my intention to open fire. We quietly released the safety catches; jumped out from behind the building; and standing erect, opened fire on the enemy nearby. Some were killed or wounded on the spot; but the majority took cover behind steps, garden walls, and woodpiles and returned our fire. Thus, at very close range, a very hot fire fight developed. I stood taking aim alongside a pile of wood. My adversary was twenty yards ahead of me, well covered, behind the steps of a house. Only part of his head was showing. We both aimed and fired almost at the same time and missed. His shot just missed my ear. I had to load fast, aim calmly and quickly, and hold my aim. That was not easy at twenty yards with the sights set for 400 meters, especially since we had not practised this type of fighting in peacetime. My rifle cracked; the enemy's head fell forward on the step.'

The might of Mauser

The Mauser Gewehr 98 fired a 7.92mm (.312in) cartridge from a five-round internal box magazine that was fed by a brass stripper clip. Loading was accomplished with relative ease as the stock was cut

◀ Mannlicher M1903
Imperial German Army / Landwehr Regiment 77, 1915

The Mannlicher M1901/M1903 utilized a spring and cam system to manage the action of the slide during rearward traverse, thus operating on a delayed blowback principle. Originally chambered for 8mm (.314in) ammunition, it was later modified to 7.65mm (.3in). The M1903 used a six-round magazine, while the M1901 magazine held eight rounds.

Specifications

Country of Origin: Austria	Overall Length: 239mm (9.4in)
Date: 1903	Barrel Length: 165mm (6.5in)
Calibre: 7.65mm (.3in)	Muzzle Velocity: 312m/sec (1025ft/sec)
Operation: Blowback	Feed/Magazine: 6-round magazine
Weight: .94kg (2.1lb)	Range: 30m (98ft)

▶ Bergmann 1896
Imperial German Army / Reserve Infantry Regiment 242, 1915

The Bergmann 1896 corrected a dangerous element in the operation of its predecessor. Rather than impacting the next unfired round while extracting the spent case, the new closed design ejected it safely. This design was active for a number of years.

Specifications

Country of Origin: Germany	Overall Length: 254mm (10in)
Date: 1896	Barrel Length: 102mm (4in)
Calibre: 7.63mm (.3in)	Muzzle Velocity: 380m/sec (1250ft/sec)
Operation: Blowback	Feed/Magazine: 5-round magazine
Weight: 1.13kg (2.5lb)	Range: 30m (98ft)

▶ Parabellum M1908
Imperial German Army / Infantry Regiment 132, 1915

Commonly known as the Luger, the Parabellum M1908 utilized a toggle-locking system rather than a slide as in most semiautomatic pistols. More than two million were made during the world wars.

Specifications

Country of Origin: Germany	Barrel Length: 127mm (5in)
Date: 1908	Muzzle Velocity: 351m/sec (1150ft/sec)
Calibre: 9mm (.35in)	Feed/Magazine: 8-round detachable box
Operation: Toggle locked, short recoil	magazine
Weight: .96kg (2.125lb)	Range: 30m (98ft)
Overall Length: 222mm (8.8in)	

down on the right side to allow the rifleman to insert the cartridge more rapidly and safely than with the downward motion of the thumb which was required with the British Lee-Enfield. The bolt-action weapon served well although it was prone to jamming if exposed to excessive amounts of debris or dust.

The action of the heavy bolt required a steady hand in combat, as the soldier often was tasked with realigning his vision through the sights after operating the mechanism. The Mauser Gewehr 98 was ideally suited for mobile warfare as conducted in the early months of the Great War; however, when relegated to the trenches it was a somewhat ponderous weapon with an unloaded weight of four kilograms (nine pounds) and a length of 1250mm (49.2in). Its five-round magazine held fewer cartridges than the British Lee-Enfield; however, a skilled and well-trained user could manage a rate of fire up to 12 rounds per minute.

Sniper variant

In the spring of 1915, the order was given to equip more than 15,000 of the Mauser Gewehr 98 with telescopic sights to employ them as highly accurate sniper rifles. By the end of the war, adaptations had been completed for the sights and more than 18,000 of the sniper variants had actually been issued. Prior to World War I, a shortened version, the Karabiner 98a, was produced as a cavalry weapon. However, this experiment was disappointing and production discontinued. The Belgian Army fielded a modified version of the Mauser Gewehr 98, while the armies of Serbia and Turkey were equipped with it as well.

One of the most popular weapons to emerge from World War I was the Pistole Parabellum M1908, commonly known as the Luger in reference to its designer, Georg J. Luger, who patented the weapon in 1898. Perhaps due to its distinctive profile, the Luger has been highly sought after by collectors for decades, while its reputation is one of reliability, accuracy and ease of operation. It was commonly carried by officers of the German Army during World War I, including those of the Fourth Army during the four separate engagements that constituted the Second Battle of Ypres. Not until the late 1930s was the weapon scheduled for replacement with the Walther P38. Even then, though, its popularity did not wane.

The Pistole Parabellum M1908 utilizes a toggle-locking system rather than the slide that is more often found on semiautomatic pistols, while locating its magazine in the handgrip made the weapon shorter overall and more compact than placing it in front of the trigger. The chamber was spring fed, and as the weapon was fired the backward action advanced the next round upwards through the detachable eight-round box magazine. Reloading was accomplished with relative ease.

Production of the Luger was begun in 1900 by Imperial German arsenals and various private manufacturers, particularly the Deutsche Waffen und Munitionsfabriken, and continued until 1945 with wartime production exceeding two million. The pistol was originally designed to fire the 7.65mm (.301in) Parabellum round but later was reconfigured and came to be recognized as the pistol that popularized the 9mm (.35in) Parabellum cartridge.

Specifications		▲ **Mauser Gewehr 98**

Specifications

Country of Origin: Germany	Overall Length: 1250mm (49.2in)
Date: 1898	Barrel Length: 740mm (29.1in)
Calibre: 7.92mm (.312in)	Muzzle Velocity: 640m/sec (2100ft/sec)
Operation: Bolt action	Feed/Magazine: 5-round box magazine
Weight: 4.2kg (9.25lb)	Range: 500m (1640ft)

▲ **Mauser Gewehr 98**

Imperial German Army / Infantry Regiment 136, 1915

Although it is respected as one of the finest infantry shoulder arms ever made, the Mauser Gewehr 98 was not well suited for trench warfare. An estimated five million were manufactured, and the weapon is prized by sporting riflemen today.

French Army at Verdun
1916–17

Remembered as one of the costliest battles in human history, the 10-month struggle at Verdun resulted in the deaths of more than 300,000 soldiers with a half million wounded.

CONTROVERSY SURROUNDS the actual motive of the German high command for its offensive against the fortified city of Verdun in northeastern France. While some historians assert that the motivation was to reduce a troublesome French salient in the stalemated trenchlines, achieve a decisive breakthrough and then march on Paris, others contend that the intention was purely to bleed the French Army white.

Actually, it was German chief of staff Erich von Falkenhayn (1861–1922) who asserted that a decisive breakthrough was not achievable after both the Allies and the Central Powers had repeatedly failed to accomplish one. Therefore, in his personal memoirs he related that the purpose of the bloodbath at Verdun was to inflict such high casualties on the French that they would be compelled to ask for surrender terms. In the end, both French and German losses at Verdun were catastrophic during the protracted ordeal that lasted from February 1916 through to the end of the year.

While artillery played a major role in delivering death and destruction at Verdun, small arms were responsible for a good deal of the carnage as well. Hand-to-hand combat occurred on numerous occasions, and pistols, knives and bayonets were regularly employed. While serving as an infantry officer at Verdun, Charles de Gaulle, future leader of the Free French in World War II and architect of the nation's Fifth Republic, was seriously wounded by shrapnel from a hand grenade and a bayonet thrust to the hip and taken prisoner.

When the fighting at Verdun had finally ebbed, the longest battle of the Great War was assessed as a tactical victory for the French, who prevented a German breakthrough but suffered horrendous casualties. From a strategic perspective, the battle must be considered a draw, emphasizing the terrible waste and apparent futility of war.

By 1915, the shortcomings of the Lebel rifle were well known to the French high command, and the decision was made to replace it with the Fusil Berthier Mle 1907/15; however, the Lebel was never completely phased out of service and the Berthier was limited in heavy combat due to its woefully inadequate three-round magazine. The following year, a modified Berthier, the Fusil Mle 1907/15-M16 (Mle 1916), with a five-round magazine, was authorized. The improved model did not reach frontline units of the French Army until the summer of 1918, generally too late to have a positive impact on the prosecution of the war. In the meantime, a number of French officers insisted on equipping their troops with the older Lebel. Thus, the French Army

▲ **Fusil Berthier Mle 1907/15**

French Army / 87th Infantry Regiment, 1916

By 1915, it had become apparent that an upgrade to the old Lebel rifle was needed; almost 440,000 examples of the Berthier Mle 1907/15 were produced during World War I.

Specifications	
Country of Origin: France	Overall Length: 1306mm (51.4in)
Date: 1915	Barrel Length: 797mm (31in)
Calibre: 8mm (.314in)	Muzzle Velocity: 640m/sec (2100ft/sec)
Operation: Bolt action	Feed/Magazine: 3-round box magazine
Weight: 3.8kg (6.4lb)	Range: 500m (1640ft)

struggled with the development and deployment of an adequate shoulder arm for the duration of the war. At Verdun, the Lebel was present in great numbers.

The development of French machine guns lagged following the perceived poor performance of the Reffye *mitrailleuse* during the Franco-Prussian War. In 1914, the air-cooled 8mm (.314in) St. Etienne Mle 1907 was the standard machine gun of the French Army. The adjustable rate of fire of the St. Etienne was from eight to 650 rounds per minute, and it was a considerable improvement over its predecessor, the Puteaux M1905.

By the summer of 1917, the reliable Hotchkiss Mle 1914 (M1914) was being deployed and the St. Etienne was shuttled to reserve units. The M1914 was the last in a series of machine guns developed by the French arms manufacturer Hotchkiss et Cie, which had been founded by American inventor Benjamin B. Hotchkiss (1826–85). The weapon ejected spent cartridges with a gas system rather than through recoil. It was fed by strips of 24 rounds which could be linked together, and was operated by a crew of three. Its weight of 23.6kg (52lb) was cumbersome for an infantry weapon. Production of the hefty Hotchkiss steadily increased, and nearly 50,000 were delivered to the French Army by 1918. It remained in service until 1945.

FRENCH INFANTRY COMPANY, 1916		
Unit	Officers	Men
Company HQ	1	
Four Sections each	2	
1st Half-section	1	
1st Squad (grenadiers)	1	
throwers		2
ammo suppliers		2
assistants		2
floater		1
2nd Squad (automatic riflemen)	1	
gunners		2
ammo suppliers		2
assistants		2
2nd Half-section	1	
3rd Squad (troopers)	1	
VB rifle-grenadiers		2
ammo suppliers		1
riflemen		8
4th Squad (troopers)	1	
VB rifle-grenadiers		2
ammo suppliers		1
riflemen		9
Total Strength	32	144

▲ **Hotchkiss Mle 1914**

French Army / 151st Infantry Regiment, 1916

The Hotchkiss Mle 1914 entered service as the standard machine gun of the French Army in 1917 and was deployed in significant numbers until the 1940s. When production ceased in 1920 more than 65,000 had been manufactured.

Specifications

Country of Origin: France

Date: 1914

Calibre: 8mm (.314in)

Operation: Gas operated, air cooled

Weight: 23.6kg (52lb)

Overall Length: 1270mm (50in)

Barrel Length: 775mm (30.5in)

Muzzle Velocity: 725m/sec (2380ft/sec)

Feed/Magazine: Strip fed

Cyclic Rate: 600rpm

Range: 2000m (6580ft)

The Somme
1916–17

Concentrated fire from machine guns and other small arms took a fearful toll in British and Commonwealth lives on the Somme, calling into question the judgment of senior Allied commanders who had ordered the units into action.

THE BRITISH ARMY lost nearly 60,000 dead and wounded on the first day of the Battle of the Somme. Such carnage was unprecedented, and the fighting was to last five months, from July to November 1916. The offensive against the German trenches in northern France was initially undertaken in an effort to coordinate with the Russian armies on the Eastern Front. Allied war planners reasoned that German forces would be stretched to the breaking point as British and French troops launched simultaneous attacks in the West while the Russians assumed the offensive in the East.

The German offensive at Verdun, begun in February 1916, altered Allied planning to a degree and required the British rather than the French to assume the primary role along the Somme River as French troops battled the emerging threat at Verdun. Therefore, the Somme offensive developed a twofold

▲ **Infantry support**
A British or Commonwealth infantryman aims a Lewis Gun somewhere on the Western Front. The American-designed Lewis Gun was one of the first infantry support weapons to be widely deployed.

▲ Lee-Enfield Rifle No. 1 Mk III SMLE

British Army / 1st Tyneside Irish Brigade, 1916

The Lee-Enfield No. 1 Mk III SMLE, the best known version of the 10-round rifle, began production in 1904 and entered service with Commonwealth forces three years later. The Mk III* was initially a wartime expedient version but continued in production into the 1950s.

Specifications

Country of Origin: United Kingdom
Date: 1907
Calibre: 7.7mm (.303in)
Operation: Bolt action
Weight: 3.93kg (8.625lb)
Overall Length: 1133mm (44.6in)
Barrel Length: 640mm (25.2in)
Muzzle Velocity: 634m/sec (2080ft/sec)
Feed/Magazine: 10-round box, loaded with
5-round charger clips
Range: 500m (1640ft)

▲ Ross

Canadian Corps / 24th Battalion Victoria Rifles, 1916

Prone to jamming due to a susceptibility to dirt and debris and inherent mechanical problems, the Canadian Ross rifle proved a disappointment in the field after performing well on the firing range.

Specifications

Country of Origin: Canada
Date: 1903
Calibre: 7.7mm (.303in)
Operation: Bolt action
Weight: 4.48kg (9.875lb)
Overall Length: 1285mm (50.6in)
Barrel Length: 765mm (30.1in)
Muzzle Velocity: 792m/sec (2600ft/sec)
Feed/Magazine: 5-round magazine
Range: 500m (1640ft)

▲ Lewis Gun Mk I

60(R) Squadron Royal Air Force, 1917

The American-designed Lewis Gun was modified by British manufacturers and widely used from 1916 until the end of the Great War. It was a familiar weapon among Allied air forces as well.

Specifications

Country of Origin: United States
Date: 1914
Calibre: 7.7mm (.303in)
Operation: Gas operated, air cooled
Weight: 11.8kg (26lb)
Overall Length: 965mm (38in)
Barrel Length: 665mm (26.25in)
Muzzle Velocity: 600m/sec (1970ft/sec)
Feed/Magazine: Magazine fed
Cyclic Rate: 550rpm
Range: 1000m (3280ft)

BRITISH INFANTRY PLATOON, 1917	
Unit	Strength
Rifle section	9
scout	1
sniper	1
Bombing (grenade) section	5
expert bombers	2
ammunition carriers	3
Rifle grenade section	9
rifle grenadiers	4
riflemen	5
Lewis Gun section	9

purpose – to stretch the Germans thin both East and West and to relieve mounting pressure against the French defenders of Verdun. As the Somme offensive began, 24 Allied divisions, 13 from the British Fourth Army and 11 of the French Sixth Army, confronted slightly more than 10 divisions of the German Second Army. Eventually, German strength committed on the Somme was to swell to more than 50 divisions.

The ordeal of the Tyneside Irish Brigade is indicative of the horrific losses endured on that fateful first day on the Somme front. The brigade was assigned to a support role as its sister brigades, the 101st and 102nd of the 34th Division, attacked. Crossing no-man's-land, the Tyneside Irish were caught in the open when the initial attack failed to progress satisfactorily. With the brigade brought to a halt, elements of two battalions (the 1st and the 4th) were able to reach positions on the German side, but these were killed or captured to a man. When the slaughter abated, the 1st and 4th Tyneside Irish battalions had lost nearly 1200 dead.

Canadian divisions

Of the 780 Newfoundlanders who moved forward on the morning of 1 July 1916, only 68 were fit for duty the following day. The Newfoundland Regiment was decimated in less than 20 minutes and without advancing beyond the British trenchline. From July to September, three Canadian divisions were heavily engaged in the vicinity of the Somme. On 15 September, the Canadian Second Division attacked at Courcelette, supported by tanks for the first time.

When the fighting ended on the Somme, Allied forces had gained only a few kilometres of territory.

In total, the British had lost 420,000 casualties. On the first day alone, more than 20 per cent of the effective British fighting force had been killed or wounded. The Battle of the Somme raised questions concerning the proper commitment of troops before enemy positions defended with modern small arms. Its shadow continues to loom across the British psyche to this day.

The British and Commonwealth soldiers at the Somme carried the standard issue Lee-Enfield Rifle No. 1 Mk III, the famous 7.7mm (.303in) Short Magazine Lee-Enfield (SMLE). This bolt-action rifle entered service with the British Army in 1907, and along with its predecessor the MLE (Magazine Lee-Enfield) was the primary shoulder arm of the British soldier from 1895 to 1957. Named for designer James Paris Lee and the Royal Small Arms Factory at Enfield, the Mk III incorporated a 10-round box magazine loaded from the top with five-round chargers. Unlike that of its Mauser counterpart, the Mk III's bolt action was smooth to the point that the rifleman could maintain his sight picture while operating it, thus providing a more stable and accurate shooting perspective.

The British Army placed a high priority on the concentrated, efficient rifle fire of its infantry, and the Mk III was ideally suited for this purpose. Well-trained soldiers often achieved a sustained rate of fire of 15 rounds per minute. At the height of combat, British troops sometimes referred to the 'mad minute' during which up to 30 rounds were discharged. In fact, on more than one occasion during the Great War German infantrymen taken under fire by British

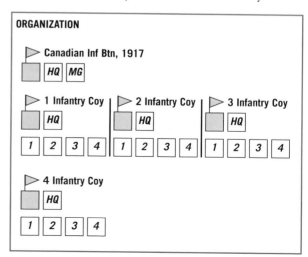

ORGANIZATION

Canadian Inf Btn, 1917 — HQ, MG

1 Infantry Coy — HQ; 1, 2, 3, 4

2 Infantry Coy — HQ; 1, 2, 3, 4

3 Infantry Coy — HQ; 1, 2, 3, 4

4 Infantry Coy — HQ; 1, 2, 3, 4

◀ Colt New Service

Canadian Corps / 4th Battalion (Central Ontario) Canadian Infantry,
Hill 145, 1917

The Colt New Service revolver fired an 11.43mm (.45in) cartridge and was adopted by the US armed forces as the Model 1909. It was later developed into the M1917 for the US military. Actually, the revolver had been in production since 1898. A large number were purchased by the Canadian Army prior to World War I and by the British during the war.

Specifications

Country of Origin: United States	Overall Length: 273mm (10.75in)
Date: 1909	Barrel Length: 140mm (5.51in)
Calibre: 11.43mm (.45in)	Muzzle Velocity: 198m/sec (650ft/sec)
Operation: Revolver	Feed/Magazine: 6-round cylinder
Weight: 1.3kg (2.9lb)	Range: 20m (66ft)

▶ Smith & Wesson Triple Lock

Canadian Corps / 27th Battalion (City of Winnipeg) Canadian Infantry,
Battle of Courcelette, 1916

The triple lock designation for this revolver arose from the third locking lug on the cylinder crane enabling the weapon to handle its cartridge. It is also known as the Smith & Wesson .44 Hand Ejector.

Specifications

Country of Origin: United States	Overall Length: 298mm (11.75in)
Date: 1908	Barrel Length: 185mm (7.3in)
Calibre: 11.2mm (.44in)	Muzzle Velocity: 198m/sec (650ft/sec)
Operation: Revolver	Feed/Magazine: 6-round cylinder
Weight: 1.08kg (2.4lb)	Range: 30m (98ft)

Specifications

Country of Origin: United States

Date: 1895

Calibre: 7.62mm (.3in), 6mm (.23in)

Operation: Gas operated

Weight: 16kg (35.25lb)

Overall Length: 1040mm (40.94in)

Barrel Length: 711mm (28in)

Muzzle Velocity: 732m/sec (2400ft/sec)

Feed/Magazine: Belt fed

Cyclic Rate: 400rpm

Range: 2740m (8990ft)

▲ M1895 Colt-Browning

2nd Canadian Division / 13th Canadian Machine Gun Company,
Vimy Ridge, April 1917

This gas-operated machine gun saw extensive service with Allied forces. It was produced in a number of calibres, including 7.7mm (.303in) and led to improvements with the development of the water-cooled M1917, one of the most famous families of machine guns in military history.

troops equipped with the Mk III actually believed they were confronted by machine guns.

The basic Mk III rifle was modified several times through the years, and a sniper variant served with Commonwealth forces into the 1990s. An estimated 17 million examples of the MLE, SMLE and variants have been manufactured.

The emergent Lewis Gun

By late 1915, the British Army had adopted the light Lewis Gun as an infantry support alternative to the heavier Vickers weapon in conjunction with the reorganization of the infantry machine-gun battalions into the Machine Gun Corps. The Lewis and the Vickers were designated as light and heavy machine guns respectively. By the end of World War I, the Lewis outnumbered the Vickers in service with the British Army by approximately three to one.

The Lewis Gun was of American design, and it was widely used by British and Commonwealth forces through World War I and into the Korean Conflict. British manufacturers modified the weapon to fire the 7.7mm (.303in) cartridge rather than the original 7.62mm (.3in) in use by the Americans, who never

▲ **Machine-gun team**
A German machine-gun squad operate a Maxim '08 from wooded cover during the latter stages of the war. The Maxim was the most widely used heavy machine gun of World War I.

officially adopted the Lewis Gun. It was produced from 1913 to 1942, and over 100,000 were sold by the British to Imperial Russia. British production of the Lewis Gun far exceeded that in the United States, and by the end of World War I more than 145,000 were in service with Commonwealth forces. In contrast to the heavier Vickers, the gas-operated, air-cooled Lewis Gun weighed only 11.8kg (26lb). It was easily identified with its drum-pan magazine that held up to 97 rounds and its long cooling sleeve. The Lewis Gun gained equal notoriety with Allied air forces during World War I, often mounted aboard fighter and reconnaissance aircraft with its cooling sleeve removed.

▶ Mauser M1912

Imperial German Army / Infantry Regiment 23 (Upper Silesian), 1916

The military version of the Mauser C96, nicknamed the Broomhandle, the M1912 semiautomatic pistol was originally chambered for 7.63mm (.3in) ammunition but retooled for 9mm (.35in).

Specifications

Country of Origin: Germany	Barrel Length: 140mm (5.51in)
Date: 1912	Muzzle Velocity: 427m/sec (1400ft/sec)
Calibre: 7.63mm (.3in)	Feed/Magazine: 6-, 10- or 20-round integral or
Operation: Short recoil	detachable magazine
Weight: 1.25kg (2.75lb)	Range: 100m (328ft)
Overall Length: 295mm (11.6in)	

Specifications

Country of Origin: Germany	Barrel Length: 719mm (28.33in)
Date: 1908	Muzzle Velocity: 829m/sec (2925ft/sec)
Calibre: 7.92mm (.312in)	Feed/Magazine: Belt fed (250-round fabric belt)
Operation: Short recoil, water cooled	Cyclic Rate: 300–450rpm
Weight: 26.44kg (58.25lb)	Range: 1500m (4921ft)
Overall Length: 1175mm (46.25in)	

▲ Maxim Maschinengewehr 08

Imperial German Army / Infantry Regiment 180 (Württemberg), 1917

A variant of the British Maxim Gun originally built under licence, the Maschinengewehr 08 served as the primary machine gun of the German Army during World War I. Its service life was extended into the 1940s due to shortages of newer types.

The Michael Offensive
1918

With Russia out of World War I, the Germans planned a decisive offensive for the spring of 1918. The main thrust of four separate attacks was codenamed Michael, and intended to crush the British Army from the Somme to the Channel.

A S THE GREAT WAR STRETCHED into its fourth year, Imperial Germany had reason for optimism with the Treaty of Brest-Litovsk, which ended Russian participation in the fighting. At long last, the German Army was able to transfer as many as 50 fresh divisions to the Western Front, amassing enough strength on the ground for what General Erich Ludendorff (1865–1937), Chief Quarter Master of the Army and joint senior commander with Field Marshal Paul von Hindenburg (1847–1934), hoped would be the decisive campaign against the British and French.

War fatigue was beginning to plague Germany. The strangulation of a blockade by the Royal Navy created shortages of foodstuffs and war materiel. The casualty rolls were lengthy, and manpower shortages were becoming an issue. Perhaps the most daunting prospect for the continuation of the war was the mobilization of the United States, which had entered the conflict on the Allied side in April 1917. Ludendorff knew that the immense military and industrial potential of the United States could doom Germany to defeat, and some American troops were already fighting in France. The window of opportunity was closing when the Michael Offensive commenced on 21 March 1918.

Although the British sustained more than 20,000 casualties on the first day of the offensive and components of both the Fifth and Third Armies were compelled to retreat to avoid being outflanked, isolated pockets of resistance held out. German penetrations utilizing new 'stormtrooper tactics' were significant in some areas; however, these were of little strategic importance. At key positions the British held their ground, repulsing German attacks and buying precious time.

Eventually, the Michael Offensive slowed and lost momentum. Supply lines were stretched thinly, and artillery could not maintain the pace of advance necessary. The Germans failed to capture the vital rail and road links through the town of Amiens in northern France, and by the first week of April Ludendorff ordered a halt to the attacks. Although Allied and German losses were comparable at about 250,000, the Allied losses were replaceable – particularly with the pending arrival of more

▲ **Parabellum M1908 Artillery Model**

Imperial German Army / Infantry Regiment 121 (Württemberg), 1918

The artillery version of the legendary Parabellum M1908 pistol, popularly known as the Luger after its designer, Georg Luger, featured a lengthened barrel and a wooden stock which allowed it to function as a carbine.

Specifications

Country of Origin: Germany

Date: 1913

Calibre: 9mm (.35in)

Operation: Toggle locked, short recoil

Weight: .96kg (2.125lb)

Overall Length: 324mm (12.75in)

Barrel Length: 190mm (7.5in)

Muzzle Velocity: 351m/sec (1150ft/sec)

Feed/Magazine: 8- or 32-round magazine

Range: 80m (260ft)

American troops – while the German dead and wounded were not. Elsewhere during the spring offensive, the outcome was predictably similar. The last, best opportunity for German victory was extinguished.

The Spandau spectre

In addition to the employment of stormtrooper tactics, which involved rapid movement and the isolation of strongpoints to be mopped up by slower-moving units, the potential for success in the Michael Offensive relied on the capabilities of the Maxim Maschinengewehr 08 (MG 08), the heavy machine gun that had become the stalwart defender of the German trenches for most of World War I. The MG 08 had proved its worth in a defensive capacity on numerous occasions, most notably at the Somme where the butcher's bill exacted from the British was catastrophic.

The greatest issue with the MG 08, however, was its heavy weight at 26.44kg (58.25lb). The weapon was so heavy that it was either transported on sleds or carried by several soldiers who hoisted it to their shoulders or bore it like a stretcher. The solution was the introduction of the Maxim Maschinengewehr 08/15, a bipod version of the same weapon that was somewhat lighter at 18kg (39.75lb). With added firepower and mobility, the German offensive in the spring of 1918 suffered primarily from unrefined tactics to exploit the initial gains won by the stormtroopers and ill-defined objectives once significant progress was made.

Nevertheless, the performance of the MG 08 during World War I was outstanding. The workhorse remained in service with the German Army of the Weimar Republic and into World War II to bridge shortages in newer models such as the Maschinengewehr 34 (MG 34). The reputation of

▶ Langenham pistol

Imperial German Army / 2nd Grenadier Regiment 'King Friedrich Wilhelm IV'
(1st Pomeranian), 1918

More than 50,000 Langenham pistols were made during the Great War for the German Army. The weapon was fed by an eight-round box magazine. A pocket version was also made for the civilian market.

Specifications

Country of Origin: Germany	Overall Length: 165mm (6.5in)
Date: 1914	Barrel Length: 101.5mm (4in)
Calibre: 7.65mm (.301in)	Muzzle Velocity: 282m/sec (925ft/sec)
Operation: Blowback	Feed/Magazine: 8-round box magazine
Weight: .77kg (1.7lb)	Range: 30m (98ft)

◀ Dreyse M1907

Imperial German Army / Reserve Infantry Regiment 40, 1918

Heavily influenced by the early Browning pistol designs, the Dreyse was issued to German and Austrian officers and later used by the German *Volkssturm* units in World War II.

Specifications

Country of Origin: Germany	Barrel Length: 92mm (3.6in)
Date: 1907	Muzzle Velocity: 300m/sec (984ft/sec)
Calibre: 7.65mm (.301in)	Feed/Magazine: 7-round detachable single stack
Operation: Blowback	magazine
Weight: .71kg (1.6lb)	Range: 50m (164ft)
Overall Length: 160mm (6.3in)	

the MG 08 was so fearsome that every German automatic weapon came to be known as a Spandau, for the arsenal where many of the machine guns were manufactured.

The Maxim Maschinengewehr 08 was a variant of an original German licence-produced copy of the British Maxim Gun, designed by American-born inventor Hiram Maxim. It fired the 7.92mm (.312in) Mauser round and was capable of a cyclic rate of fire of up to 450 rounds per minute. Using the short-recoil and toggle-lock mechanism, the weapon continued to fire as long as the trigger was depressed or until the 250-round fabric belt of ammunition was exhausted. Truly the most outstanding defensive weapon of World War I, the gun was produced in large quantities from 1916 forward, achieving a peak of 14,400 examples per month.

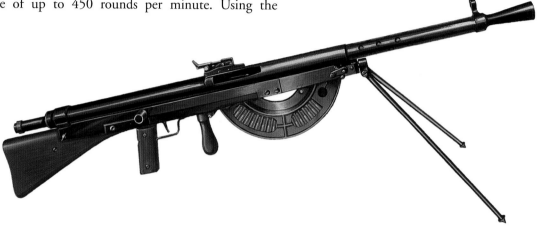

Specifications

Country of Origin: France	Barrel Length: 470mm (18.5in)
Date: 1915	Muzzle Velocity: 700m/sec (2300ft/sec)
Calibre: 8mm (.314in) Lebel	Feed/Magazine: Magazine fed
Operation: Recoil, air cooled	Cyclic Rate: 250rpm
Weight: 9kg (20lb)	Range: 1000m (3280ft)
Overall Length: 1145mm (45in)	

▲ **Fusil Mitrailleur M'15**

French Army / 118th Chasseurs, 1918

Deployed in large numbers by both the French and US Armies, the Fusil Mitrailleur M'15 weighed 9kg (20lb) but proved unfit for heavy combat. The weapon was produced in both French and US versions, firing the 8mm (.314in) and 7.62mm (.3in) cartridge respectively.

▲ **Mousqueton Berthier Mle 1892/M16 carbine**

French Army / 87th Infantry Regiment, 1918

The crowning achievement of the Berthier system was this carbine variant of the five-shot Mle 1916 Berthier rifle. Light troops, cavalry and reconnaissance units favoured the weapon.

Specifications

Country of Origin: France	Barrel Length: 453mm (17.8in)
Date: 1916	Muzzle Velocity: 640m/sec (3000ft/sec)
Calibre: 8mm (.314in)	Feed/Magazine: 5-round charger-loaded
Operation: Bolt action	magazine
Weight: 3.1kg (6.8lb)	Range: 500m (1640ft)
Overall Length: 945mm (37.2in)	

Specifications

Country of Origin: Germany

Date: 1918

Calibre: 9mm (.35in) Parabellum

Operation: Blowback

Weight: 4.2kg (9.25lb)

Overall Length: 815mm (32in)

Barrel Length: 195mm (7.75in)

Muzzle Velocity: 395m/sec (1300ft/sec)

Feed/Magazine: 32-round detachable drum
  magazine

Range: 70m (230ft)

▲ **Bergmann MP 18**

Imperial German Army / 73rd Fusilier Regiment, 1918

The world's first operational submachine gun for ground troops, the Bergmann MP 18 fired up to 500 rounds per minute and served as a basis for the design of automatic infantry weapons into the 1960s.

The Maschinengewehr 08/15 reached the army in great numbers in the spring of 1917 and rapidly became a success on the battlefield, although it remained somewhat cumbersome and required a crew of four to operate. By the time of the Michael Offensive approximately six MG 08/15s were fielded by each infantry company and up to 72 by each regiment, eclipsing the number of heavy Maschinengewehr 08 weapons in service.

Approximately 130,000 MG 08/15s were manufactured during World War I, primarily at the arsenals of Spandau and Erfurt and the works of civilian arms manufacturer Deutsche Waffen und Munitionsfabriken. Other variants of the MG 08 were used aboard aircraft, while the Chinese Army and some Southeast Asian forces deployed versions of the weapon until the 1960s.

First submachine gun

One of the most innovative weapons utilized by German troops during the Michael Offensive was the Bergmann MP 18, the first blowback-operated submachine gun in the world. Development of the Bergmann MP 18 was undertaken by Hugo Schmeisser (1884–1953) in 1916, and production was initiated by Theodor Bergmann Waffenbau Abteilung. Within a few months the weapon was issued on the Western Front and proved effective in providing suppressive fire against fixed objectives and in clearing trenches of massed enemy troops.

Although exact figures are unknown and full-scale production did not begin until early 1918, it is believed that between 5000 and 10,000 MP 18s were manufactured by the end of World War I. The spring offensive of 1918 saw the most prolific deployment of the MP 18, and its presence on the battlefield was noted by the Allied troops who encountered its distinctive report, high degree of mobility and rate of fire of up to 500 rounds per minute. The relatively few MP 18s available in the spring of 1918 were placed in the hands of the newly formed stormtrooper units, whose primary task was to rapidly penetrate enemy lines and clear the way for larger numbers of troops to advance.

The Treaty of Versailles outlawed the manufacture of the Bergmann MP 18; however, production continued on a clandestine basis into the 1920s. Although technically the MP 18 was not the world's first submachine gun, preceded by the Italian Villar-Perosa in 1915, it is considered the first serviceable weapon of its kind for ground troops. The Villar-Perosa was initially intended for use in aircraft and was later adapted for infantry.

The technology of the MP 18 was advanced for its time; however, limited production prevented it from effecting the course of World War I and potentially breaking the stalemate of trench warfare. Still, the battle-tested weapon formed the basis for the development of submachine guns and individual automatic weapons for the next half-century.

MACHINE GUN COMPARISON

Equipment	Crew	Calibre	Cyclic Rate
German MG 08/15	4	7.92mm	300–450 rpm
British Vickers Mk I	3	7.7mm	600 rpm
French Hotchkiss M1914	3	8mm	600 rpm
U.S. Browning M1917	4	7.62mm	450 rpm

Vickers Mk I

MG 08/15

Hotchkiss M1914

Browning M1917

▶ **Webley & Scott 1912**

British Army / 5th Battalion West Yorkshire Regiment, Le Havre, 1917

Issued to airmen of the Royal Flying Corps and personnel of the Horse Artillery, the Webley & Scott 1912 fired a heavy 11.55mm (.455in) cartridge and was fed by a six-round magazine.

Specifications

Country of Origin: United Kingdom

Date: 1912

Calibre: 11.55mm (.455in)

Operation: Self-loading

Weight: .66kg (1.5lb)

Overall Length: 216mm (8.5in)

Barrel Length: 127mm (5in)

Muzzle Velocity: 220m/sec (720ft/sec)

Feed/Magazine: 6-round magazine

Range: 20m (66ft)

Specifications*

Country of Origin: United Kingdom

Date: 1916

Calibre: 7.7mm (.303in)

Operation: Bolt action

Weight: 3.93kg (8.625lb)

Overall Length: 1133mm (44.6in)

Barrel Length: 640mm (25.2in)

Muzzle Velocity: 634m/sec (2080ft/sec)

Feed/Magazine: N/A

Range (Grenade): 100m (328ft)

(*Of rifle without grenade)

▲ **Lee-Enfield Rifle No. 1 Mk III SMLE with Grenade Launcher**

British Expeditionary Force / 4th Battalion Duke of Wellington's Brigade
(West Riding Regiment), 1917

The body and upper barrel of the Mk III SMLE were wrapped in brass wire and soldered together to prevent the rifle from bursting when converted as a grenade launcher. The grenade is a No. 5 Mk I 1916.

American Expeditionary Force
1917–18

When the United States entered World War I in April 1917, it was far from prepared to provide troops and war materiel in great quantities. However, the first soldiers of the American Expeditionary Force reached France within 90 days.

WHEN THE FIRST AMERICAN SOLDIERS arrived in France a contingent marched through Paris, and its commander, General John J. Pershing (1860–1948), was reported to have commented, 'LaFayette, we are here!' American troops were eventually deployed in large numbers, and by May 1918 more than a million had reached the Western Front. Half of these were in the trenches and forward Allied positions. The American troops were welcomed by the war-weary French and British Armies; however, friction developed when some Allied commanders wanted the Americans to fight under foreign leadership. Pershing sought to maintain independent command for US forces. While some American units gained combat experience with British and French troops, Pershing trained his soldiers tirelessly.

Under French command, the US 1st Division engaged in the initial American offensive action at Cantigny on 18 May 1918. Later during the Second Battle of the Marne at Belleau Wood and Chateau Thierry, US Army troops and Marines defeated opposing German forces. Subsequently, American troops fought major actions in the autumn of 1918 during the reduction of the St. Mihiel salient and the Meuse-Argonne Offensive. At St. Mihiel, Pershing led the American First Army, which consisted of seven infantry divisions and 500,000 men. It was the largest US military operation in history up to that time. During their participation in the Great War, the Americans suffered casualties amounting to nearly 117,000 dead and 204,000 wounded. At the peak of his command tenure, Pershing led more than a million American and French combat troops.

Springfield special

Although the American Expeditionary Force arrived in France within weeks of the declaration of war in 1917, the rapid movement required that most of its heavy equipment be left behind. Therefore, many of the aircraft and artillery pieces fielded by the Americans were of British or French manufacture. When it came to shoulder arms, however, the primary rifle of the US Army was the Springfield Model 1903, a descendant of the prolific German

Mauser G98 design which was put into production at the Springfield Arsenal in Massachusetts.

While there were some minor alterations to the original Mauser design, which the Americans had fought against during the Spanish-American War, the basic weapon varied little from its German configuration. In fact, Mauser eventually filed a suit against the US government and received royalty payments. US military leaders had struggled for years to find an appropriate rifle, purchasing both the German Mauser G98 and the Norwegian Krag-Jørgensen. The Springfield 1903 entered service in

▶ Colt M1911

American Expeditionary Force / 2nd Division / 9th Regiment, 1917

For more than 70 years, the Colt Model 1911 remained in service with the US Army and was later known as the M1911A1. Designed by John Browning, it used a swinging-link, short-recoil system.

Specifications

Country of Origin: United States	Overall Length: 216mm (8.5in)
Date: 1911	Barrel Length: 127mm (5in)
Calibre: 11.43mm (.45in)	Muzzle Velocity: 262m/sec (860ft/sec)
Operation: Short recoil	Feed/Magazine: 7-round magazine
Weight: 1.1kg (2.425lb)	Range: 30m (98ft)

▶ Smith & Wesson M1917

American Expeditionary Force / 26th Division / 102nd Regiment, 1917

Loaded using two three-round half-moon clips, the Smith & Wesson M1917 was called into service to ease a shortage of handguns in the US Army. The clips were required for the ejector to grip the rimless 11.43mm (.45in) round.

Specifications

Country of Origin: United States	Overall Length: 208mm (11.75in)
Date: 1917	Barrel Length: 185mm (7.3in)
Calibre: 11.43mm (.45in)	Muzzle Velocity: 198m/sec (650ft/sec)
Operation: Revolver	Feed/Magazine: 6-round cylinder
Weight: 1.08kg (2.4lb)	Range: 20m (66ft)

▶ Colt .45 Army 1917

American Expeditionary Force / 42nd Division / 165th Infantry Regiment, 1918

The last standard issue US military revolver, the Colt .45 Army 1917 was pressed into service during World War I until enough of the semiautomatic M1911 were available.

Specifications

Country of Origin: United States	Overall Length: 273mm (10.75in)
Date: 1917	Barrel Length: 140mm (5.5in)
Calibre: 11.43mm (.45in)	Muzzle Velocity: 198m/sec (650ft/sec)
Operation: Revolver	Feed/Magazine: 6-round cylinder
Weight: 1.13kg (2.5lb)	Range: 20m (66ft)

COLT M1911 MILITARY PRODUCTION FIGURES	
Period	Total
1912	20,000
Jan 1913 – Jan 1915	90,000
Feb 1915 – Oct 1918	440,000
Nov 1918 – April 1919	180,000

1905 and was not officially replaced until the M1 Garand was adopted in 1937. Its sniper version is still in use to this day. The M1903A4, which appeared in 1942, was the first attempt by the US military to standardize a sniper rifle.

The Springfield 1903 fired the 7.62mm (.3in) .30-03 and subsequently .30-06 cartridges. Although smaller than other contemporary rifles, it was accurate and sturdy and remained popular with the troops. The experienced soldier was capable of firing an average of 15 rounds per minute with ammunition fed from a five-round stripper clip to an internal box magazine. Production numbers topped 800,000 prior to World War I and eventually several million were manufactured.

Browning brawler

Despite the fact that only about 1200 Browning M1917 heavy machine guns reached the front prior to the end of World War I, the gun managed to acquire a reputation as a first-rate defensive weapon. Weighing 47kg (103lb) including gun, tripod, water for cooling the barrel and a standard supply of ammunition, it compared favourably in weight with the German MG 08 and the British Vickers Mk I, while its rate of fire was

comparable at 450 rounds per minute. The gun itself was actually considerably lighter than the MG 08 or the Vickers Mk I.

Due to the shortage of Browning weapons, most American troops in France were equipped with British Vickers machine guns built by Colt or French Hotchkiss models. The service life of the Browning M1917 extended for more than half a century as it was improved and later designated the Model 1917A1. The development of the M1917 began around the turn of the twentieth century as John Browning sought to produce a serviceable recoil-operated, water-cooled machine gun. Its sliding-block mechanism was a significant departure from the toggle lock favoured by Hiram Maxim, the father of the prominent European models. When the US government requested designs from several potential manufacturers in the spring of 1917, Browning's entry fired 20,000 rounds without jamming or overheating.

A scant one-third of the US divisions sent to France received the Browning M1917, and its combat use during the Great War was only about 10 weeks in duration. The M1917A1 refined the successful design with an improved bottom plate; however, the basic original design proved more than adequate for defensive purposes until supplanted by the M60.

▶ **Expeditionary troops**

The first contingent of US servicemen to arrive in England in 1917 for deployment to the Western Front stand at ease, their Springfield 1903 rifles arranged in front of them.

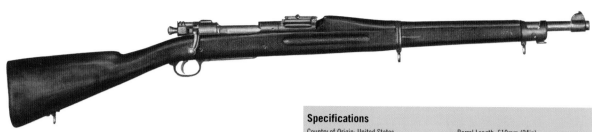

▲ Springfield Model 1903

American Expeditionary Force / 42nd Division / 168th Infantry Regiment, 1917

Based on a Mauser design, the Springfield 1903 entered service with the US Army in 1905 and remained the standard issue rifle until replaced by the M1 Garand in 1937. Its service life, however, was extended for decades.

Specifications

Country of Origin: United States	Barrel Length: 610mm (24in)
Date: 1903	Muzzle Velocity: 823m/sec (2700ft/sec)
Calibre: 7.62mm (.3in)	Feed/Magazine: 5-round stripper clip, box
Operation: Bolt action	magazine
Weight: 3.9kg (8.625lb)	Range: 750m (2460ft)
Overall Length: 1115mm (43.9in)	

▲ M1917 Enfield Rifle

American Expeditionary Force / 41st Division / 161st Infantry Regiment, 1918

An adaptation of the earlier P14, the M1917 was the product of a joint effort by British and American designers. It fired the US 7.62mm (.3in) .30-06 cartridge.

Specifications

Country of Origin: United Kingdom/United States	Barrel Length: 660mm (26in)
Date: 1917	Muzzle Velocity: 823m/sec (2700ft/sec)
Calibre: 7.62mm (.3in)	Feed/Magazine: 6-round magazine, 5-round clip-
Operation: Bolt action	fed reloading
Weight: 4.17kg (9.2lb)	Range: 500m (1640ft)
Overall Length: 1175mm (46.25in)	

Specifications

Country of Origin: United States	Overall Length: 1194mm (47in)
Date: 1917	Barrel Length: 610mm (24in)
Calibre: 7.62mm (.3in)	Muzzle Velocity: 853m/sec (2800ft/sec)
Operation: Gas operated	Feed/Magazine: 20-round straight box
Weight: 7.26kg (16lb)	Range: 1000–1500m (3280–4921ft)

▲ Browning BAR

American Expeditionary Force / 1st Division / 16th Infantry Regiment, 1918

The Browning Automatic Rifle (BAR) provided automatic fire support for advancing infantry of the US Army. The weapon was heavy and limited by an ammunition supply of only 20 rounds.

Specifications

Country of Origin: United States	Barrel Length: 610mm (24in)
Date: 1917	Muzzle Velocity: 850m/sec (2800ft/sec)
Calibre: 7.62mm (.3in)	Feed/Magazine: Belt fed
Operation: Recoil, water cooled	Cyclic Rate: 450rpm
Weight: 15kg (32.75lb)	Range: 2000m (6560ft)
Overall Length: 980mm (38.5in)	

▶ **Browning M1917**

American Expeditionary Force / 1st Division /
1st Machine Gun Battalion, 1918

An excellent defensive weapon, the Browning M1917
machine gun was capable of firing at 450 rounds per
minute, while an improved version, the M1917A1,
could reach 600rpm. The M1917 served with US and
other forces for more than half a century.

Dardanelles Campaign
1915

The Dardanelles campaign, conceived as a blow against Ottoman Turkey with the possible capture of Constantinople, ended in a bloody debacle for Commonwealth troops who landed under heavy enemy fire at Gallipoli.

I N THE FIRST MAJOR CAMPAIGN undertaken during
World War I by the Australian and New Zealand
Army Corps (ANZAC), these Commonwealth
troops suffered tremendous losses but gained a
measure of national identity for their countries in the
process. Although they failed to advance on
Constantinople, the capital of Ottoman Turkey, or to
open a supply route to Russia, they fought heroically
although being at times poorly led.

In early 1915, the Royal Navy and the French
Navy mounted a series of abortive naval attacks
against Turkish fortifications in the Dardanelles, a
strait running between the Aegean Sea and the Sea of
Marmara. These resulted in embarrassing losses, and
it was determined that a land campaign was necessary
to secure passage through the strait and on towards
the Bosporus and the Black Sea. On 25 April British
and French forces landed at Helles on the tip of the
Gallipoli peninsula, while ANZAC troops went
ashore at Gaba Tepe on the coast of the Aegean Sea.
In memory of their sacrifice there, the small inlet at
Gaba Tepe has since been known as ANZAC Cove.

▲ FN-Mauser Infantry Rifle Model 1889

Turkish Army / 57th Infantry Regiment, 1915

Delivered to the Turks to complete a contract for the earlier Model 1887, the FN-Mauser Model 1889 was a standard rifle of the Belgian Army as well. The Turkish version was known as the M90, and a small number were produced as shorter-barrelled carbine versions.

Specifications

Country of Origin: Belgium	Overall Length: 1295mm (51in)
Date: 1889	Barrel Length: 780mm (30.6in)
Calibre: 7.65mm (.301in)	Muzzle Velocity: 610m/sec (2000ft/sec)
Operation: Bolt action	Feed/Magazine: 5-round box magazine
Weight: 4.1kg (8.8lb)	Range: 1000m (3280ft)

▶ Mauser C96

Turkish Army / 35th Regiment, 1915

The semiautomatic Mauser C96 pistol was front-loading and chambered for the high-powered 7.63mm (.3in) cartridge. At least 1000 C96s were delivered to the Turkish Army and designated the 1897 Turkish Army Mauser.

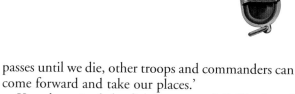

Specifications

Country of Origin: Germany	Barrel Length: 140mm (5.51in)
Date: 1896	Muzzle Velocity: 305m/sec (1000ft/sec)
Calibre: 7.63mm (.3in)	Feed/Magazine: 6- or 10-round integral or
Operation: Short recoil	detachable magazine
Weight: 1.045kg (2.3lb)	Range: 100m (328ft)
Overall Length: 295mm (11.6in)	

The landings in both locations were bitterly contested. At Helles, senior commanders failed to exploit advances in poorly defended sectors. Instead, their soldiers suffered heavy casualties on and near the beaches. The transport ship *River Clyde* was intentionally run aground, and those unfortunate troops who were required to vacate the ship through sally ports found themselves under withering Turkish machine-gun fire. Only 21 of the initial 200 soldiers of the Royal Hampshires and Royal Munster Fusiliers managed to reach the beach.

Although Turkish troops were hard pressed at both Helles and ANZAC Cove, they held off the Commonwealth and French forces, which were supported by naval gunfire. At Helles, Turkish Lieutenant-Colonel Mustafa Kemal realized that his situation was desperate and issued an order to his 57th Infantry Regiment which read: 'I do not expect you to attack. I order you to die. In the time which passes until we die, other troops and commanders can come forward and take our places.'

Kemal survived the fighting around Gallipoli and went on the become the 'Father of Modern Turkey'. As the first president of the Turkish Republic, he earned the name Atatürk.

Deadly stalemate

Rather than being a rapidly successful campaign, the Dardanelles adventure lapsed into a deadly stalemate. Commonwealth troops were withdrawn in late 1915 and early 1916. The affair at Gallipoli had been the brainchild of First Lord of the Admiralty Winston Churchill, who suffered a severe political setback as a result of its failure. However, Churchill emerged as a hero a generation later, leading Great Britain as prime minister during the dark days of World War II. During the Dardanelles campaign, Commonwealth casualties amounted to 44,000 dead and 97,000

▶ **Webley & Scott Mk VI**

British Commonwealth Army / 5th Australian Brigade / 20th Battalion, 1915

One of several sturdy revolvers produced by Webley & Scott, the Mark VI entered service in 1915 and fired a large 11.55mm (.455in) cartridge. A bayonet was produced but found little practical usage.

Specifications

Country of Origin: United Kingdom	Overall Length: 279mm (11in)
Date: 1915	Barrel Length: 152mm (6in)
Calibre: 11.55mm (.455in)	Muzzle Velocity: 198m/sec (650ft/sec)
Operation: Revolver	Feed/Magazine: 6-round cylinder
Weight: 1.1kg (2.425lb)	Range: 20m (66ft)

▲ **Lee-Enfield Rifle No. 1 Mk III SMLE**

British Commonwealth Army / 5th Australian Brigade / 20th Battalion, 1915

The Lee-Enfield No. 1 Mk III SMLE equipped many regiments of the Commonwealth troops that fought alongside British units. The definitive version of the SMLE entered service with the British military in 1907 and fired a high-velocity 7.7mm (.303in) cartridge.

Specifications

Country of Origin: United Kingdom	Barrel Length: 640mm (25.2in)
Date: 1907	Muzzle Velocity: 634m/sec (2080ft/sec)
Calibre: 7.7mm (.303in)	Feed/Magazine: 10-round box, loaded with
Operation: Bolt action	5-round charger clips
Weight: 3.93kg (8.625lb)	Range: 500m (1640ft)
Overall Length: 1133mm (44.6in)	

wounded. A total of 87,000 Turkish troops were killed and 165,000 wounded.

Among the shoulder arms carried by the Turkish Army during the Dardanelles campaign and throughout World War I was a weapon similar to the FN-Mauser Model 1889 and known as the Mauser M90, which was delivered to the Turks in completion of an order that had been originally filled with the earlier Mauser Model 1887. A clause in the Turkish contract with the German arms manufacturer stated that if any other nation purchased an improved version of the Model 1887 the Turks would be entitled to an upgrade to complete their deliveries. When Belgium purchased the Model 1889, Mauser made up the Turkish order with the M90, which was based on the Model 1889.

Like the Model 1889, the bolt-action Mauser M90 fired the 7.65mm (.301in) cartridge and was fed by a five-round vertical box magazine, a considerable improvement over tubular magazines in older weapons. With the rifle's open action, the magazine was loaded using a charger.

The Mauser C96 front-loading semiautomatic pistol was another import from Germany that equipped Turkish soldiers during the Dardanelles campaign. Known as the Mauser Broomhandle, the weapon was chambered for a high-velocity 7.63mm (.3in) cartridge and fed by a six- or 10-round integral or detachable magazine. Many of the C96 pistols in service with the Turks had been delivered under the first arms contract between Mauser and the Turkish government which was placed in 1897 for 1000 weapons. These pistols were designated the 1897 Turkish Army Mauser and bore distinctive markings such as the year stamp 1314 to correspond with the Muslim calendar.

Chapter 2

World War I: Eastern Front, Italy and the Balkans

The Great War had begun in the Balkans with the assassination of Archduke Franz Ferdinand at Sarajevo. Subsequently, the web of alliances and treaties negotiated for mutual protection, military support and potential territorial expansion triggered a trail of mobilizations and declarations of war. The global nature of World War I became readily apparent as nations fought on three major fronts – in the east, west, and south of Europe – as well as in the Middle East, equatorial Africa and across the oceans of the world. The vastness of Russia and its seemingly endless supply of manpower loomed in the East, compelling the Central Powers to weaken their troop strength elsewhere as the prospects for a war of attrition taxed German resources beyond capacity.

◀ **Trench warfare**
Russian troops eat during a respite in the fighting, sometime during a spring thaw. Their Mosin-Nagant rifles are left resting on the trench lip, ready to be fired if their position is attacked.

Introduction

Military, political and ideological confrontation fuelled World War I in the East as the Central Powers, particularly Germany, found themselves fighting a costly war on multiple battlefields from the wide expanse of the steppes to the rugged Carpathian mountains.

THE GREAT WAR on the Eastern Front was played out in territory stretching from the Baltic Sea in the north to the Black Sea in the south, roughly 1600km (1000 miles). Because the forces of the various belligerents were thinly stretched at times, the stagnation of trench warfare did not develop as in the West. Although large numbers of soldiers were deployed by the warring nations, concentrations of troop strength were often difficult or impossible to accomplish from a logistical standpoint; therefore, successful offensive actions resulting in a breakthrough of enemy lines might be accomplished, and subsequently halted not by enemy action but by severe strains on supply lines.

With the outbreak of hostilities, the German high command anticipated that its primary adversary would be France and accordingly deployed the majority of its military assets in the West. At the same time, the army of Imperial Russia was twice the size of the 10 divisions arrayed in the East by the Germans. The capacity of the Russians to conscript and mobilize additional forces was considerably greater than that of the Germans or their Austro-Hungarian allies. However, the discipline, military structure and relative availability of weapons and equipment equalized this imbalance in manpower to some degree.

Given the political climate throughout Europe and the burgeoning potential for hostilities, the German high command fully expected a war on at least two fronts, as France and Great Britain took up arms in the West and the Russians went to war in the East. In

▲ **Tannenberg campaign**
Carrying full packs and wearing their distinctive boiled-leather *Pickelhaube* helmets, German infantry climb a slope during the Tannenberg campaign.

▲ **Power of the Revolution**
Dressed in imperial uniforms, early Russian revolutionaries point their Mosin-Nagant rifles at some imagined enemy.

late 1905, German Army chief of staff General Alfred von Schlieffen (1833–1913) had introduced a war contingency plan that envisioned a rapid, sweeping attack against France while a defensive deployment on the Eastern Front was intended to hold the Russians at bay. Schlieffen reasoned that the swift defeat of France would make Britain and Russia reluctant to continue the war, resulting in an advantageous round of peace negotiations.

The Russians also considered the likelihood of war with Germany and neighbouring Austria-Hungary. The response was Plan 19 developed in 1910 by General Yuri Danilov (1866–1937), correctly anticipating that German attention would focus on France and advocating a Russian offensive into East Prussia with a strength of 19 corps grouped in four field armies. By 1912, Plan 19 was altered to deal more directly with the perceived threat from Austria-Hungary. The subsequent shuffle of troops effectively halved the number of Russian soldiers intended to fight in East Prussia and redirected

substantial forces to the front opposite the Austro-Hungarian Army.

The high standards of German firearms and equipment production were well known to the Russians, as was the strict regimen of military training and the efficiency of the conscription system that generated nearly 300,000 new recruits to the German Army annually. However, the armies of Austria-Hungary and Ottoman Turkey were forces with which to be reckoned. In 1914, the standing Turkish Army amounted to only 250,000; however, that number increased by more than half a million within months. For some time, German advisors had assisted the Turks with training, provided some arms, and helped to instil a measure of military order.

As in the West, the armies in the East relied on the bolt-action rifle and the availability of the machine gun. Weapons were developed within the national arsenals and private manufacturers of Germany, Austria-Hungary and Russia, while Italian-made weapons went into action on Italy's northern border.

Balkan Prelude
1914–15

Shots from a single pistol assassinated Austro-Hungarian royalty and plunged the world into the most costly military conflict in history to that time.

WHEN BOSNIAN SERB and Serbian nationalist Gavrilo Princip (1894–1918) assassinated Austro-Hungarian Archduke Franz Ferdinand (1863–1914) and his wife Sophie, Duchess of Hohenberg (1868–1914), in Sarajevo on 28 June 1914, the shots from his pistol literally changed the course of history and set in motion the horrific conflagration of World War I. Princip had chosen as his weapon the Browning FN Model 1910 blowback-operated semiautomatic pistol. By that time, Browning had already produced several successful designs for Colt and for the Belgian manufacturer Fabrique Nationale. However, when Colt decided to forego production of the Model 1910, Browning gravitated towards Europe and patented the weapon there. The pistol used by Princip held a seven-round detachable box magazine of 7.65mm (.301in) ammunition. A number of these weapons found their way into the hands of ultra-nationalists and terrorist elements in the Balkans, including the shadowy group known as the Black Hand, to which Princip had been reported sympathetic.

With the Austro-Hungarian declaration of war on Serbia, the major powers followed suit. Germany honoured its obligation to support Austria-Hungary, while Russia had guaranteed the sovereignty of Serbia. And so the dominoes fell into conflict. In 1914, the Serbian Army consisted of five divisions. This was rapidly doubled, and the strength of Serbian men under arms rose to 180,000. Many of these were armed with Russian weapons that had flowed to the Serbian state for more than 20 years.

Prominent among the shoulder arms used by the Serbian Army was the Berdan series of rifles developed by American inventor Hiram Berdan (1824–93) and produced in Russia from the late 1860s until 1891. The trapdoor-breechblock Berdan I and the single-shot bolt-action Berdan II were used extensively by the Russian military even after the arrival of the Mosin-Nagant rifle in the early twentieth century. The Berdan series was also in service with the armies of Finland and Bulgaria, and by 1914 more than 75,000 had been exported to Serbia. The early Berdan rifle fired a heavy 10.75mm (.42in) cartridge, and an accomplished soldier was capable of a rate of fire of six to eight rounds per minute.

Among the sidearms in service in the Balkans was the Montenegro revolver produced by the Austrian firm Gasser. Firing an 11.2mm (.44in) cartridge, the Montenegro was originally developed for the Austro-Hungarian cavalry around 1870, while the Smith & Wesson No. 2 was popularized as a private purchase handgun during the American Civil War. It fired an 8.1mm (.32in) cartridge.

▶ **Gasser Montenegro**

Austro-Hungarian Army / 41st Infantry Brigade, 1914

The star-shaped automatic ejector of the Montenegro assisted the ejection of spent cartridges by pushing them outwards when the barrel was tipped down for reloading.

Specifications

Country of Origin: Austria-Hungary	Overall Length: 185mm (7.28in)
Date: 1870	Barrel Length: 135mm (5.3in)
Calibre: 11.2mm (.44in)	Muzzle Velocity: 168m/sec (550ft/sec)
Operation: Revolver	Feed/Magazine: 5-round cylinder
Weight: 1.3kg (2.9lb)	Range: 20m (66ft)

▲ Berdan Rifle

Serbian Army / 2nd Timok Infantry Division, 1914

Large numbers of the extremely accurate Berdan rifle were produced in two variants for the Russian military prior to World War I and exported to friendly neighbouring countries.

Specifications

Country of Origin: United States/Russia

Date: 1869

Calibre: 10.75mm (.42in)

Operation: Berdan I: 'Trapdoor'; Berdan II: 'Bolt'

Weight: 4.2kg (9.25lb)

Overall Length: 1300mm (51.18in)

Barrel Length: 830mm (32.67in)

Muzzle Velocity: Not known

Feed/Magazine: Single shot, breech-loader

Range: 280m (919ft)

▶ Browning FN Model 1910

Gavrilo Princip, assassination of Archduke Ferdinand, June 1914

The Model 1910 was notable for an innovative spring location around the barrel and its triple safety feature, with an external safety flipper plus safeties at the grip and magazine. The spring design served as a basis for future famous pistols such as the German Walther PPK.

Specifications

Country of Origin: Belgium

Date: 1910

Calibre: 7.65mm (.301in), 9mm (.35in)

Operation: Blowback

Weight: .57kg (1.25lb)

Overall Length: 154mm (6in)

Barrel Length: 88.5mm (3.5in)

Muzzle Velocity: 299m/sec (981ft/sec)

Feed/Magazine: 7-round magazine

Range: 30m (98ft)

▼ Road march

Bayonets fixed, Serbian troops march to their camp near Mikra, April 1916. Following the Austro-Hungarian-led invasion of 1914, Britain and France set about re-equipping the Serbian Army from 1915.

War in Russia
1914–17

War with the Central Powers and civil unrest within combined to doom the Czarist regime in Russia after the nation had suffered nearly seven million killed, wounded or taken prisoner.

THE WIDENING CLASS DISTINCTION among the people of Imperial Russia had sparked violence in the streets of major cities from time to time since the turn of the century, while ethnic diversity and latent nationalism simmered beneath the surface of the mammoth Eastern European nation, destabilizing the monarchy of Czar Nicholas II (1868–1918). As the Czar and his ministers sought to maintain strong ties with Serbia in the restive Balkans and solidify their relations with France in the event of hostilities with Germany, Russia also was intent on expanding its influence with the smaller nations of Eastern Europe, particularly the Baltic states of Lithuania, Estonia and Latvia and the Scandinavian territory of Finland.

To the south, the Russians had long nurtured designs on a warm-water port. Victory over the Central Powers, including Ottoman Turkey, might pave the way for control of the Bosporus and the Dardanelles, which controlled marine transport from the Black Sea to the Mediterranean.

The Great Bear

With the outbreak of World War I, Grand Duke Nicholas (1856–1929), cousin of the Czar, was named initial commander of all Russian forces in the field. Russian troop strength was estimated at slightly more than 1.4 million soldiers; however, with mobilization the ranks were expected to swell to near five million. In reality, a series of legal modifications, exemptions and administrative missteps resulted in the pace of conscription and mobilization slowing appreciably. Although its population greatly outnumbered that of Germany, Russia's effort to augment its armed forces was only slightly more productive in raw numbers.

A diversity of ethnic backgrounds, harbouring centuries-old rivalries and hatreds among certain groups, posed a challenge to forming a cohesive Russian Army, while the majority of Russian soldiers were of peasant stock and had little, if any, formal education. Literate soldiers were often sent to the artillery or to occupy staff positions, while the officer corps was seriously deficient in junior and senior level commanders.

Although senior Russian military officers were familiar with the advancing technology of the day and Russian weapons manufacturers had demonstrated the capabilities of producing modern small arms, the country's industrial establishment had not successfully implemented a programme of

▲ **Mosin-Nagant Model 1891**

Imperial Russian Army / 5th Rifle Brigade, 1915

Both Belgian and Russian designers contributed to the Mosin-Nagant, and this sturdy rifle equipped Russian infantry units for many years. An estimated 37 million were eventually produced.

Specifications

Country of Origin: Russia	Overall Length: 1305mm (51.4in)
Date: 1891	Barrel Length: 802mm (31.6in)
Calibre: 7.62mm (.3in)	Muzzle Velocity: 810m/sec (2657ft/sec)
Operation: Bolt action	Feed/Magazine: 5-round box magazine
Weight: 4.37kg (9.625lb)	Range: 500m (1640ft)

production to keep pace with that of its potential adversaries. Further, the military had allowed the implementation of advanced weapons to drift to a great extent.

As a result, in 1914 the Russian Army could field only a single machine gun per infantry battalion, and the total number of such weapons deployed with Russian troops was just over 4000. Artillery production and maintenance were woefully deficient, with only one factory manufacturing field guns and only a handful of others capable of keeping them battleworthy. Only two-thirds of the estimated rifles needed to equip the mobilized army could be procured, leaving the fighting forces short at least 400,000 shoulder arms. During the war, the production of rifles rose from about 70,000 per month in 1915 to more than 110,000 per month the

following year. However, the estimated need of 200,000 per month was never realized.

Plan 19 and disaster at Tannenberg

In August 1914, General Alexander Samsonov (1859–1914) set the Russian Second Army in motion, implementing the altered Plan 19 for the invasion of East Prussia that had been adopted two years earlier. Samsonov advanced eastwards at a snail's pace, and the initial plan of linking up with another Russian army coming from the north under General Paul von Rennenkampf (1854–1918) was thwarted by rapid German movement. By the end of the month, Samsonov had been surrounded at Tannenberg.

Attempts to relieve the Second Army were bungled or intentionally undermined by Samsonov's rivals in the Russian command structure. Nearly 100,000

▶ Nagant M1895

Imperial Russian Army / 3rd Cavalry Division, 1914

A formidable sidearm, the Nagant M1895 revolver featured a cylinder that moved forward when the weapon was cocked, creating a tighter gas seal and higher muzzle velocity.

Specifications

Country of Origin: Russia	Overall Length: 229mm (9in)
Date: 1895	Barrel Length: 110mm (4.33in)
Calibre: 7.62mm (.3in)	Muzzle Velocity: 178m/sec (584ft/sec)
Operation: Revolver	Feed/Magazine: 7-round cylinder
Weight: .79kg (1.75lb)	Range: 20m (66ft)

▲ Madsen Let Maschingevaer

Imperial Russian Army / 3rd Guards Infantry Division, 1915

The Danish Madsen was the world's first true light machine gun. It was infantry-portable, adopted by the Danish Army in 1902, and deployed by Russian forces during World War I.

Specifications

Country of Origin: Denmark	Barrel Length: 585mm (23in)
Date: 1897	Muzzle Velocity: 715m/sec (2350ft/sec)
Calibre: 8mm (.314in) M89	Feed/Magazine: 25-, 30- or 40-round box
Operation: Recoil, air cooled	magazine
Weight: 9kg (20lb)	Cyclic Rate: 450rpm
Overall Length: 1145mm (45in)	Range: 1000m (3280ft)

Russian troops were captured and 30,000 killed. Samsonov committed suicide, and the Battle of Tannenberg is remembered as one of the greatest victories in German military history. German commanders Paul von Hindenburg (1847–1934) and Erich Ludendorff (1865–1937) were hailed as national heroes.

Soon, a German thrust towards Warsaw in the winter of 1914 was stopped at Lodz by the Russians, who suffered 120,000 casualties in the process and were forced to abandon an offensive action in Silesia. Russian losses continued to mount, compounding the difficulties of conscription and replenishing their rapidly depleting ranks. By the end of 1915, it was estimated that the Russian Army had lost two million men killed, wounded or captured within the previous six months.

On the Austro-Hungarian front, Russian troops made early gains during an offensive into Galicia. An Austro-Hungarian counterattack threw the Russians back, but the Autro-Hungarian forces were, in turn, compelled to retreat to the foothills of the Carpathian mountains. By the autumn of 1915, the Russians had been completely ejected from Galicia.

Red regime rising

The Germans considered the potential for the success of future offensive actions in the East to be limited, and for much of 1916 the fighting on the Eastern Front was inconclusive. The Russian Kerenski Offensive launched in the summer of 1917 ended in failure. Even though the Russians had absorbed horrendous losses and conscription riots had erupted in major cities, their vast manpower resource presented an obstacle that senior German commanders believed insurmountable in terms of achieving absolute and total victory. Therefore, greater numbers of German troops were concentrated in the West, while a campaign to foment continuing civil unrest in Russia was emphasized.

The German government facilitated the return of Bolshevik leader Vladimir Lenin (1870–1924) to Russia from exile, and by the autumn of 1917 the October Revolution had brought the Communists to power in Russia. The Treaty of Brest-Litovsk was concluded in the spring of 1918 and effectively ended Russian participation in World War I. Although they had won a victory in the East, the Central Powers sustained a high number of casualties in more than

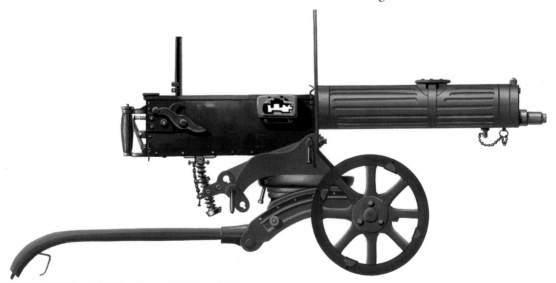

Specifications

Country of Origin: Russia	Barrel Length: 720mm (28.35in)
Date: 1910	Muzzle Velocity: 863m/sec (2831ft/sec)
Calibre: 7.62mm (.3in)	Feed/Magazine: Belt fed
Operation: Recoil, water cooled	Cyclic Rate: 520–600rpm
Weight: 23.8kg (52.47lb)	Range: Not known
Overall Length: 1107mm (43.6in)	

▲ **Pulemot Maksima Obrazets 1910**

Imperial Russian Army / 4th Infantry Division, 1916

Licensed and built as a copy of the Maxim Gun, the PM M1910 was of simpler overall design. It was mounted on a cumbersome carriage rather than a tripod.

three years of fighting. German losses alone are estimated at 1.4 million.

Eastern armaments

Those Russian-manufactured arms that reached their troops at the front were generally of good quality although never available in adequate numbers. Among the most prevalent rifles in the Russian ranks was the Mosin-Nagant bolt-action Model 1891, designed by Russian Army officer Sergei Mosin (1849–1902) and Belgian arms manufacturer Léon Nagant (1833–1900). The weapon was initially produced in Belgium and later adopted by the Russian military and built at locations in Russia as well as the United States.

▲ **Red columns**

A unit of revolutionary soldiers marches, Mosin-Nagant rifles shouldered and bayonets fixed. Most are wearing Russian Army uniform, and many of the combatants of the revolution and ensuing civil war were former Imperial soldiers.

The 7.62mm (.3in) bolt-action Mosin-Nagant rifle was fed by a five-round box magazine, and the weapon proved to be robust under the harsh conditions often encountered on the Eastern Front. Improvements to the rifle were made during the 1930s, including the introduction of a feed mechanism, greatly decreasing incidences of failure in combat. As production reached sufficient levels, the Mosin-Nagant was widely distributed to Russian Army units, and by the Russo-Japanese War of

▶ **Mauser Zig-Zag**

German Army / 43rd Infantry Regiment, 1915

The innovative series of external grooves that moved the cylinder of the Mauser Zig-Zag was a departure from the more traditional pawl-and-ratchet system.

Specifications

Country of Origin: Germany	Overall Length: 298mm (11.75in)
Date: 1878	Barrel Length: 165mm (6.5in)
Calibre: 10.9mm (.42in)	Muzzle Velocity: 198m/sec (650ft/sec)
Operation: Revolver	Feed/Magazine: 6-round cylinder
Weight: 1.19kg (2.625lb)	Range: 20m (66ft)

1904–05 nearly four million had been delivered. During World War I, the Russian government ordered an additional 3.2 million rifles from the American firms of Remington and Westinghouse. The Bolshevik Revolution, however, halted these deliveries. Variants of the Mosin-Nagant were in service with the Russian and Soviet armies for decades, and when production ceased in 1965 an estimated 37 million had been made.

The Russian variant of the often-imitated Maxim Gun was the Pulemot Maksima Obrazets 1910, more often referred to as the PM M1910. Adapted by the Russians to fire their 7.62mm (.3in) cartridge, this heavy machine gun was fed by a 250-round belt. Unlike the versions deployed by other nations, the Russian PM M1910 was mounted on a two-wheeled Sokolov carriage rather than a tripod, adding to its 23.8kg (52.47lb) weight and making the gun difficult to transport in some conditions. The Russians also added a gun shield which increased the weapon's unwieldy character. Regardless of its shortcomings, the PM M1910 proved durable and served with the Imperial Russian Army and later the Red Army through to the end of World War II.

▲ **Maxim Maschinengewehr 08/15 'light'**

German Air Force / Jagdstaffel 11, 1917

The MG 08/15 'light' was an air-cooled version of the original MG 08 intended for use aboard aircraft. About 23,000 were manufactured during World War I.

Specifications

Country of Origin: Germany	Barrel Length: 719mm (28.33in)
Date: 1915	Muzzle Velocity: 900m/sec (2953ft/sec)
Calibre: 7.92mm (.312in) Mauser	Feed/Magazine: 50-, 100- or 250-round fabric
Operation: Short recoil	belt
Weight: 18kg (39.75lb)	Cyclic Rate: 450rpm
Overall Length: 1398mm (55in)	Range: 1500m (4921ft))

▲ **Parabellum Maschinengewehr Model 14**

German Air Force / Jagdstaffel 16, 1917

The Parabellum Model 14 was specially adapted for use with aircraft. An air-cooled version was mounted to fixed-wing planes, while a water-cooled version was placed aboard Zeppelins. In 1918 a ground-mounted variant was introduced.

Specifications

Country of Origin: Germany	Barrel Length: 705mm (27.75in)
Date: 1914	Muzzle Velocity: 890m/sec (2925ft/sec)
Calibre: 7.92mm (.312in) Mauser	Feed/Magazine: Belt fed (belt contained in drum)
Operation: Recoil, water or air cooled	Cyclic Rate: 650–750rpm
Weight: 9.8kg (21.5lb)	Range: 2000m (6560ft) +
Overall Length: 1225mm (48.25in)	

▲ **Maxim Maschinengewehr 08/15**

German Army / 4th Infantry Brigade, 1916

As the need for mobile fire support for infantry was realized, it became apparent that heavy machine guns were better suited to defensive roles. In response, the lighter MG 08/15 was adapted from the original MG 08 design and proved effective as a portable automatic weapon.

Specifications

Country of Origin: Germany	Overall Length: 1398mm (55in)
Date: 1915	Barrel Length: 719mm (28.33in)
Calibre: 7.92mm (.312in) Mauser	Muzzle Velocity: 900m/sec (2953ft/sec)
Operation: Short recoil, water cooled	Feed/Magazine: 250-round box
Weight: 18kg (40lb)	Cyclic Rate: 450rpm
	Range: 3500m (11,483ft)

Austro-Hungarian Army
1914–18

The monarchy of Austria-Hungary had long considered Slavic Serbia a threat to its hold on the population within its borders, and the assassination of the heir to the nation's throne presented an immediate *casus belli*.

THE STANDING PEACETIME ARMY of Austria-Hungary numbered about 500,000 men, and by the summer of 1914 it had expanded to about one million. Plans to rapidly increase its numbers to 1.5 million and eventually to more than 3.3 million were formulated. Although the average number of conscripts prior to the war had numbered a respectable 160,000, the troops who wore the uniform were potentially problematic in themselves. The ethnic diversity within Austria-Hungary had long been an issue for the government, and fully 60 per cent of its people were of varied Slavic ancestry. Ardent nationalism among these ethnic peoples within the borders of Austria-Hungary was fuelled by the Slavic Serbs; therefore, the reliability of some troops was always suspect.

The Austro-Hungarian military establishment considered neighbouring Serbia a nuisance and anticipated a campaign that would be easily won despite a lack of military spending and relatively little

modernization of weaponry in the years preceding World War I. Confident that their German allies would provide the needed support to win a decisive victory over the Serbs, the Austro-Hungarians embarked on a belligerent course for which they were significantly underprepared.

With the outbreak of hostilities, the Austro-Hungarian Army fielded more than 100 infantry regiments. Each infantry company included four platoons and a complement of 267 soldiers, five of them officers. As was the case with their Russian enemies, machine guns were relatively scarce. Therefore, machine-gun detachments were organized at the battalion level and fielded only a pair of the adequately serviceable Schwarzelose M07.

The shortcomings within the Austro-Hungarian Army became starkly apparent in 1914 with the decisive defeat at the Battle of Cer Mountain only weeks after the assassination of Archduke Franz Ferdinand. During three days of fighting, well-placed

◀ Frommer Model 1910

Austro-Hungarian Army / 11th Infantry Regiment, 1914

The Frommer Model 1910 pistol was characterized by a long recoil that extended beyond the length of the cartridge it fired. An improved model, the Frommer Stop, was introduced in 1912.

Specifications

Country of Origin: Austria-Hungary	Overall Length: 184mm (7.25in)
Date: 1910	Barrel Length: 108mm (4.25in)
Calibre: 7.65mm (.301in)	Muzzle Velocity: 335m/sec (1100ft/sec)
Operation: Blowback	Feed/Magazine: 7-round magazine
Weight: .59kg (1.3lb)	Range: 20m (66ft)

◀ Schönberger

Austro-Hungarian Army / 24th Infantry Regiment, 1915

The Schönberger was the first semiautomatic sidearm to enter commercial production. Based on its predecessor, the Laumann 1892, it was a failure with the civilian market.

Specifications

Country of Origin: Germany	Overall Length: Not known
Date: 1892	Barrel Length: Not known
Calibre: 8mm (.314in)	Muzzle Velocity: 300m/sec (1200ft/sec)
Operation: Recoil	Feed/Magazine: 5-round fixed magazine
Weight: Not known	Range: 30m (98ft)

▲ Steyr-Mannlicher M1895

Austro-Hungarian Army / 90th Infantry Brigade, 1916

The standard issue rifle of the Austro-Hungarian Army during World War I, the Steyr-Mannlicher M1895 featured a straight-pull bolt action. It remained in service for decades after the war ended.

Specifications

Country of Origin: Austria-Hungary	Overall Length: 1272mm (50.12in)
Date: 1895	Barrel Length: 765mm (30.14in)
Calibre: 8mm (.314in)	Muzzel Velocity: Not known
Operation: Straight-pull bolt action	Feed/Magazine: 5-round en-bloc clip, internal
Weight: 3.8kg (8.36lb)	box magazine
	Range: 500m (1640ft)

Serbian artillery and infantry units rained shells and small-arms fire on the Austro-Hungarian forces inflicting 23,000 casualties, including 18,500 killed and wounded.

Nevertheless, the Austro-Hungarian Army was instrumental in maintaining a counterbalance to the overwhelming manpower of the Russians on the Eastern Front, although on repeated occasions its commanders were compelled to call upon the Germans for military assistance. Although they were initially pushed back by the Russian offensive in Galicia in 1914, the Austro-Hungarians rallied to drive the enemy back and held the line at the Carpathians.

The primary shoulder arm of the Austro-Hungarian Army in World War I was the Steyr-Mannlicher M1895 straight-pull bolt-action rifle. The Steyr-Mannlicher performed admirably during the war and facilitated a higher rate of fire (up to an astonishing 35 rounds per minute) than other contemporary rifles due to the fact that the rifleman was not required to turn the bolt during the reloading process. However, the bolt was a challenge to pull back and offered more resistance to its basic manipulation than other models.

Fed via an internal box magazine by a five-round en-bloc clip which was updated to a stripper clip in subsequent variants, the Steyr-Mannlicher fired an 8mm (.314in) cartridge. The rifle was produced from 1895 to 1918, and more than three million were manufactured. It remained in service with the armed forces of numerous countries through to the end of World War II and has since been discovered in the hands of paramilitary and guerrilla fighters around the globe.

Designed by Ferdinand Ritter von Mannlicher (1848–1904), the straight-pull bolt-action of the rifle

◀ Steyr M1911/1912

Austro-Hungarian Army / 1st Tyrolean Kaiserjäger Regiment, 1915

The M1911 and M1912 Steyr pistols were of Austrian design and differed only in the enhanced front sight on the later model. The Austro-Hungarian Army issued the weapon at the outbreak of the war, and some were converted to automatic capability.

Specifications

Country of Origin: Austria-Hungary	Overall Length: 216mm (8.5in)
Date: 1911	Barrel Length: 128mm (5.1in)
Calibre: 9mm (.35in)	Muzzle Velocity: 340m/sec (1115ft/sec)
Operation: Short recoil	Feed/Magazine: 8-round magazine
Weight: 1.02kg (2.25lb)	Range: 30m (98ft)

◀ Roth-Steyr M1907

Austro-Hungarian Army / 2nd Cavalry Division, 1916

The first semiautomatic sidearm to be adopted by the military of a major power, the Roth-Steyr 1907 was initially issued to cavalry units. It fired a cartridge unique to the weapon.

Specifications

Country of Origin: Austria-Hungary	Overall Length: 233mm (9in)
Date: 1907	Barrel Length: 131mm (5in)
Calibre: 8mm (.314in)	Muzzle Velocity: 332m/sec (1089ft/sec)
Operation: Short recoil	Feed/Magazine: 10-round magazine
Weight: 1.03kg (2.25lb)	Range: 30m (98ft)

earned it the nickname Ruck-Zuck from the soldiers who carried it. Although the rate of fire achieved with the straight pull was an advantage, improving the overall sturdy performance of the weapon, it also created issues with maintenance and demanded regular cleaning since there was little to assist the bolt action itself in the ejection of the spent cartridge.

The Steyr-Mannlicher was purchased by the Bulgarian government in 1903 and equipped the majority of that nation's infantry units during World War I. The weapon's straight-pull bolt further served as a model for the Canadian Ross rifle, which proved to be a bitter disappointment.

The Roth-Steyr M1907 pistol holds the distinction of being the first semiautomatic pistol adopted for regular use by the army of a major world military power. Czech designer Karel Krnka (1858–1926) developed the pistol, which was manufactured from 1908 to 1914 and acquired by the Austro-Hungarian military. It entered service in 1909, and nearly 100,000 were produced at the Steyr-Mannlicher works in Steyr, Austria, and at the Fegyvergyar factory near Budapest, Hungary.

Issued primarily as a cavalry weapon prior to World War I, the Roth-Steyr M1907 fired an 8mm (.314in) cartridge that was unique to this weapon.

The pistol's distinctive locked breech and long bolt facilitate the recoil of the barrel and bolt together through the hollow receiver. The 10-round magazine is fixed and cannot be detached.

Following the break-up of Austria-Hungary after World War I, the Roth-Steyr M1907 remained in service with the armies of both Austria and Hungary, as well as Yugoslavia, Italy, Czechoslovakia and Poland. About 54,000 were originally issued to military units, while the remainder were purchased by civilians.

Another long-serving pistol that was adopted by the Austro-Hungarian Army was the Steyr M1917 blowback 9mm (.35in) pistol. The M1917 was developed from the earlier M1912, which, in turn, traced its roots to the M1907.

Also commonly known as the Steyr Hahn, or Steyr Hammer, the M1912 was produced for the Austro-Hungarian military and remained in service with various armies until the end of World War II. Its eight-round magazine was fixed and loaded from above with a stripper clip. The pistol proved a sturdy sidearm that stood up to harsh treatment with little maintenance. Its reputation for reliability was borne out in the varied and rugged conditions that were prevalent on the Eastern Front in World War I. In response to a shortage of sidearms in the Austro-Hungarian Army, production of the M1912 and later the M1917 were increased substantially during the

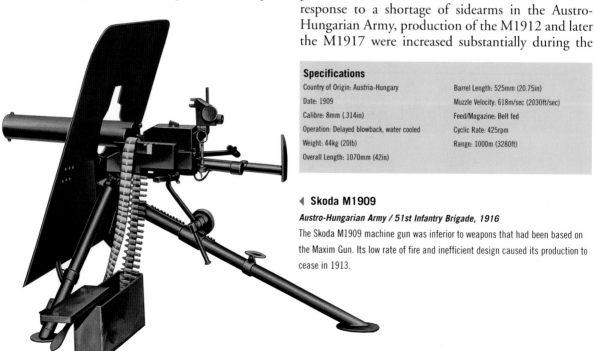

Specifications

Country of Origin: Austria-Hungary	Barrel Length: 525mm (20.75in)
Date: 1909	Muzzle Velocity: 618m/sec (2030ft/sec)
Calibre: 8mm (.314in)	Feed/Magazine: Belt fed
Operation: Delayed blowback, water cooled	Cyclic Rate: 425rpm
Weight: 44kg (20lb)	Range: 1000m (3280ft)
Overall Length: 1070mm (42in)	

◀ **Skoda M1909**

Austro-Hungarian Army / 51st Infantry Brigade, 1916

The Skoda M1909 machine gun was inferior to weapons that had been based on the Maxim Gun. Its low rate of fire and inefficient design caused its production to cease in 1913.

Great War, and more than 300,000 were manufactured before production ended in 1945.

The Frommer Model 1910 was a blowback, 7.65mm (.301in) semiautomatic pistol that utilized a long recoil of the barrel and bolt, exceeding the entire length of the cartridge. The cartridge itself was fashioned specifically for the Model 1910 with a crimp in the casing of the round. The pistol held a seven-round magazine and was effective to a range of 20m (66ft). Designer Rudolf Frommer (1868–1936) incorporated a short-recoil system into later models; however, in the years preceding World War I the long recoil was a hallmark of his handguns. In 1912, the Frommer Stop was introduced and offered a more traditional configuration in an updated version of the Model 1910. The Frommer Stop survived World War I as the standard issue sidearm of the Hungarian armed forces.

▶ Steyr M1917

Austro-Hungrian Army / 26th Infantry Brigade, 1917

Reloaded from the top using a charger, the Steyr M1917 semiautomatic pistol was an upgrade of the M1912 and remained in service with the Austrian and Hungarian armies through to the end of World War II.

Specifications

Country of Origin: Austria-Hungary	Overall Length: 216mm (8.5in)
Date: 1917	Barrel Length: 128mm (5.03in)
Calibre: 9mm (.35in)	Muzzle Velocity: 335m/sec (1100ft/sec)
Operation: Blowback	Feed/Magazine: 8-round fixed magazine
Weight: .99kg (2.18lb)	Range: 30m (98ft)

Specifications

Country of Origin: Austria-Hungary	Barrel Length: 525mm (20.75in)
Date: 1907	Muzzle Velocity: 618m/sec (2030ft/sec)
Calibre: 8mm (.314in)	Feed/Magazine: Belt fed
Operation: Blowback, water cooled	Cyclic Rate: 425rpm
Weight: 20kg (44lb)	Range: 1000m (3280ft) +
Overall Length: 1070mm (42in)	

▲ Schwarzlose M07/12

Austro-Hungarian Army / 88th Infantry Brigade, 1917

Though produced in four variants, the delayed-blowback operation of the Schwarzlose caused it to utilize a short barrel, which limited the range of the weapon and shortened its service life compared with other machine guns.

Austrian machine guns

The Austro-Hungarian Army deployed the water-cooled, 8mm (.314in) Schwarzlose M07/12 medium machine gun during World War I and exported the weapon to the armed forces of The Netherlands, Greece and Sweden as well. The Schwarzlose operated with a toggle-delayed blowback mechanism and was fed by a 250-round ammunition belt. Mounted on a tripod and served by a crew of three, it was initially capable of a cyclic rate of fire of 400 rounds per minute; however, this was later increased to 580 rounds with the addition of a more efficient spring. The weapon remained in service beyond the end of World War II, equipping the Czech Army during the early Cold War period.

Like its contemporaries, the Schwarzlose M07/12 had a design based on the Maxim Gun, but the weapon was of overall simpler construction. As an infantry weapon it may be deemed a success. However, in contrast to other medium machine guns, conversions to anti-aircraft or heavier support roles were disappointing.

Prior to Czech independence from Austria-Hungary in 1918, the famed arms works of Skoda in the city of Plzen produced weapons for the monarchy's armed forces. The M1909 machine gun was manufactured by Skoda from 1909 to 1913 and operated with a delayed blowback mechanism. The weapon was water-cooled and fired an 8mm (.314in) cartridge. It was fed by a 250-round belt, and later versions achieved an improved rate of fire above the initial 250 rounds per minute. Nevertheless, the M1909's overall performance was rated inferior to Maxim-inspired designs.

▲ **Defensive line**

Austrian troops set up a temporary defensive line with machine-gun pits and a shallow trench somewhere in the Caporetto area.

Italian Army
1915–18

Longstanding rivalry with Austria-Hungary pushed Italy towards the Allies and a protracted war of attrition along the nation's rugged mountainous border regions.

WHEN WAR BROKE OUT IN EUROPE IN 1914, Italy was not yet prepared to commit to either the Allies or the Central Powers. A relatively new nation in itself, a united Italy had emerged from the jumble of city states and minor monarchies a little over 50 years earlier. From a military standpoint, the Italian Army had embarked on an ill-fated venture into Ethiopia in 1896 and fought a costly war against Turkey for control of Libya in 1911–12.

Following the Italian declaration of war against the Central Powers, initially Austria-Hungary, in 1915, it was apparent to the country's military establishment that the army was not yet ready for combat. Its complement of just under a million men was raised considerably by spring 1915 when active operations began. However, the 35 divisions at the disposal of General Luigi Cadorna (1850–1928), the army chief of staff and overall commander, were woefully short

▲ **Moschetto 1891 per Cavalleria**

Italian Army / 8th Cavalry Regiment, 1915

A shortened stock facilitated use of this carbine by Italian cavalry units during World War I. The weapon was noted for its folding bayonet that was permanently fixed and could be deployed when the trooper dismounted.

Specifications

Country of Origin: Italy	Overall Length: 920mm (36.2in)
Date: 1891	Barrel Length: 610mm (24in)
Calibre: 6.5mm (.256in)	Muzzle Velocity: 700m/sec (2275ft/sec)
Operation: Bolt action	Feed/Magazine: 6-round integral box magazine
Weight: 3kg (6.6lb)	Range: 600m (1968ft)

Specifications

Country of Origin: Italy	Overall Length: 1291mm (50.79in)
Date: 1891	Barrel Length: 780mm (30.6in)
Calibre: 6.5mm (.256in)	Muzzle Velocity: 730m/sec (2400ft/sec)
Operation: Bolt action	Feed/Magazine: 6-round integral box magazine
Weight: 3.8kg (8.375lb)	Range: 1000m (3280ft)

▲ **Mannlicher Carcano Model 1891**

Italian Army / 37th Infantry Division, 1915

The primary rifle of the Italian infantry until it was modified in 1938, the Model 1891 fired a 6.5mm (.256in) cartridge. The Mannlicher Carcano name is somewhat misleading due to limited Austrian design influence.

of ammunition, machine guns and artillery as Italian arms manufacturers lacked the capacity to keep pace with demand.

Along a 644km (400-mile) line in the north of the country, Cadorna divided the front into three departments, the Isonzo, Alpine and Trentino. The bloodiest fighting was to take place along the Isonzo where some areas of hilly terrain provided space for troop manoeuvring but at length would expose an advancing army to killing fire from enemy-occupied higher ground.

Opposing the 35 Italian divisions across the frontier were 20 Austro-Hungarian divisions, and Cadorna assumed the offensive in the region in May 1915, nearly 10 months after the war had begun elsewhere. Throughout the summer and into 1916, the Italians repeatedly threw themselves against strong Austro-Hungarian defences along the Isonzo line, losing 60,000 soldiers in the first two weeks alone. Numerical superiority was of little advantage, and Italian casualties were horrific, often numbering more than 30,000 dead, wounded or taken prisoner in a single attack. Little ground was gained, and the landscape of trenches resembled that of the Western Front in France, although the hazardous terrain compounded the logistical difficulties faced by both sides on the Italian front.

Catastrophe at Caporetto

After 11 costly but indecisive battles on the Isonzo, the German high command at last responded to Austro-Hungarian appeals for reinforcements, allowing a combined army of the Central Powers to assume the offensive. On 24 October 1916, the 12th Battle of the Isonzo, perhaps better known as Caporetto, was launched with a tremendous German and Austro-Hungarian artillery bombardment followed by a devastating gas attack. The attackers realized early success, spurred by the rapid movement of their infiltrating stormtrooper formations.

The battle ended in disaster for the Italians, who were driven back great distances and finally made a stand a scant few kilometres from the great city of Venice. They had more than 10,000 dead and 300,000 wounded or captured, and losses in weapons and equipment were staggering as well. Britain, France and later the United States committed reinforcements to stabilize the front, and a wave of conscripts and recruits replenished the depleted Italian ranks. War-weary Austro-Hungarian troops essentially ceased offensive operations through 1917 while the Italians marshalled their forces.

Barely two weeks before the armistice of 11 November 1918, the Italians attacked, capturing the town of Vittorio Veneto as a demoralized Austro-Hungarian enemy fled or surrendered in large numbers and their government collapsed. From 1915 to 1918, Italy deployed just over five million troops and suffered 420,000 dead and more than 950,000 wounded.

Italian small arms

Italian infantry units in World War I were regularly armed with the Mannlicher Carcano Model 1891 bolt-action rifle, which incorporated elements of both the German Mauser and the Austrian

◀ **Glisenti Model 1910**

Italian Army / 54th Infantry Regiment, 1915

Although somewhat underpowered, the Glisenti Model 1910 was nevertheless adopted by the Italian Army. Its low muzzle velocity hampered performance during close combat; however, the handgun was common with Italian forces into World War II.

Specifications

Country of Origin: Italy	Overall Length: 210mm (8.25in)
Date: 1910	Barrel Length: 99mm (3.9in)
Calibre: 9mm (.35in)	Muzzle Velocity: 305m/sec (1000ft/sec)
Operation: Short recoil, locked breech	Feed/Magazine: 7-round magazine
Weight: .82kg (1.8lb)	Range: 20m (66ft)

Mannlicher shoulder arms. Engineer Salvatore Carcano (1827–1903) developed the rifle and chambered it for the 6.5mm (.256in) rimless cartridge fed by en-bloc charger clips into a six-round box magazine. The rifle is more properly identified as the Model 91, and the only real link to Mannlicher designs lies in the ammunition clip and feed system.

Production of the weapon in long rifle and carbine versions was undertaken at Turin, and it was adopted by the Italian Army in 1891. The carbine was issued primarily to cavalry and specialized units such as alpine troops. A half-stocked cavalry carbine known as the Moschetto 1891 per Cavalleria was produced by several manufacturers, including FNA Brescia,

Specifications

Country of Origin: Italy	Barrel Length: 320mm (12.6in)
Date: 1915	Muzzle Velocity: 320m/sec (1050ft/sec)
Calibre: 9mm (.35in)	Feed/Magazine: Box magazine
Operation: Blowback	Cyclic Rate: 350rpm
Weight: 6.5kg (14.33lb)	Range: 2000m (6560ft) +
Overall Length: 558.8mm (21in)	

▼ Villar-Perosa M1915

Italian Army / 8th Alpini Regiment, 1916

The world's first submachine gun, the Model 1915 provided a substantial rate of fire, but its use was inhibited by the need for a bipod or a platform slung across a soldier's shoulders.

▼ Villar-Perosa OVP M1918

Italian Army / 6th Alpini Regiment, 1917

Essentially a half-size version of the Model 1915 submachine gun, the Model 1918 was capable of automatic or single-shot modes, employed a rifle stock and was primarily issued to alpine troops to provide mobile fire support.

Specifications

Country of Origin: Italy	Barrel Length: Not known
Date: 1915	Muzzle Velocity: 301.82m/sec (990ft/sec)
Calibre: 9mm (.35in)	Feed/Magazine: 25-round detachable box
Operation: Blowback	magazine
Weight: 3.62kg (8lb)	Range: 70m (230ft)
Overall Length: 901.69mm (35.5in)	

and featured a folding bayonet permanently fixed to a muzzle mounting and hinged for storage backwards in a slot beneath the stock.

The Model 91 operated with a rotating bolt action and produced an adequate rate of fire, which was enhanced due to the fact that its clip was open and could be loaded from either end. The original rifle was standard issue with the Italian Army until 1938 when it was rechambered to fire the heavier 7.35mm (.29in) cartridge. It was produced until 1945, and thousands were sold as surplus, one of which gained infamy as the weapon used by assassin Lee Harvey Oswald (1939–1963) to kill US president John F. Kennedy (1917–1963).

The 9mm (.35in) Glisenti Model 1910 short-

▲ **Hidden emplacement**

Italian troops man a machine-gun emplacement protected by sandbags. They are firing through a small loophole and much care has been taken to conceal their position.

▼ **Fiat-Revelli Modello 14**

Italian Army / 3rd Bersaglieri Regiment, 1917

Prone to jamming, the Modello 14 was difficult to fire and proved unpopular with Italian troops. Its loading system was cumbersome and performed poorly in combat.

Specifications

Country of Origin: Italy

Date: 1914

Calibre: 6.5mm (.256in) M95

Operation: Delayed blowback, water cooled

Weight: 17kg (37.75lb)

Overall Length: 1180mm (46.5in)

Barrel Length: 655mm (25.75in)

Muzzle Velocity: 640m/sec (2100ft/sec)

Feed/Magazine: Magazine fed

Cyclic Rate: 400rpm

Range: 1500m (4921ft)

recoil pistol was common among Italian troops during World War I. The semiautomatic locked-breech handgun was fed by a seven-round detachable box magazine and was effective to a range of 20m (66ft). Produced by Real Factory D'arma Glisenti, the weapon was adopted in 1910 and served with Italian forces through World War II. Although it was intended to fire a unique cartridge, it could operate with the 9mm (.35in) Parabellum with substantial recoil that was difficult to manage and even dangerous.

Automatic weapons

Two Italian automatic weapons, the Villar-Perosa M1915 and OVP M1918 could be described as variants of the first deployed submachine gun. The M1915 was originally designed to provide mobile fire support for alpine troops. Its double barrel provided a substantial rate of fire, but the weapon was highly inaccurate. Although it was mobile, it was somewhat unwieldy and was fired from a bipod or a platform worn over the shoulders of the soldier in 'cigarette girl' fashion. The single-barrelled OVP M1918 utilized a rifle stock and was basically a 'half-version' of the M1915.

Italian machine-gun development lagged behind that of other belligerents prior to World War I, and two types, the Fiat-Revelli Modello 14 and the Perino M1913, were primarily used during the Great War. The Fiat-Revelli was indicative of an Italian penchant for overengineered loading mechanisms that required ammunition to be lubricated for firing and unsurprisingly this resulted in numerous incidents of jamming or failure in the field.

Fed from 10-round clips inserted in a revolving drum, the delayed-blowback-operating Modello 14 often split cartridges in the chamber. A later version, the Modello 35, eliminated some of the issues with loading and employed a belt-feed system. The Modello 14 was chambered for the 6.5mm (.256in) cartridge and was water-cooled, firing at a cyclic rate of 400 rounds per minute.

The Perino M1913, which worked on a combined recoil and gas-operated system, was both water- and air-cooled. It was a successor to at least two improvements to an original machine gun designed by engineer Giuseppe Perino in 1901. Perino is credited with developing the first Italian machine gun, and the M1913 fired a 6.5mm (.256in) cartridge at a cyclic rate of 500 rounds per minute.

Specifications

Country of Origin: Italy

Date: 1913

Calibre: 6.5mm (.256in) M95

Operation: Combined recoil/gas operated, water/air cooled

Weight: 13.65kg (30lb)

Overall Length: 1180mm (46.5in)

Barrel Length: 655mm (25.75in)

Muzzle Velocity: 640m/sec (2100ft/sec)

Feed/Magazine: Strip fed

Cyclic Rate: 500rpm

Range: 1500m (4921ft)

▶ **Perino M1913**

Italian Army / 151st Infantry Regiment, 1917

A descendant of the first operational Italian machine gun, the Model 1913 was a lighter version of the original, which was produced in 1901, and utilized a combined gas and recoil operating system.

Chapter 3

Interwar Years

During the turbulent twentieth century, the years between the world wars remained restive. Nascent nationalism, ideological awakenings and imperialistic ambitions steadily heightened tensions across the globe. In concert, the proliferation of rifles, machine guns and other small arms gave rise to military operations on both a grand and localized scale. While isolated battles were often fought between rival factions, larger conflicts served as proving grounds for new and innovative small arms, including a generation of machine guns and automatic weapons that increased the firepower of individual soldiers to unprecedented levels and raised casualty figures appreciably. Meanwhile, the war-proven shoulder arms from Mauser, Springfield, Lee-Enfield and other sources were refined, upgraded and supplemented as new rifles emerged to arm the legions of soldiers destined to prosecute the greatest military conflict the world has ever known.

◀ **House search**
Spanish troops loyal to General Franco search buildings somewhere in Spain during the Spanish Civil War. They are armed with Lebel Berthier 1915 bolt-action rifles.

Introduction

Ethnic and civil wars, the rise of totalitarian regimes and the reach for empire made the interwar years a turbulent period.

THE INTRODUCTION OF SMALL ARMS on a grand scale heightened an uneasy peace between the great powers and gave rise to guerrilla warfare and revolution. The Treaty of Versailles included 440 clauses. Of these, more than 400 were related to the guilt of Germany for fomenting World War I or the nation's responsibility to pay reparations and disarm. The terms of the treaty crippled Germany and exacerbated the impact of the Great Depression, which plunged the world into economic chaos in the autumn of 1929.

The treaty limited the *Reichswehr*, the German Army of the Weimar Republic, to 84,000 rifles, 18,000 carbines, 792 heavy machine guns and 1134 light machine guns. These were to be parcelled evenly throughout a standing army that numbered no more than 100,000 troops and consisted of seven infantry and three cavalry divisions. Therefore, a standard *Reichswehr* infantry division was to be allocated 12,000 rifles, while a cavalry division received 6000 carbines. Only 108 heavy and 162 light machine guns were theoretically available for each infantry division. The number of officers and non-commissioned officers was severely restricted to deprive the German armed forces of cohesive, experienced leadership.

In truth, however, Germany had never completely disarmed and a covert, shadow army remained active, with training in the use of small arms in effective offensive operations at its core. Even before the rise of the Nazi Party to power in 1933, the Germans were actively circumventing the harsh terms of the treaty. With General Hans von Seeckt (1866–1936) as its prime mover, the German military covertly exceeded the 100,000-man limitation on troop strength specified at Versailles, while clandestine arrangements were made with the Soviet Union to train soldiers and gain familiarity with infantry weapons and small-arms tactics. Major German arms manufacturers such as Krupp and Rheinmetall contracted with foreign companies or their own subsidiaries outside the borders of Germany to produce new weapons systems. With the outbreak of civil war in Spain, Nazi Germany took advantage of an opportunity to

◀ **Czechoslovakian manoeuvres**
Czechoslovakian soldiers armed with the Czechoslovakian version of the Mauser Kar 98 rifle, the vz. 24, and Maschinengewehr 08/15 Maxim-style machine guns carry out manoeuvres, mid-1930s. Many of the Czechoslovakians' impressive arsenal of weaponry fell into the hands of the *Wehrmacht* following the Nazi occupation of the Sudetenland in 1938.

▲ **Defence of the people**
Government troops fire on rebels from the shelter of a hastily erected barricade, Toledo, July 1936.

support the Nationalist forces of Generalissimo Francisco Franco (1892–1975), and along with Fascist Italy sent troops, planes (and pilots to fly them) and other war materiel to fight the Republican forces. Italy under Benito Mussolini (1883–1945) also invaded a virtually defenceless Ethiopia and occupied tiny Albania across the Adriatic Sea in the turbulent Balkans.

By the spring of 1935, German chancellor Adolf Hitler (1889–1945) had repudiated the Treaty of Versailles and told the world that Germany was rearming, albeit for peaceful and defensive purposes only. On 16 March, Hitler boldly declared Germany's initial compliance with the treaty and alleged that other nations had failed to take advantage of opportunities to disarm and promote peace. He claimed that Germany had actually destroyed more than six million rifles, 130,000 machine guns and 244,000 barrels, 340,000 tonnes (335,000 tons) of ammunition cartridges, more than 16.5 million hand and rifle grenades, 180 machine-gun sleds, and 174,000 gas masks among other weapons of war, large and small.

In the process of unveiling German rearmament to the world, Hitler further twisted the words of British prime minister Stanley Baldwin (1867–1947), who stated, 'A nation that is not willing to take the necessary precautionary measures for its own defence will never have any power in the world, neither of the moral nor of the material kind.'

As for Great Britain and France, post-war malaise persisted in the wake of a catastrophic global conflict that had nearly bankrupted their national treasuries, while various political factions sought to curb military preparedness and pointed to the tremendous casualty tolls of 1914–18 as the rationale for their protests. In the process, appeasement came to have heavy influence on British and French foreign policy. In the United States, a resurgence of isolationism emerged and the standing army dwindled towards 100,000 – not by treaty but by design and steady decline. Meanwhile, in Asia the war machine of Imperial Japan prepared for offensive action to expand territorial control and prestige throughout the region.

French Forces: North Africa
1920–39

European influence in North Africa was heavily contested in Morocco as Spain, later joined by France, sought to consolidate rule over tribal regions east of their mountainous holdings.

THE TREATY OF FEZ was concluded in 1912, and like other treaties of its time became the basis for future conflict. As a portion of Morocco became a French protectorate, the government of Spain was given territory in the mountainous western region of the country. Subsequently, it was decided that the Spanish would extend their rule into eastern areas populated by the Rif and Jabala tribes.

Although the Spanish troops deployed were better armed and equipped, the natives under the leadership of Abd el-Krim (1882–1963) resisted resolutely and five years of insurgency, counter-insurgency and open warfare ensued. Eventually, the Spanish were joined by French troops and succeeded in asserting control in the region. However, Abd el-Krim proved to be a resourceful tactician and builder of consensus among the various native factions taking part in the resistance to European rule, sowing the seeds of pan-North African nationalism that was to rise with great force a half-century later.

Another unintended consequence of the Rif Wars was the emergence of Francisco Franco (1892–1975), a leader of Spanish troops who distinguished himself during the fighting in Morocco and gained a

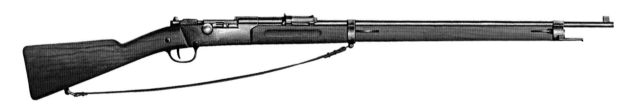

▲ **Fusil Mle 1886**

French Army / 2nd Foreign Legion Regiment, Morocco, 1920

The bolt-action Lebel Model 1886 was the standard French Army rifle from the late nineteenth century until the 1930s. Nearly three million were produced, and it remained in service alongside other weapons intended as replacements.

Specifications

Country of Origin: France	Overall Length: 1303mm (51.3in)
Date: 1886	Barrel Length: 798mm (31.4in)
Calibre: 8mm (.314in) Lebel	Muzzle Velocity: 725m/sec (2379ft/sec)
Operation: Bolt action	Feed/Magazine: 8-round tubular magazine
Weight: 4.245kg (9.375lb)	Range: 400m (1312ft)

▲ **Fusil Automatique Modèle 1917**

French Army / 4th Foreign Legion Regiment, Morocco, 1925

Intended to supplant the Lebel Model 1886 rifle in the French Army, the Modèle 1917 entered production late in World War I and eventually saw service in the Rif Wars. Its semiautomatic operation was aided by gas cartridge ejection.

Specifications

Country of Origin: France	Overall Length: 1331mm (52.4in)
Date: 1917	Barrel Length: 798mm (31.4in)
Calibre: 8mm (.314in) Lebel	Muzzle Velocity: 853m/sec (2800ft/sec)
Operation: Gas, rotating bolt	Feed/Magazine: 5-round box magazine
Weight: 5.25kg (11.6lb)	Range: 300m (984ft)

following among military personnel who had become disenchanted with the instability of government at home. By the end of the Rif Wars in 1926, Franco had become the youngest general in any European army and gained additional notoriety suppressing labour unrest. The emergence of a left-wing Popular Front government precipitated a failed coup d'etat by Franco and members of the Falange Party, bringing about the bloody Spanish Civil War.

French firepower

A pair of French rifles were prominent during the Rif Wars and beyond. The Lebel Model 1886 and its successor, the Fusil Automatique Modèle 1917, were available in large numbers among the French regular troops and Foreign Legionnaires who took part in the Moroccan fighting. The Lebel 1886 was an 8mm (.314in) bolt-action rifle that entered service in large numbers with French forces in the spring of 1887. Fed by an eight-round tubular magazine, the Lebel was the primary shoulder arm of the French Army during World War I.

During the course of the weapon's production from 1887 to 1920, more than 2.8 million Lebel Model 1886 rifles were produced by state-run arms-manufacturing facilities in Châtellerault, Saint-Etienne and Tulle. The rifle was distributed in large quantities to French colonial troops during World War I; therefore, thousands of them found their way into the hands of rebels, insurgents, and militia that later fought the French and Spanish militaries during the Rif Wars. Early setbacks for European forces also resulted in the capture of many of these weapons.

The Fusil Automatique Modèle 1917 was the result of a French attempt to replace the Lebel rifle and became operational with units of the French Army in the spring of 1916. The rifle was also known as the Modèle 1917 RSC, for its design collaboration team of Ribeyrolles, Sutter, and Chauchat. By the end of World War I in November 1918, approximately 86,000 of these had been built by the French government at its Manufacture d'armes de Saint-Etienne facility. The Modèle 1917 fired an 8mm (.314in) cartridge and was operated by bolt action with a long recoil and gas-operated ejection assistance for spent cartridges, which provided some benefits of semiautomatic operation. Its internal box magazine was fed by a five-round clip. Although it appeared late in World War I, French troops rapidly formed a negative opinion of the Modèle 1917, particularly because its length of 1331mm (52.4in) was too cumbersome for trench warfare.

A substantial improvement to the design was completed in 1918 and included the change from a proprietary ammunition clip to the universal Berthier clip. About 4000 of the 1918 variant were produced, and many of these performed satisfactorily during the Rif Wars.

▲ **Fusil Mitrailleur Mle 24/29**

French Army / 21st Colonial Infantry Regiment, Morocco, 1924

An improvement over the Mle 1915 of World War I, the Modèle 24/29 served with the French armed forces into the 1950s and was the army's principal light machine gun of World War II.

Specifications

Country of Origin: France	Barrel Length: 500mm (19.75in)
Date: 1924	Muzzle Velocity: 825m/sec (2707ft/sec)
Calibre: 7.5mm (.295in) M29	Cyclic Rate: 450rpm
Operation: Gas operated, air cooled	Feed/Magazine: 25-round box magazine
Weight: 9.25kg (20.25lb)	Range: 1000m (3280ft) +
Overall Length: 1080mm (42.5in)	

Spanish Civil War
1936–39

The bloody Spanish Civil War raged for three years and served as a harbinger of the global war that followed as Nazi Germany and Fascist Italy sent direct military aid to the forces of Francisco Franco.

FOR NEARLY A CENTURY prior to the outbreak of the Spanish Civil War on 17 July 1936, Spain had experienced periods of tumult and chaos as rival liberal and conservative factions vied for preeminence and the long-embattled monarchy endured despite numerous efforts to undermine or abolish it. The Republican government of Spain had attempted to quell right-wing discontent among the army leadership and demoted General Francisco Franco (1892–1975) to command in the Canary Islands. However, he was later able to escape capture and rally troops in North Africa for landings at Seville. The war dragged on until the conservative government, dominated by Franco and his Falange Party, consolidated power in April 1939.

Atrocities were widespread on both sides during the Spanish Civil War, and civilian deaths numbered in the hundreds of thousands. Both Nazi Germany and Fascist Italy sent military personnel, arms and equipment in support of Franco, while the Soviet Union provided limited support for the Republicans. Eventually, Franco controlled the country while the monarchy survived with limited authority.

During the Spanish Civil War, a flood of small arms from around the world equipped the forces of both the Nationalists and Republicans. In addition to the French Lebel, German Mauser, British Lee-Enfield and Austrian Mannlicher rifles that had been so prevalent during World War I, the American Springfield Model 1903 and numerous other shoulder arms such as the antiquated Norwegian Krag-Jørgensen saw service during the conflict.

Machine guns in Spain

Numerous types of machine gun were deployed during the Spanish Civil War. Prominent among them was the German Maschinengewehr 34, commonly known as the MG 34, which entered service with the German Army in great numbers following Hitler's repudiation of the Versailles Treaty in the spring of 1935. The MG 34 was tested in combat by German troops aiding Franco's Nationalists, and its characteristics as an automatic weapon with a heavy sustained rate of fire, providing substantial support to infantry in defensive positions but highly mobile as well, were demonstrated to the world in horrific fashion.

French machine guns, including improved versions of World War I-vintage Fusil Mitrailleur and Hotchkiss models, were deployed by both sides. At

▶ **Unceta Victoria**

Spanish Nationalist Army / 2nd CCNN Division Fiamme Nere (Black Flames),
Guadalajara, 1937

Closely related to the Browning family of pistols, the Unceta Victoria was also closely associated with the Ruby pistol of the French Army during World War I. It was adopted by the French after entering service in 1911.

Specifications

Country of Origin: Spain	Barrel Length: 81mm (3.2in)
Date: 1911	Muzzle Velocity: 229m/sec (750ft/sec)
Calibre: 7.65mm (.301in)	Feed/Magazine: 7-round detachable box
Operation: Blowback	magazine
Weight: .57kg (1.25lb)	Range: 30m (98ft)
Overall Length: 146mm (5.75in)	

the end of World War I, the French military assessed the shortcomings of the Mitrailleur Modèle 1915 and determined to provide a more functional and reliable weapon to its soldiers. In competition with the newly developed American Browning Automatic Rifle (BAR), the French arms producer Manufacture d'Armes de Saint-Etienne (MAS) won a competitive bid to produce the Modèle 24/29.

This updated machine gun was to serve as the basic French light infantry support weapon for the next quarter-century and has surfaced as late as the last decade in the hands of various militia and paramilitary groups. It also remained in service with the French *Gendarmerie Nationale* until 2006. The Modèle 24/29 was known for its in-line stock, bipod mount and pistol grip, which was favoured by infantrymen for ease of aiming and control of the weapon's vibration. It was fed by a 25-round top-fitted magazine, and the bolt held itself open for reloading when the last round was fired. A Lieutenant-Colonel Reibel, credited with the weapon's design, recognized the need for a comparatively high cyclic rate of fire and achieved that at 450 rounds per minute.

The weapon first entered service as the Modèle 1924 and fired a 7.5mm (.295in) cartridge, a departure from the traditional 8mm (.314in) ammunition. Problems encountered through trying to use captured 8mm (.314in) rounds during the Rif Wars, though, led to the production of a modified

version of the weapon, which became the Modèle 24/29. The machine gun armed French troops during the opening days of the Nazi offensive against France during the spring of 1940 and emerged as a prominent weapon during the Algerian war for independence in the 1950s. A further modification was accomplished in 1931 and included a heavier barrel and drum feed, increasing the rate of fire to 600 rounds per minute.

Another French light machine gun, the Hotchkiss M1922/26, suffered from a woefully underfunded French arms research and development industry in the 1920s. Although the design itself was promising, with a muzzle-climb compensator and an adjustable rate of fire, the weapon almost came to nothing and its production numbers were limited. A handful of these 6.5mm (.256in) machine guns with a cyclic rate of fire of 500 rounds per minute were in action during the Rif Wars and in the Spanish Civil War. Most of the production run was sold to the Greek armed forces.

Spanish export

The blowback-operated Unceta Victoria pistol fired a 7.65mm (.301in) cartridge and utilized a seven-round detachable box magazine. It was developed by the Spanish firm that later came to be known as Astra and entered service in 1911. The pistol initially saw action with Allied forces in 1914 and was officially adopted by the French Army. Patterned after the

▲ **Hotchkiss M1922/26**

Nationalist Army / Flechas Negras (Black Arrows) Division, Catalonia, 1938

An adjustable rate of fire and muzzle-climb compensator were two outstanding features of the Hotchkiss M1922/26; however, the weapon was produced in limited numbers due to French arms budget constraints. Most were exported to Greece, while a relative few were fielded during the Spanish Civil War.

Specifications

Country of Origin: France	Barrel Length: 575mm (22.75in)
Date: 1922	Muzzle Velocity: 745m/sec (2444ft/sec)
Calibre: 6.5mm (.256in)	Feed/Magazine: 25- or 30-round strip
Operation: Gas operated, air cooled	Cyclic Rate: 500rpm
Weight: 9.5kg (21lb)	Range: 1000m (3280ft) +
Overall Length: 1215mm (47.75in)	

▲ **Republican column**
Republican soldiers move up to the front lines in the Guadarrama Mountains, September 1936.

American Browning Model 1903, it is considered by many to be an almost identical copy of the Ruby pistol that was widely used by the French Army as a sidearm during World War I.

Automatic weapons

Although the Treaty of Versailles prohibited the deployment of submachine guns with the German armed forces, they had nevertheless utilized them during the waning months of World War I and recognized their tremendous firepower enhancement capabilities. Therefore, the Germans continued the development of the submachine gun during the interwar years, and its prowess on the battlefield was validated in combat in Spain. Typically, German submachine gun designations included the initials 'MP' for *Maschinenpistole.*

The German Erma MPE was one of the most widely used submachine guns of the Spanish Civil War and was exported in large numbers to several nations in Central and South America whose governments were right-wing. Designed in the 1920s by Heinrich Vollmer (1885–1961), the Erma MPE

was used by both French Foreign Legion and German troops during the 1930s and was eventually replaced by the MP 38. It was fed by a 32-round detachable box magazine that was loaded from the left side, and featured a wooden stock and pistol grip for control.

In another effort to circumvent the Treaty of Versailles, the German government facilitated the acquisition of the Swiss firm of Solothurn by Rheinmetall, and production of a prototype began on what came to be known as the MP 34. Rheinmetall in turn purchased a controlling interest in the Austrian arms manufacturer Steyr, and the result was a highly successful submachine gun that developed a reputation for operational excellence. The Austrian version of the MP 34 was known as the Steyr-Solothurn S1-100. The blowback-operated weapon fired a 9mm (.35in) cartridge and was fed by a detachable box magazine holding from 20 to 32 rounds. It featured a selective shot option, either single-round or fully automatic. Although the weapon was extremely well made, production of the MP 34/Steyr-Solothurn S1-100 was somewhat limited due to high materials costs.

▲ Erma MPE

Guardia Civil

Widely used during the Spanish Civil War, the Erma MPE began production in 1930. Its service life was extended by a significant export market for the submachine gun in Central and South America.

Specifications

Country of Origin: Germany	Barrel Length: 254mm (10in)
Date: 1930	Muzzle Velocity: 395m/sec (1300ft/sec)
Calibre: 9mm (.35in) Parabellum	Feed/Magazine: 32-round box magazine
Operation: Blowback	Cyclic Rate: 500rpm
Weight: 4.15kg (9.13lb)	Range: 70m (230ft)
Overall Length: 902mm (35.5in)	

Specifications

Country of Origin: Austria	Barrel Length: 200mm (7.87in)
Date: 1930	Muzzle Velocity: 418m/sec (1370ft/sec)
Calibre: 9mm (.35in)	Feed/Magazine: 20- or 32-round box magazine
Operation: Blowback	Cyclic Rate: 500rpm
Weight: 4.48kg (9.88lb)	Range: 100m (328ft)
Overall Length: 850mm (33.46in)	

▲ Steyr-Solothurn S1-100

Army of Africa / Spanish Foreign Legion, 1937

The Austrian version of the extraordinarily well-engineered MP 34 submachine gun, the Steyr-Solothurn S1-100 was a successful effort to circumvent the Treaty of Versailles.

▲ Star S135

Spanish Republican Army / 3rd Mixed Brigade, Catalonia, 1937

The Star S135 submachine gun was a complicated design that eventually was discarded for simpler and less expensive models. Originating in Spain, it did offer selective rates of fire and a mechanism that held the bolt open for easy reloading of an empty magazine.

Specifications

Country of Origin: Spain	Barrel Length: 269mm (10.6in)
Date: 1935	Muzzle Velocity: 410m/sec (1345ft/sec)
Calibre: 9mm (.35in) Largo	Feed/Magazine: 10-, 30- or 40-round detachable
Operation: Delayed blowback	box magazine
Weight: 3.74kg (8.25lb)	Cyclic Rate: 300 or 700rpm
Overall Length: 900mm (35.45in)	Range: 50m (164ft)

Sino-Japanese War
1937–45

Japanese expansion on the mainland of Asia was set in motion in a series of violent clashes with the Chinese; however, the vastness of China plus Allied aid prevented Japan from achieving complete victory.

JAPAN AND CHINA had fought intermittently since the turn of the twentieth century, and modern conflict had developed in 1931 with the Japanese using a trumped-up incident in Manchuria as a pretext for the invasion of this northern region of China. The Japanese secured control of Manchuria, installed a puppet regime, and renamed the province Manchukuo.

Fighting continued sporadically for several more years until another armed incident at the Marco Polo Bridge near Beijing marked the beginning of the Sino-Japanese War between Imperial Japan and the Republic of China. The war officially commenced on 7 July 1937, and lasted until Japan's defeat by the Allies in August 1945. The war was spawned by an insatiable Japanese hunger for land and raw materials on the Asian mainland and a political desire to dominate the affairs of their giant neighbour to the west. Following the Japanese attack on Pearl Harbor and US entry into World War II, the Sino-Japanese War effectively merged into the greater global conflict and formed the largest component of the China-Burma-India theatre.

With its victory over Russia in the Russo-Japanese War of 1904–05, Japan established itself as the preeminent power in East Asia. In 1910, the Japanese were granted a mandate over the Korean peninsula and effectively ruled that country for the next 35 years. Influenced heavily by the military technology of the West, the Japanese built an army which was equivalent in size and strength to many of those of the European powers. Its support of the Allies during World War I resulted in further territorial influence in Asia during the interwar years.

An increasingly imperialistic Japan provided its troops with an array of small arms, including the Arisaka series of rifles and the pistols and machine guns manufactured to the specifications of prolific arms designer Kijiro Nambu (1869–1949). European influence was further apparent in the design and manufacture of several of these key small arms.

Type 38

The primary Japanese shoulder arm of the early twentieth century was the Arisaka 38th Year rifle, simply known as the Type 38 and named for the weapon's adoption during the 38th year of the Meiji restoration. It entered service in 1905 and was intended as a replacement for the Type 30 rifle that had served with the Japanese Army for a brief seven years. The Type 38 fired a 6.5mm (.256in) cartridge which was underpowered by many Western

▲ **Chinese Gew 88 (Hanyang 88)**

Chinese National Revolutionary Army / 127th Infantry Brigade, Shanghai, 1937

The Gew 88 was more commonly known as the Hanyang 88 and equipped large numbers of Chinese infantrymen during the Sino-Japanese War. Patterned after the German Mauser design, it was produced at Hanyang Arsenal.

Specifications

Country of Origin: China	Overall Length: 1110mm (43.7in)
Date: 1895	Barrel Length: 600mm (23.6in)
Calibre: 7.92mm (.312in)	Muzzle Velocity: 810m/sec (2657ft/sec)
Operation: Bolt action	Feed/Magazine: 5-round box magazine
Weight: 4.08kg (9lb)	Range: 500m (1640ft)

standards, and the rifle's length of 1280mm (50.39in) presented challenges in handling to the average Japanese soldier of the period, who stood but 1.6m (5ft 3in) tall.

By 1939, the Japanese had embarked on a programme to replace the Type 38 with the new Type 99 rifle; however, the outbreak of World War II impeded the progress of this initiative. A total of 3.4 million of the bolt-action Type 38 were produced, and the weapon was prominent among Japanese forces during the Pacific War. It was fed by a five-round box magazine, and a skilled rifleman was said to be capable of firing 30 rounds per minute.

Mauser copy

Like its Japanese Type 38 counterpart, the Chinese Gew 88 rifle was influenced by the German Mauser design. The Republic's forces depended on the Gew, or Gewehr 88, heavily during the Sino-Japanese War. Those weapons in Chinese service were often referred to as the Hanyang 88 in reference to their production at the Hanyang Arsenal. A virtual copy of the Gewehr 88, the Hanyang 88 fired a 7.92mm (.312in) Mauser round and its external box magazine was fed by a five-round clip.

The Hanyang 88 was relatively inexpensive to produce and rather well suited for China's weak industrial posture in relation to its Japanese adversary. One distinct advantage over its Japanese counterpart was the fact that the Hanyang 88 fired a heavier round than the 6.5mm (.256in) Japanese Arisaka, which tipped the scales slightly towards the Chinese in early close-quarters fighting. Although it had been in service since 1895 and pre-dated the most recent Japanese rifles, the Hanyang 88 performed well during the Sino-Japanese War. Despite the fact that its

▲ Arisaka 38th Year rifle

Japanese Tenth Army / 6th Infantry Division, Nanjing, 1937

The Type 38 rifle entered service in 1905, and plans to replace it with the updated Type 99 were only partially completed. The Type 38 remained in service through to the end of World War II.

Specifications

Country of Origin: Japan	Overall Length: 1280mm (50.7in)
Date: 1905	Barrel Length: 800mm (31.5in)
Calibre: 6.5mm (.256in)	Muzzle Velocity: 765m/sec (2509ft/sec)
Operation: Bolt action	Feed/Magazine: 5-round internal magazine
Weight: 3.95kg (8.7lb)	Range: 500m (1640ft)

◀ Baby Nambu

Imperial Japanese Army / Central China Expeditionary Army / 14th Independent Brigade, September 1939

The Baby Nambu pistol fired an underpowered 7mm (.275in) cartridge and has become the most recognized of the Nambu series of pistols adopted as sidearms for Japanese officers.

Specifications

Country of Origin: Japan	Overall Length: 230mm (9.06in)
Date: 1906	Barrel Length: 117mm (4.61in)
Calibre: 7mm (.275in)	Muzzle Velocity: 289.6m/sec (950ft/sec)
Operation: Recoil spring	Feed/Magazine: 8-round box magazine
Weight: .9kg (1.98lb)	Range: 50m (164ft)

rate of fire was relatively slow, the Hanyang remained in production until 1947, and over 1.1 million were built during the course of more than 50 years.

A principal Japanese heavy machine gun of the Sino-Japanese War was the Type 3, also referred to as the Taisho 14 machine gun. Patterned after the French Hotchkiss Model 1914, the Type 3 was produced in Japan under licence and fired the 6.5mm (.256in) standard Arisaka cartridge rather than the heavier 8mm (.314in) ammunition of the Hotchkiss.

The air-cooled Type 3 was adapted by Japanese designer Kijiro Nambu in 1914 and was fed by a 30-round ammunition strip. It was capable of a rate of fire up to 450 rounds per minute.

The Nambu nemisis

A career officer of the Japanese Army, Nambu rose to the rank of lieutenant-general and founded the Nambu Arms Manufacturing Company in Tokyo in 1927. He was responsible for the design and

▲ **Taisho 14**

Japanese Tenth Army / 6th Infantry Division, Nanjing, 1937

The Taisho 14 heavy machine gun was built in Japan under licence as a duplicate of the French Hotchkiss Model 1914. Designer Kijiro Nambu modified the French weapon to fire the Japanese 6.5mm (.256in) cartridge.

Specifications

Country of Origin: Japan	Barrel Length: 750mm (29.5in)
Date: 1914	Muzzle Velocity: 760m/sec (2500ft/sec)
Calibre: 6.5mm (.256in) Arisaka	Feed/Magazine: Strip fed
Operation: Gas operated, air cooled	Cyclic Rate: 400rpm
Weight: 28kg (62lb)	Range: 1500m (4921ft)
Overall Length: 1155mm (45in)	

▶ **94 Shiki Kenju (Type 94)**

Japanese Northern China Area Army / 2nd Independent Mixed Brigade, northern China, 1940

Issued primarily to the crewmen of aircraft and vehicles, the Type 94 pistol was intended for cheap manufacture but eventually became prohibitively expensive. Like most other Japanese pistols, it fired an underpowered 8mm (.314in) round.

Specifications

Country of Origin: Japan	Overall Length: 183mm (7.2in)
Date: 1934	Barrel Length: 96mm (3.78in)
Calibre: 8mm (.314in)	Muzzle Velocity: 305m/sec (1000ft/sec)
Operation: Not known	Feed/Magazine: 6-round box magazine
Weight: .688kg (1.52lb)	Range: Not known

production of a number of Japanese small arms carried through the Sino-Japanese War and the duration of World War II. Among his most famous weapons designs is the Baby Nambu pistol, one of a series of pistols that were common sidearms of Japanese officers and soldiers.

The Baby Nambu was officially known as the Type A Model 1902 Modified and fired a 7mm (.275in) round compared with the larger 8mm (.314in) round of the Type A Model 1902 Grandpa Nambu. Essentially a scaled-down version of the Grandpa, the Baby Nambu included modifications to the sights, grip, safety and magazine finger pad along with a swivelling lanyard ring and an aluminium magazine base. Both pistols were fed by an eight-round box magazine. The Grandpa Nambu was notorious for misfiring due to weak magazine springs, while the Baby Nambu has become one of the most highly sought-after Japanese firearms. Slightly more than 10,000 Baby Nambu pistols were built, and a small number of these were produced by Tokyo Gas and Electric.

Production of the Nambu series of pistols was begun in 1906, and in 1925 the Type A was replaced by the Type 14, which was produced through to the end of World War II in numbers that eventually exceeded 250,000. The Type 14 short-recoil semiautomatic fired an 8mm (.314in) Nambu cartridge and was fed by an eight-round detachable box magazine. It was an improvement over earlier models with an enlarged trigger guard. The Nambu series proved to be accurate pistols; however, they fired substantially underpowered rounds with inferior knockdown capability and remained prone to misfiring throughout their service lives.

▲ **Invasion and occupation**

Bayonets fixed on their Arisaka rifles, a Japanese infantry battalion marches through a town somewhere in China during the Sino-Japanese War.

◀ **Nambu Type 14**

Japanese Twelfth Army / 115th Infantry Division, Zhengzhou, 1939

Replacing the Type A series in 1925, the semiautomatic Nambu Type 14 pistol provided some limited improvements such as an enlarged trigger guard but remained prone to misfiring.

Specifications

Country of Origin: Japan	Barrel Length: 121mm (4.76in)
Date: 1925	Muzzle Velocity: 335m/sec (1100ft/sec)
Calibre: 8mm (.314in) Nambu	Feed/Magazine: 8-round detachable box
Operation: Short recoil	magazine
Weight: .9kg (1.98lb)	Range: 30m (98ft)
Overall Length: 227mm (8.93in)	

Czechoslovakian Arsenal
1920–45

Prior to the collapse of the Austro-Hungarian Empire, the provinces that would constitute the nation of Czechoslovakia were known for their production of quality small arms.

CONSIDERED one of the premier producers of arms in Europe, the Skoda manufacturing works at Plzen turned out the Model 1909 machine gun for the Austro-Hungarian Army, and by that time the company was a half-century old. Although the firm was better known for its production of heavy artillery and even turrets for battleships, the reputation of Skoda and other Czech arms producers enticed Hitler to assert control over the Central European nation prior to World War II.

At the end of World War I, another Czech arms manufacturer, Zbrojovka Brno, was established and began to produce the ZB-53 medium machine gun, which fired the 7.92mm (.312in) Mauser cartridge at a rate of up to 800 rounds per minute, fed by a 225-round metal-link belt. Copied by the British and built under licence as the Besa machine gun, the weapon was primarily mounted on vehicles. By the late 1930s, the ZK-383 submachine gun was being

produced by Zbrojovka Brno, and many entered service with the German Army. Although production volume was low, it continued until 1966.

The company's Lehky Kulomet ZGB vz.33 light machine gun also served with the German Army and was exported to many countries. Capable of a rate of fire of up to 500 rounds per minute, it was fed by a 30-round detachable box magazine. It shared a similar lineage and was virtually identical to the fabled British Bren Gun, a derivative of the earlier ZB vz.26, which entered production in 1924.

Initially ordered by the Czech Army, the blowback-operated CZ Model 38 pistol was designed by Frantisek Myska and underwent field testing in 1938. A few of the weapons were shipped to Bulgaria; however, the majority of the 10,000 produced wound up in service with various German security forces. The pistol fired a 9mm (.35in) cartridge and was fed by a eight-round magazine.

▲ **Lehky Kulomet ZGB vz.33**

German Army Group Centre / 1st SS Infantry Brigade, Zhitomir, Belorussia, 1942

Virtually identical in design to the British Bren Gun, the ZGB vz.33 entered service just prior to the Bren and was one of many highly successful Czech light machine guns.

Specifications

Country of Origin: Czechoslovakia	Barrel Length: 635mm (25in)
Date: 1933	Muzzle Velocity: 730m/sec (2400ft/sec)
Calibre: 7.92mm (.312in) Mauser	Feed/Magazine: 30-round box magazine
Operation: Gas operated, air cooled	Cyclic Rate: 500rpm
Weight: 10.25kg (22.5lb)	Range: 1000m (3280ft)
Overall Length: 1150mm (45.25in)	

◀ CZ Model 38
German police unit, 1939

The CZ Model 38 pistol was a failure in the field due to a heavy trigger pull and its weak 9mm (.35in) short cartridge. Due to a shortage of handguns, the German Army and police pressed the Model 38 into service.

Specifications

Country of Origin: Czechoslovakia	Overall Length: 198mm (7.8in)
Date: 1938	Barrel Length: 119mm (4.69in)
Calibre: 9mm (.35in) Short	Muzzle Velocity: 296m/sec (970ft/sec)
Operation: Short recoil	Feed/Magazine: 8-round box magazine
Weight: .909kg (2lb)	Range: 30m (98ft)

▲ ZK-383
German Army Group North / 4th SS Polizei Division, Luga, August 1941

Large numbers of the ZK-383 submachine gun were exported from Czechoslovakia prior to World War II. Following the German occupation of Czech territory, most of the weapons were issued to the *Waffen*-SS.

Specifications

Country of Origin: Czechoslovakia	Overall Length: 875mm (34.45in)
Date: 1938	Barrel Length: 325mm (12.8in)
Calibre: 9mm (.35in) Parabellum	Muzzle Velocity: 365m/sec (1200ft/sec)
Operation: Blowback	Feed/Magazine: 30-round box magazine
Weight: 4.83kg (10.65lb)	Range: 100m (328ft)

▲ Besa
British Army / 2nd Royal Tank Regiment, Tobruk, Libya, 1942

The British version of the Czech ZB-53 medium machine gun, the Besa was commonly mounted on armoured vehicles. It was chambered for the 7.92mm (.312in) Mauser cartridge and could fire captured German ammunition.

Specifications

Country of Origin: Czechoslovakia	Barrel Length: 736mm (29in)
Date: 1936	Muzzle Velocity: 825m/sec (2700ft/sec)
Calibre: 7.92mm (.312in) Mauser	Feed/Magazine: 225-round belt
Operation: Gas operated, air cooled	Cyclic Rate: 750–850rpm
Weight: 21.5kg (47lb)	Range: 2000m (6560ft) +
Overall Length: 1105mm (43.5in)	

Chapter 4

World War II: Poland and Western Theatre

World War II raged in the West for five years, from the campaign against France in 1940 to VE Day. It spanned the Low Countries, the deserts of North Africa and the boot of Italy. Throughout the period, millions of soldiers fought with countless varieties of small arms, some antiquated and others actually ahead of their time. While bolt-action rifles ruled the day, the semiautomatic shoulder arm made its combat debut and automatic weapons became regular issue for some units, increasing the firepower of the individual soldier substantially. A new generation of heavy machine guns provided devastating fire from fixed positions, while lighter models were transportable and highly effective with infantry on the move.

◀ **Ship's armoury**
A US naval rating examines a row of Springfield M1903 rifles during a visit to England, 1944. Although superseded by the Garand M1 for many frontline troops, the Springfield was in service with other branches of the US military.

Introduction

From static warfare to rapid mobility, World War II in the West was characterized by the attack and defence of small infantry units employing offensive and defensive tactics to cope with the increasing firepower of the enemy.

WHEN THE GERMAN ARMY executed Case Yellow in May 1940, and the Phoney War in the West, derisively referred to as the 'Sitzkrieg', became a shooting war, the swift advance of the *Blitzkrieg* carried German armour from the French frontier to the coast of the Channel in a matter of days. While the tanks rolled westwards, risking the threat of counterattack against open flanks, it was the German infantry that secured and held the ground gained and eventually came to grips with the British Expeditionary Force evacuating at Dunkirk.

In many respects, the battle between the Germans and the defending British and French forces was a renewal of the conflict of a generation earlier. However, this time there would be no prolonged war of attrition in the trenches. In just over a month,

France had surrendered and the British had been ejected from the European continent. German soldiers patrolled the streets of Paris with their Mausers slung over their shoulders.

The British Expeditionary Force had evacuated northern France with little of its precious equipment intact. Thousands of Vickers machine guns and Lee-Enfield SMLE rifles were left lying on the beaches at Dunkirk. The legions of French prisoners of war turned over their arms to the Germans. Rearming and re-equipping many of the 350,000 Allied soldiers evacuated at Dunkirk was a formidable task, and for more than a year Great Britain stood alone against the Nazis, forced to content itself with an ill-fated foray into Greece and an ultimately unsuccessful attempt to maintain control of the island of Crete.

▲ **Defensive fire**

Armed with a mixture of Garand M1 rifles and M1 carbines, a US infantry anti-tank crew returns fire on German troops who machine-gunned their vehicle somewhere in the Netherlands, November 1944.

◀ *Wehrmacht* firepower

German soldiers man an MG 34 during the invasion of Denmark and Norway, April 1940.

Pressing needs to supply the armed forces in Crete and North Africa stretched both fronts thin, limiting the successes in North Africa and dooming the defence of Crete to failure.

America's arsenal

The Nazi invasion of the Soviet Union in June 1941 brought an unlikely ally into the war, and Hitler's declaration of war on the United States at the end of the year finally buoyed British hopes for a reversal of fortune. Although the US had been savagely attacked by the Japanese at Pearl Harbor, it was agreed by President Franklin D. Roosevelt and Prime Minister Winston Churchill that the defeat of Nazi Germany was to take precedence over the war in the Pacific. The commitment of American troops and arms was tremendous, substantially exceeding the lifeline of Lend-Lease that had helped keep Britain in the war during the dark days of 1940–41. Although Allied forces for such an undertaking were deemed to be insufficient for some time, the US and Britain began

planning a cross-Channel invasion of the Nazi-occupied European continent almost immediately.

US forces relied heavily on their World War I-era weapons, including the Springfield Model 1903 bolt-action rifle and the Browning Model 1917 machine gun, which had undergone some improvements in the 1930s. By 1937, the M1 Garand rifle and the smaller M1 carbine had been adopted by the US Army and were gradually coming into service with American troops. The M1 was the first semiautomatic rifle officially to enter service with any army and proved a decided advantage for US soldiers in combat.

German designers, however, had not called a halt to their innovative weapons design programmes and continued to deploy the stalwart Maschinengewehr 34, or MG 34, with its high rate of fire and reasonable mobility, in large numbers. In addition, the Germans improved the MG 34 design and deployed the Maschinengewehr 42 (MG 42) in substantial numbers. Although the durable and simply constructed MG 42 was intended to replace the MG 34, both continued in widespread production throughout the war.

Perhaps the most significant harbinger of the future of ground warfare was the German development of the Sturmgewehr 44, a fully automatic rifle that was capable of tremendous firepower in the hands of a single soldier and bolstered the long-serving Mauser bolt-action Karabiner 98k rifle. Although initially available in relatively low quantities, it was a shock to Allied soldiers battling in the hedgerows of Normandy following the D-Day landings on 6 June 1944. The Sturmgewehr 44 is considered by many to be the first fully operational assault rifle to see combat.

By 1945, the Allies had driven deep into Germany from the west and threatened the Reich from the south as they drove through mountainous northern Italy. While the Soviets pressed from the east, US and British forces halted their advance along the Elbe River and met the vanguard of the Red Army there. Along with the fighting stamina of the Allied soldiers in the West, the arms they carried proved sufficient to win the victory, even in the face of German innovation.

Polish Army

SEPTEMBER 1939

The overmatched Polish Army fought heroically to stem the German *Blitzkrieg*; however, it was overwhelmed by the *Wehrmacht* and the Red Army in a matter of weeks.

DURING THE 1930s, THE POLISH GOVERNMENT and its military commanders became increasingly concerned with the possibility of war with Germany and formulated plans for the defence of their country. Organized into six field armies with several additional units of corps size known as operational groups, the Polish Army consisted of up to 30 infantry divisions, 11 cavalry brigades, nine reserve divisions, three mountain brigades and two motorized brigades. During the years immediately following World War I, the Poles had received military assistance and training from a cadre of French officers.

The swiftness of the German advance into Poland prevented the coordinated defensive effort envisioned by the Polish high command, and mutual support of Polish operations of division size or greater was quite limited. Nevertheless, by 1 September 1939, the Polish Army numbered 700,000 troops. Although heavy weapons and armoured vehicles were relatively few in number, the Poles possessed more than three battalions of French-made Renault light tanks and 11 armoured car battalions, each with eight armoured cars and 13 tankettes.

▲ **Horse power**
These Polish lancers carry Karabinek wz.29 rifles across their backs. The Polish Army used their cavalry as mounted infantry, rather than in a purely cavalry role.

The Polish infantry battalion of 1939 included three rifle companies and a machine-gun company. The rifle company included a complement of 232 troops organized in three rifle platoons. Each of the platoons included three rifle sections of 19 men. The primary shoulder arm of the Polish infantry was the Karabinek wz.29, a bolt-action rifle based on the German Mauser-designed Karabiner Model 1898, a close relative of the German standard rifle of World War II, the Mauser Karabiner 98k. The Karabinek wz.29 fired the 7.92mm (.312in) cartridge that was standard for Mauser rifles.

The Karabinek was fed by a five-round internal box magazine, and an average rate of fire was 15 rounds per minute. It entered production at the Polish National Arms Factory in Radom in 1930, and 264,000 were manufactured. It remained in service with Polish resistance units and in some organized units of Polish origin that fought with the Allies.

A machine-gun company consisted of 12 Ckm wz.30 heavy machine guns, and a platoon of three machine guns was typically assigned by battalion command to support each infantry company. The Ckm wz.30 was a Polish-made copy of the American Browning Model 1917 water-cooled machine gun. It was chambered to fire the 7.92mm (.312in) Mauser cartridge. Only about 7800 were built between 1930 and 1939. Although an agreement had been reached with Colt to produce the Model 1917, confusion arose between the American company and Fabrique Nationale, its European liaison, and the patent was never authorized in Poland. Therefore, Polish designers moved forward with their own version of the weapon.

In each 19-man rifle section, one soldier was armed with an Rkm wz.28 rifle, a licence-built version of the American Browning Automatic Rifle (BAR), which added some limited mobile firepower to the formation. The rifle company also fielded nine light machine guns, three anti-tank rifles and three light mortars.

▲ Karabinek wz.29 (Kbk wz.29)

Polish Army / 55th Infantry Regiment, Lodz, September 1939

Based on the German Mauser Karabiner Model 1898, the bolt-action Karabinek was the standard rifle of the Polish Army in September 1939. It was chambered to fire the 7.92mm (.312in) Mauser cartridge.

Specifications

Country of Origin: Poland	Overall Length: 1110mm (43.7in)
Date: 1930	Barrel Length: 600mm (23.62in)
Calibre: 7.92mm (.312in) Mauser M98	Muzzle Velocity: 845m/sec (2772ft/sec)
Operation: Bolt action	Feed/Magazine: 5-round integral box magazine
Weight: 3.9kg (8.6lb)	Range: 500m (1640ft) + with iron sights

▲ Pistolet maszynowy wz.39 Mors

Polish Army / 36th Infantry Regiment, Lublin, September 1939

Following trials with the German Erma, Polish designers developed the Mors wz.39 between 1937 and 1939. Production was begun in 1939; however, only about 40 were manufactured before the German invasion of Poland.

Specifications

Country of Origin: Poland	Barrel Length: 300mm (11.8in)
Date: 1939	Muzzel Velocity: 400m/sec (1312ft/sec)
Calibre: 9mm (.35in)	Feed/Magazine: 24-round magazine
Operation: Blowback	Range: 440m (1444ft) + with adjustable iron
Weight: 4.25kg (9.37lb) (without magazine)	sights
Overall Length: 970mm (38in)	

▶ Radom wz.35

Polish Army / Wilenska Cavalry Brigade, Warsaw, September 1939

The 9mm (.35in) Radom wz.35 was developed for the Polish Army in 1935, and more than 360,000 were manufactured. Also known as the Vis pistol, the semiautomatic handgun was utilized by the Germans following their invasion of Poland.

Specifications

Country of Origin: Poland	Barrel Length: 115mm (4.53in)
Date: 1935	Muzzle Velocity: 350m/sec (1150ft/sec)
Calibre: 9mm (.35in) Parabellum	Feed/Magazine: 8-round detachable box
Operation: Short recoil	magazine
Weight: 1.022kg (2.25lb)	Range: 30m (98ft)
Overall Length: 197mm (7.76in)	

Wehrmacht

SEPTEMBER 1939 – JUNE 1940

The German Army that rolled to victory in Poland and then crushed French and British forces the following spring demonstrated tremendous speed and coordination.

WHEN ADOLF HITLER (1889–1945) came to power in January 1933, the German Army had already taken steps to circumvent the Treaty of Versailles. By autumn, the Nazi chancellor had taken his country out of the League of Nations and quietly authorized a build-up of the army to 300,000 soldiers, triple the strength authorized by the treaty. In concert with that build-up of troop strength, training proceeded under the guise of sports leagues and Nazi youth development programmes.

Following the *Anschluss* with Austria, the annexation of the Sudetenland and the occupation of the remainder of Czechoslovakia, and the acquisition of other territory during the full flower of the Allied appeasement doctrine, Hitler turned to war and invaded Poland on 1 September 1939. When war broke out, the German Army hurled more than 60 infantry and armoured divisions against the Polish Army, which was outnumbered 10 to one.

When German forces attacked Poland on 1 September 1939, the standard field army, or *Feldheer*, infantry division averaged a strength of about 17,500 troops including support personnel. The combat infantry element of the division consisted of three regiments, each commanded by a

GERMAN INFANTRY BATTALION, *CIRCA* 1939–40		
Unit	Officers	Men
Battalion Headquarters	5	15
Communications Platoon		19
Battle Train	2	17
Rations Train		8
Baggage Train		7
Machine Gun Company	4	173
Company HQ	1	20
Battle Train		11
Rations Train		3
Mortar Platoon	1	67
Two Machine-Gun Platoons, each	1	36
Three Rifle Companies, each	4	186
Company HQ	1	11
Battle Train		18
Rations and Baggage Trains		6
Machine-Gun Section		16
Three Rifle Platoons, each	1	45
Platoon HQ	1	3
Light Mortar Section		3
Three Rifle Squads, each		13
Total Strength of 820 all ranks	23	797

▶ **Parabellum M1908**

German Army / 50th Infantry Division, Poland, September 1939

Popularly known as the Luger after its designer, the semiautomatic Parabellum M1908 utilized a toggle-locking system rather than a slide, and its magazine was located in the handgrip. Although newer handguns were introduced, the weapon was popular with German officers throughout World War II.

Specifications

Country of Origin: Germany

Date: 1908

Calibre: 9mm (.35in)

Operation: Toggle locked, short recoil

Weight: .96kg (2.125lb)

Overall Length: 222mm (8.8in)

Barrel Length: 127mm (5in)

Muzzle Velocity: 351m/sec (1150ft/sec)

Feed/Magazine: 8-round detachable box
    magazine

Range: 30m (98ft)

colonel who reported to the general in command of the division. Based on an organizational alignment from 1938, the regiments consisted of approximately 3100 officers and men.

Each regiment consisted of three battalions, while each of these included three infantry companies with light and heavy machine gun and light mortar components. An infantry company typically comprised up to 200 troops, with a battalion populated by 825 officers and soldiers. A separate heavy weapons company contained additional mortars and heavy machine guns that could be deployed at the discretion of the battalion commander. The small-arms complement of the German infantry division of 1939 included nearly 650 machine guns along with rifles, submachine guns

German Infantry Rifle Squad, 1940

Intended for effective fire and manoeuvre, the German rifle squad of 1940 included 13 soldiers. Seven of these were riflemen carrying the Mauser K98k shoulder arm, while three soldiers made up the machine-gun section. The squad leader or assistant squad leader was often armed with an MP 40 submachine gun capable of firing up to 550 rounds of 9mm (.35in) ammunition per minute. Augmented by the powerful MG 34 machine gun, the squad was capable of a significant volume of fire.

Rifle Squad (1 x MP 40 SMG, 9 x K98k rifle)

Machine-gun Section (1 x machine-gunner with pistol and MG 34, 1 x loader with pistol, 1 x loader with K98k rifle)

▲ Mauser Karabiner 98k

German Army / 213th Infantry Division, Poland, September 1939

The iconic Mauser K98k was the standard rifle of the German Army throughout World War II. Its bolt action had been modified from the earlier Gewehr 98, and its average rate of fire was 15 rounds per minute. The rifle remains popular with marksmen today.

Specifications

Country of Origin: Germany	Overall Length: 1110mm (43.7in)
Date: 1935	Barrel Length: 600mm (23.62in)
Calibre: 7.92mm (.312in) Mauser M98	Muzzle Velocity: 745m/sec (2444ft/sec)
Operation: Bolt action	Feed/Magazine: 5-round internal box magazine
Weight: 3.9kg (8.6lb)	Range: 500m (1640ft) + with iron sights

INFANTRY RIFLE COMPANY: 1939

Although German infantry battalions were nominally reorganised several times during the war, the overall structure of the battalion and company remained largely unaltered from the beginning of the war to the end. The officer and three messengers of the platoon HQ carried a pistol and rifles respectively. The three men of the light mortar section carried rifles and served a single 5cm (2in) mortar. The three rifle squads were each 13 strong. Each squad included a machine gun group of four men, armed with three pistols and one rifle and serving a single MG34. In Poland the 13 man squad proved too large in action, and from 1940 a 10 man squad was introduced.

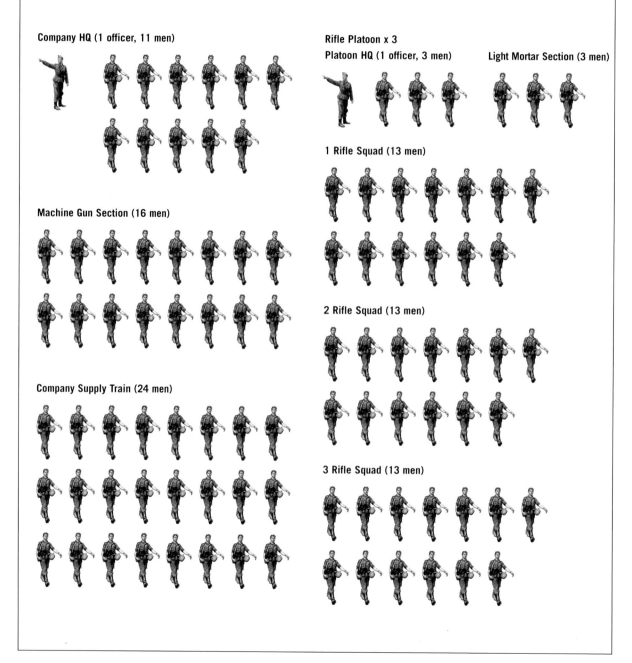

Company HQ (1 officer, 11 men)

Machine Gun Section (16 men)

Company Supply Train (24 men)

Rifle Platoon x 3
Platoon HQ (1 officer, 3 men)   **Light Mortar Section (3 men)**

1 Rifle Squad (13 men)

2 Rifle Squad (13 men)

3 Rifle Squad (13 men)

and pistols to equip the individual soldiers. During the course of the war, the composition of the infantry division was changed, as was the strength of the standard infantry squad, which was reduced from 13 to 10 men following the combat experience in Poland.

The backbone of the German Army in World War II was the infantry platoon. In 1939, the platoon comprised just under 50 soldiers in three squads of 13 riflemen. A 50mm (2in) light mortar section was organic, and one officer armed with a pistol and three soldiers with rifles who normally performed courier duties served as the headquarters element.

Two noncommissioned officers served as squad leader and assistant squad leader in each of the three squads, while each squad fielded seven riflemen and four soldiers who manned an MG 34 machine gun. Usually one noncommissioned officer carried an MP 40 submachine gun. Two members of the machine-gun section carried pistols, and one was usually armed with a rifle.

▶ Landser

A young German soldier poses for the camera during the invasion of France, May 1940. He is armed with the ubiquitous Karabiner 98k rifle and the famous Model 24 stick grenade.

Specifications

Country of Origin: Germany	Barrel Length: Not known
Date: 1930	Muzzle Velocity: 890m/sec (2919.2ft/sec)
Calibre: 7.92mm (.312in) Mauser	Feed/Magazine: 25-round box magazine or
Operation: Short recoil	75-round saddle drum magazine
Weight: 13.3kg (29.32lb)	Cyclic Rate: 600rpm
Overall Length: 1443mm (56.8in)	Range: 2000m (6560ft)

▲ Maschinengewehr 13 (MG 13)

German Army / 301st Infantry Regiment, Poland, September 1939

Modified from a water-cooled weapon of World War I, the MG 13 was air-cooled and capable of firing 600 rounds per minute. It continued in service although it was intended to be replaced by the MG 34.

PERSONAL FIREARMS OF THE GERMAN INFANTRYMAN, 1939

WALTHER P38

PARABELLUM P'08

MP38

MP40

MAUSER KAR 98K

MG34

MG42

Walther P38

CALIBRE: 9mm (0.354in) Parabellum
OPERATION: Short recoil
WEIGHT: 0.96kg (2.11lb)
LENGTH: 213mm (8.38in)
MUZZLE VELOCITY: 350m/sec (1150ft/sec)
RANGE: 30m (98ft)

Parabellum P'08

CALIBRE: 9mm (0.354in) Parabellum
OPERATION: Short recoil
WEIGHT: 0.87kg (1.92lb)
LENGTH: 233mm (8.75in)
MUZZLE VELOCITY: 380m/sec (1247ft/sec)
RANGE: 30m (98ft)

MP38

CALIBRE: 9mm (0.354in) Parabellum
OPERATION: Blowback
WEIGHT: 4.1kg (9.1lb)
LENGTH: 832mm (32.75in) stock extended
MUZZLE VELOCITY: 395m/sec (1300ft/sec)
RANGE: 70m (230ft)

MP40

CALIBRE: 9mm (0.354in) Parabellum
OPERATION: Blowback
WEIGHT: 3.97kg (8.75lb)
LENGTH: 832mm (32.75in) stock extended
MUZZLE VELOCITY: 395m/sec (1300ft/sec)
RANGE: 70m (230ft)

Kar 98

CALIBRE: 7.92mm (0.31in)
OPERATION: Bolt action
WEIGHT: 3.9kg (8.6lb)
LENGTH: 1110mm (43.7in)
MUZZLE VELOCITY: 745m/sec (2444ft/sec)
RANGE: 500m (547yd)

MG34

CALIBRE: 7.92mm (0.31in)
OPERATION: Recoil-operated, air-cooled
WEIGHT: 12.1kg (26.67lb)
LENGTH: 1219mm (48in)
MUZZLE VELOCITY: 762m/sec (2500ft/sec)
RANGE: 2000m (6600ft) plus

MG42

CALIBRE: 7.92mm (0.31in)
OPERATION: Short recoil, air-cooled
WEIGHT: 11.5kg (25.35lb)
LENGTH: 1220mm (48in)
MUZZLE VELOCITY: 800m/sec (2650ft/sec)
RANGE: 3000m (10,0000ft) plus

Long-serving Mauser

In 1935, the German Army adopted the most recent rifle in the long Mauser line as its standard shoulder arm. The Mauser Karabiner 98 Kurz, which is also abbreviated as the K98k or K98, was a bolt-action rifle that was chambered for the standard Mauser 7.92mm (.312in) cartridge. During its decade-long production run from 1935 to 1945, the rifle was produced in great numbers, with over 14.6 million entering service.

The K98k was fed by a five-round stripper clip and an internal magazine. It was developed from the Mauser Gewehr 98, which had first appeared in great numbers with German forces around the turn of the century and was the primary infantry weapon of the German Army in World War I. During the years between the wars, variants of the Gewehr 98

appeared, and the K98k was intended to incorporate the best elements of each of these. It was lighter at 3.9kg (8.6lb) and shorter at 1110mm (43.7in) than the original Gewehr 98 and designated as a 'short carbine'. The right to manufacture the K98k was licensed to several other countries, including Czechoslovakia and Turkey.

The Mauser M98 bolt-action system of the Gewehr 98 was modified from a straight bolt to a turn-down bolt in the K98k for easier operation and better placement of the iron sights, which were accurate up to 500m (550 yards). The K98k was known for its ruggedness and reliability in action. Accessories included mounts for the standard infantry bayonet and a grenade launcher intended for clearing fortified buildings or other strongpoints. An average rate of fire was 15 rounds per minute. The

Specifications

Country of Origin: Germany	Barrel Length: 627mm (24.75in)
Date: 1936	Muzzle Velocity: 762m/sec (2500ft/sec)
Calibre: 7.92mm (.312in) Mauser	Feed/Magazine: 50- or 75-round drum magazine
Operation: Recoil, air cooled	or up to 250-round belt
Weight: 12.1kg (26.67lb)	Cyclic Rate: 800–900rpm
Overall Length: 1219mm (48in)	Range: 2000m (6560ft) +

▲ **Maschinengewehr 34 (MG 34)**

German Army / 207th Infantry Division, Holland, May 1940

The MG 34 became the standard by which other machine guns of the early World War II period were measured. It was an excellent weapon with a high rate of fire and ease of operation; however, its high cost and precision manufacturing process limited the number available for service by 1939.

▲ **Solothurn Maschinengewehr 30 (MG 30)**

German Army / 69th Infantry Division, Norway, April 1940

Designed by Rheinmetall, the MG 30 entered service with the Swiss Army and was subsequently adopted by the German military. Mauser designer Heinrich Vollmer modified the weapon and developed the iconic MG 34.

Specifications

Country of Origin: Germany	Barrel Length: 595mm (23.42in)
Date: 1930	Muzzle Velocity: 800m/sec (2650ft/sec)
Calibre: 7.5mm (.295in) Schmidt-Rubin	Feed/Magazine: 25-round detachable box
Operation: Recoil, air cooled	magazine
Weight: 7.7kg (17lb)	Cyclic Rate: 500rpm
Overall Length: 1175mm (46.25in)	Range: 2000m (6560ft) +

Germans deployed a sniper variant on all fronts, and 132,000 of these were produced.

Infantry support

The versatile Maschinengewehr 34, or simply MG 34, was arguably the finest machine gun in the world at the time of its adoption and deployment with the German Army in 1934–35. The MG 34 was based initially on a Rheinmetall design, the Solothurn MG 30, which had entered service with the Swiss military a few years earlier. The MG 30 was adapted and modified by Heinrich Vollmer (1885–1961) of Mauser. Vollmer moved the feed mechanism to the left of the breech and introduced a shroud for the barrel. Improvements to the operating mechanism resulted in an astonishing rate of fire of 800 to 900 rounds per minute.

The recoil-operated MG 34 served both in the light machine gun role, fed by a drum magazine that held 50 or 75 rounds of 7.92mm (.312in) ammunition, and in a somewhat heavier and more stationary defensive role, mounted on a bipod or tripod and fed by an ammunition belt. Belts were carried in boxes of five with each belt containing 50 rounds, and these lengths could be linked together for sustained fire. Changing barrels was a rapid process for the trained operator and involved disengaging a latch and swinging the receiver to the right for the insertion of the new barrel. The gun's double crescent trigger dictated either semiautomatic or fully automatic firing modes.

The MG 34 was well known for its precision engineering and high production costs. Although it was reliable and dominant on the battlefield, it was prohibitively expensive and too few were available to supplant the older MG 13 and other models when war broke out in 1939. It was manufactured from 1934 until the end of the war.

Defending Norway, France and the Low Countries
APRIL–MAY 1940

The swift German advance across Western Europe in the spring of 1940 overran the smaller armies of several neighbouring countries and forced the capitulation of France within weeks.

FOLLOWING THE DEFEAT OF POLAND in the East, Hitler bided his time before launching offensive operations against France, the Low Countries and Scandinavia in the spring of 1940. Although the French Army, consisting of 133 divisions, appeared to be a formidable foe on paper, the French military establishment shuddered to contemplate a repeat of the bloodbath of 1914–18 and contented itself with constructing the imposing fortifications of the Maginot Line across the frontier with Germany.

Recalling images of massed infantry mown down before German machine-gun fire in World War I, the French abandoned their doctrine of heavy infantry assaults against entrenched enemy positions and considered the defences of the Maginot Line a deterrent to direct German invasion. On the other hand, a repeat of the Schlieffen Plan of 1914, with large infantry formations pivoting through Belgium, was expected by some as the logical offensive stroke by the Germans. Therefore, continuing cooperation with Belgium was another linchpin of French military thinking on the eve of World War II.

The French infantry platoon in 1940 consisted of a commanding officer, three squads of 10 men each armed with rifles, and two sections of grenade launchers. Light machine guns were deployed at squad level and operated by a gunner and a loader.

French deployment of updated shoulder arms lagged behind that of other nations, and with the outbreak of war most French soldiers carried the Berthier rifle, a bolt-action firearm of World War I that entered service in 1907 and was modified in

▶ **Browning Hi-Power 35**

Belgian Army / 11th Infantry Division, May 1940

Known as Hi-Power because of its 13-round magazine, the Browning HP 35 short-recoil semiautomatic pistol has become one of the most successful handguns in history and influenced many other models.

Specifications

Country of Origin: Belgium/United States	Barrel Length: 118mm (4.65in)
Date: 1935	Muzzle Velocity: 335m/sec (1100ft/sec)
Calibre: 9mm (.35in) Parabellum	Feed/Magazine: 13-round detachable box
Operation: Short recoil	magazine
Weight: .99kg (2.19lb)	Range: 30m (98ft)
Overall Length: 197mm (7.75in)	

▲ **Krag-Jørgensen**

Norwegian Army / 4th Infantry Regiment, Oslo, April 1940

A Norwegian design that entered production in the late 1880s, the Krag-Jørgensen rifle was fed by an integral magazine that could be loaded prior to the last round being expended. At the turn of the twentieth century it equipped US Army units.

Specifications

Country of Origin: Norway	Overall Length: 986mm (38.8in)
Date: 1886	Barrel Length: 520mm (20.5in)
Calibre: 7.62mm (.3in)	Muzzle Velocity: 580m/sec (1900ft/sec)
Operation: Bolt action	Feed/Magazine: 5-round magazine
Weight: 3.375kg (7.4lb)	Range: 500m (1640ft)

▲ **Fusil Automatique Modèle 1917**

French Army / 104th Infantry Division, Maginot Line, June 1940

The Fusil Automatique Modèle 1917 was adapted to semiautomatic operation from the Model 1886 Lebel rifle. It used the same ammunition and was fed by a five-round box magazine.

Specifications

Country of Origin: France	Overall Length: 1331mm (52.4in)
Date: 1917	Barrel Length: 798mm (31.4in)
Calibre: 8mm (.314in) Lebel	Muzzle Velocity: 853m/sec (2800ft/sec)
Operation: Gas, rotating bolt	Feed/Magazine: 5-round box magazine
Weight: 5.25kg (11.6lb)	Range: 300m (984ft)

1915. The Fusil Automatique Modèle 1917, a semiautomatic gas-operated rifle that fired an 8mm (.314in) Lebel cartridge, was introduced in 1917, and its short production run that ended a year later resulted in 86,000 weapons. The Fusil Automatique Modèle 1917 proved unpopular with frontline troops during World War I, and many of the rifles were withdrawn from service by the end of the Rif Wars in 1926. At the time of the German invasion in the West on 10 May 1940, a few of these weapons were still in service.

By 1936, the shortcomings of antiquated rifles in French service were noted, and plans were made to re-equip French infantry units with the MAS-36, a bolt-action design that would finally retire the bulk of the Berthier and Lebel weapons remaining in service. However, budget constraints resulted in a relative few examples of the MAS-36 being manufactured, and only a handful produced by the government-run Manufacture d'Armes de Saint-Etienne were available in 1940. The Lebel Modèle 1886/93 did remain in service as the principal weapon of the grenade-launcher sections.

The standard French light machine gun remained the 7.5mm (.295in) Fusil Mitrailleur 24/29, which had been designed in the 1920s and entered service during the interwar years. The FM 24/29 had a rate of fire of 450 rounds per minute and a 25-round box magazine feed, and performed well enough to serve into the 1960s before being replaced.

The standing Belgian Army comprised 100,000 soldiers, and this could be expanded to 550,000 with mobilization. Among the 18 infantry and two cavalry divisions available to defend Belgium in 1939, however, there were only about 160 machine guns, 52 of these considered heavy weapons.

The Belgian infantry platoon of 1940 included a headquarters section of the commanding lieutenant, a noncommissioned officer and an orderly. The officer typically carried a 9mm (.35in) Browning pistol, while the NCO and orderly were armed with the elderly 7.65mm (.301in) FN Modèle 1889 rifle, a Mauser design built under licence in Belgium. Four infantry sections each included a machine-gun squad of a sergeant, five riflemen and a single machine-gunner with a Browning FM 30 light machine gun (which has also been described as an automatic rifle similar to the more famous BAR) plus a rifle squad of five riflemen and a noncommissioned officer.

The small Norwegian Army was taken by surprise when the Germans invaded in April 1940 and was only partially able to mobilize, with just four battalions of its six divisions deploying to defend the country. The Norwegian infantry battalion included a machine-gun company of 12 machine guns, either the outdated Hotchkiss Mitraljöse Model 1898 or the newer Colt Mitraljöse Model 29 that was utilized as an infantry and anti-aircraft weapon.

Norwegian infantry platoons included four 10-man light-machine-gun sections, each of which consisted of a sergeant, the machine-gun support and five riflemen armed with the Krag-Jørgensen Model 1894 bolt-action rifle. The Krag-Jørgensen had equipped infantry units of the US Army until replaced by the Springfield Model 1903. Its performance during the Spanish-American War had

▲ Pistolet Mitrailleur MAS modèle 38 (MAS-38)

French Third Army / 56th Infantry Division, May 1940

The highly accurate MAS-38 produced slight recoil but fired a 7.65mm (.301in) cartridge which was underpowered. The weapon itself was well designed and machined to high quality, but budget constraints limited its availability.

Specifications

Country of Origin: France	Barrel Length: 247mm (9.75in)
Date: 1938	Muzzle Velocity: 395m/sec (1300ft/sec)
Calibre: 7.65mm (.301in) Longue	Feed/Magazine: 32-round box magazine
Operation: Blowback	Cyclic Rate: 500rpm
Weight: 4.1kg (9.1lb)	Range: 70m (230ft)
Overall Length: 832mm (32.75in)	

been considered inferior to that of the Mauser rifles carried by Spanish infantrymen. Nevertheless, more than 700,000 variants of the Krag-Jørgensen were manufactured during more than half a century of production. The 6.5mm (.256in) weapon was a Norwegian design that bore the names of its originators, Ole Herman Johannes Krag

(1837–1916) and Erik Jørgensen (1848–1896). It was fed by a five-round integral magazine.

British Expeditionary Force

Four infantry divisions of the British Army were on the ground in France within a week of the British declaration of war against Nazi Germany on

▲ Bren Mk I

British Expeditionary Force / 1st Battalion Welsh Guards, Dunkirk, May 1940

Adapted from a proven Czechoslovakian design, the Bren I light machine gun was capable of only a relatively low rate of fire. However, it was highly accurate and was modified in five major variants that served with British forces in combat as late as the Falklands War of 1982.

Specifications

Country of Origin: United Kingdom	Barrel Length: 635mm (25in)
Date: 1937	Muzzle Velocity: 730m/sec (2400ft/sec)
Calibre: 7.7mm (.303in)	Feed/Magazine: 30-round box magazine
Operation: Gas operated, air cooled	Cyclic Rate: 500rpm
Weight: 10.25kg (22.5lb)	Range: 1000m (3280ft)
Overall Length: 1150mm (45.25in)	

Specifications

Country of Origin: United Kingdom	Barrel Length: 910mm (36in); 762mm (30in)
Date: 1937	airborne version
Calibre: 13.97mm (.55in)	Muzzle Velocity: 747m/sec (2450ft/sec)
Operation: Bolt action	Feed/Magazine: 5-round detachable box
Weight: 16kg (35lb)	Range: 90m (295ft) against 16–19mm
Overall Length: 1575mm (62in)	(.63–.75in) armour

▲ Boys Mk I Anti-Tank Rifle

British Expeditionary Force / 143rd Brigade / Royal Warwickshire Regiment, May 1940

The heavy Boys Anti-Tank Rifle weighed 16kg (35lb) and was steadied with a bipod and padded butt. A new generation of shoulder-fired anti-tank weapons made the Boys obsolete soon after its debut in 1937.

3 September 1939. By the following spring, 400,000 troops organized in 10 divisions had arrived. These troops generally fought well in northern France and Belgium but were victimized by a German feint to the north and cut off by a *Wehrmacht* thrust through the Ardennes, finally retreating to the beaches of Dunkirk for evacuation. Thousands of tonnes of arms and equipment were abandoned; however, more than 350,000 Allied soldiers escaped to fight the Nazis another day.

The British infantry platoon of 1940 included headquarters personnel and three rifle sections of eight soldiers each, totalling about 30 men. Each section was commanded by a corporal or lance-corporal and included seven riflemen armed with the Short Magazine Lee-Enfield Rifle (SMLE). The section's single light machine gun, the Bren, was serviced by a gunner and loader, who also carried rifles.

The Mark III Short Magazine Lee-Enfield was introduced in 1907 and remained the principal shoulder arm of the British military for half a century, with more than 17 million variants produced. It remains in limited service today with some specialized units, and the line traces its origin to 1895 when the Magazine Lee-Enfield (MLE) rifle was adopted by the British Army. The weapon was named for its designer, James Paris Lee (1831–1904) and the Royal Small Arms Factory at Enfield, where it was originally manufactured. The SMLE fired the 7.7mm (.303in) cartridge and was fed by a 10-round magazine loaded with five-round charger clips. The

▲ **Street fighting**

German infantrymen armed with a drum-fed MG 34 squad machine gun advance through the streets of Oslo during the invasion of Norway, April 1940.

rifle was modified to accept the new high-velocity spitzer ammunition, while improved sights were mounted and the magazine improved.

The Bren light machine gun, which provided mobile fire support to small groups of infantrymen, had been adapted from the Czechoslovakian ZB vz.26 and entered service with the British Army in 1938. Following competitive trials with Browning

Specifications

Country of Origin: United Kingdom	Barrel Length: 196mm (7.7in)
Date: 1941	Muzzle Velocity: 365m/sec (1198ft/sec)
Calibre: 9mm (.35in) Parabellum	Feed/Magazine: 32-round detachable box
Operation: Blowback	magazine
Weight: 3.1kg (7lb)	Range: 60m (196ft)
Overall Length: 760mm (29.9in)	

▲ **Sten Mk I**

Eastern Command / 61st Infantry Division, Colchester, August 1941

Developed from captured examples of the German MP 40 submachine gun, the Sten is easily recognized with its crude metal stock and 32-round box magazine that loaded from the left side. About 100,000 were made before production switched to the Mark II.

and Vickers models in the early 1930s, the British Army adopted the Czech weapon, which was modified to accept the 7.7mm (.303in) cartridge and nicknamed Bren after its original place of manufacture in the Czech city of Brno. Fed from detachable magazines of 20, 30 or 100 rounds, the Bren had a relatively low rate of fire at about 500 rounds per minute. Nevertheless, it proved to be a durable weapon and remains in service today.

The initial British submachine gun of World War II was the 9mm (.35in) Lanchester, generally a copy of the German Bergmann MP 28. Since the Lanchester was complicated and could not be produced in large numbers, a few American Thompsons were procured. By 1941, several captured German MP 40 submachine guns had been copied and designated Sten, incorporating the first letters of the names of its designers, Sheffield and Turpin, along with the first two letters of the Enfield small-arms facility. The Sten also fired the 9mm (.35in) cartridge. It was fed by a 32-round detachable box magazine.

▲ **Lanchester Mk I**

Royal Navy, July 1941

The Lanchester was a copy of the German Bergmann MP 28 submachine gun. Many of its components were common with the Lee-Enfield rifle; however, such construction made the weapon's production lengthy and expensive. It was first deployed by Royal Navy units.

Specifications

Country of Origin: United Kingdom	Barrel Length: 203mm (8in)
Date: 1941	Muzzle Velocity: 380m/sec (1247ft/sec)
Calibre: 9mm (.35in) Parabellum	Feed/Magazine: 50-round box magazine
Operation: Blowback	Cyclic Rate: 600rpm
Weight: 4.34kg (9.56lb)	Range: 70m (230ft)
Overall Length: 850mm (33.5in)	

Specifications

Country of Origin: United Kingdom	Barrel Length: 558mm (22in)
Date: 1940	Muzzle Velocity: 730m/sec (2300ft/sec)
Calibre: 7.7mm (.303in)	Feed/Magazine: 30-round box magazine
Operation: Gas operated, air cooled	Cyclic Rate: 600rpm
Weight: 9.75kg (20.5lb)	Range: 2000m (6560ft) +
Overall Length: 1185mm (46.75in)	

▲ **Besal Mk II**

British Army / Undeployed

The Besal Mk II light machine gun was intended to supplement the British Army's supply of Bren Guns. It was constructed to fire the same ammunition and utilize the same magazine and was lighter and easier to produce. As the war progressed it was deemed unnecessary to produce the Besal in quantity.

Special Ops: Behind Enemy Lines
1941–45

British and US intelligence organizations supported covert operations by resistance groups and launched their own clandestine missions, while the Germans conducted raids and undercover efforts of their own.

W HEN THE DARK GREEN, open-topped Mercedes carrying 37-year-old Reinhard Heydrich (1904–42), *Reichsprotektor* of Bohemia and Moravia and top lieutenant of *Reichsführer*-SS Heinrich Himmler (1900–45), turned a sharp corner in downtown Prague and the driver lurched into second gear, an unobtrusive man dressed in civilian clothes suddenly pulled a Sten submachine gun from beneath his coat, pointed it at the Nazi officer and pulled the trigger. Nothing happened. The Sten had jammed.

An accomplice tossed a pair of grenades at the vehicle and seriously wounded Heydrich, who later died in a Czech hospital. The assailants were Czech operatives, trained in Scotland and equipped with weapons supplied by British intelligence. Josef Gabcik (1912–42) and Jan Kubis (1913–42) were the cornerstones of Operation Anthropoid, an assassination attempt against Heydrich. The pair had been parachuted into Nazi-occupied Czechoslovakia and once on the ground connected with a resistance network that facilitated the covert operation.

▲ **Sten in action**

A French resistance fighter poses with a Sten Mk II submachine gun during the battle for Paris, August 1944. The Sten was widely supplied to resistance fighters across Europe, because of its easy assembly and simple operation.

▲ **Welrod**

British Special Operations Executive / SO2 Operations, Occupied France
1943

The Welrod assassination pistol was a short-range precision weapon that included an integral silencer. Although the pistol included an eight-round magazine, reloading was manual rather than automatic, so a user could only expect to get off one round at a time.

Specifications	
Country of Origin: United Kingdom	Overall Length: 310mm (12in)
Date: 1940	Barrel Length: 95mm (less silencer)
Calibre: 9mm (.35in), 8.1mm (.32in)	Muzzle Velocity: Not known
Operation: Rotary bolt	Feed/Magazine: 6- or 8-round magazine
Weight: 1.090kg (2.4lb)	Range: 20m (65ft)

Of course, when the Sten failed, the back-up plan succeeded in killing Heydrich and loosing a vengeful bloodbath against the Czech civilian population. The village of Lidice was thoroughly destroyed and its people massacred in reprisal. Gabcik and Kubis were cornered in the burial chamber beneath a church and finally killed.

With covert operations, necessity is often the mother of invention, and innovative weapons systems were deployed with intelligence agents and resistance fighters across Europe during World War II. Like Gabcik and Kubis, those willing to undertake such hazardous operations realized that it was likely they would not survive the mission. Nevertheless, the agents who were willing to participate were deployed

in attempts to kill enemy military and political figures, and weapons were developed for them, some of which could be easily concealed or broken down for transport.

Surprise and silence

Among the most innovative weapons developed for covert missions was the Welrod assassination pistol, a 9mm (.35in) or 8.1mm (.32in), manually reloaded bolt-action weapon with an integral silencer and a six- or eight-round magazine. Developed by the British Special Operations Executive (SOE), the Welrod was intended for close-quarters, single-opportunity action. The chambering of a new round from the magazine was slow, and it was likely that the

▶ **Liberator M1942**

French Resistance / Maquis Forces, Lyon, 1944

Cheaply made and often air-dropped to resistance fighters in Nazi-occupied Europe, the Liberator, or FP-45, was meant for close-in killing. It was difficult to operate, and clearing spent cases required the insertion of a dowel peg or a stick.

Specifications

Country of Origin: United States	Overall Length: 141mm (5.55in)
Date: 1942	Barrel Length: 102mm (4in)
Calibre: 11.4mm (.45in)	Muzzle Velocity: 250m/sec (820ft/sec)
Operation: Manual	Feed/Magazine: Single shot
Weight: .454kg (1lb)	Range: 8m (26.2ft)

▲ **Sten Mk II 'Silent Sten'**

British Special Operations Executive / SO2 Operations, Occupied France 1943

The Silent Sten was a variant of the British submachine gun with a suppressor to reduce the weapon's report. After 10 rounds were fired, the effectiveness of the suppressor was significantly degraded.

Specifications

Country of Origin: United Kingdom	Barrel Length: 196mm (7.7in)
Date: 1942	Muzzle Velocity: 380m/sec (1247ft/sec)
Calibre: 9mm (.35in) Parabellum	Feed/Magazine: 32-round detachable box
Operation: Blowback	magazine
Weight: 2.95kg (6.5lb)	Range: 70m (230ft)
Overall Length: 762mm (30in)	

agent would get off one shot only. To chamber a second round, a cap at the rear of the barrel was twisted and pulled back and then pushed forward. Reloading was accomplished only by removing the entire grip.

In the United States, the smoothbore 11.4mm (.45in) Liberator Model 1942 pistol was manufactured for the purpose of equipping resistance fighters. American intelligence officers reasoned that a quantity of crude, inexpensively made pistols could be manufactured and delivered quickly to resistance groups on the European continent, and the Liberator was cheaply made of stamped components. Although it was fitted with a single-shot magazine, each Liberator was packaged with 10 rounds of ammunition. Reloading was accomplished only after a suitable implement such as a stick was utilized to poke the spent shell casing from the weapon to clear the chamber. The Liberator was cocked by pulling the cocking piece to the rear; turning the piece sideways enabled reloading and ejecting spent casings.

The Special Operations Executive developed a silent version of the Sten Mk II for use by its agents. While the Sten itself was widely distributed to resistance fighters in Europe, the Silent Sten was identical to the original version with the exception that the muzzle report was suppressed. Although it was quiet for approximately the first 10 rounds, carbon build-up made the Silent Sten progressively louder as the 32-round 9mm (.35in) magazine was emptied.

The Hudson M3A1 was an improved version of the M3 submachine gun, popularly known as the 'Grease Gun'. Like the M3, the M3A1 was cheaply made. However, it was not approved for production until December 1944, and issued to few US troops during the waning months of World War II. The US Office of Strategic Services (OSS) requested a modification of the M3A1 with an integral sound suppressor. The suppressor was designed by Bell Laboratories, and approximately 1000 were ordered. The effectiveness of the suppressor was considerably below that of the British Sten. The M3A1 was capable of a rate of fire of 45 rounds per minute, although the low muzzle velocity retarded knockdown capability.

Another silenced weapon was intended specifically for assassination or long-distance killing. The De Lisle carbine was developed in the early 1940s and entered service in 1943. Designer William De Lisle based the weapon on the Short Magazine Lee-Enfield rifle, modifying the receiver to accept the 11.4mm (.45in) cartridge, replacing the barrel with a modified Thompson submachine gun barrel, and using modified magazines from the Model 1911 pistol.

A single-shot bolt-action weapon, the De Lisle was, in contrast to other silenced weapons of the time, extremely quiet. The single-shot feature was considered an advantage over semiautomatic operation, which might alert sentries or other enemy personnel when silence was required for a successful operation. The De Lisle was manufactured in quite limited numbers, and only 129 were produced from 1943 to 1945. Most of these were placed in the hands of British Commandos.

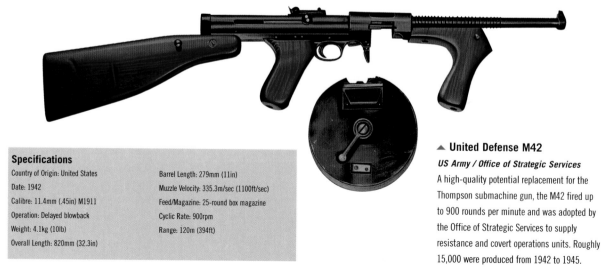

Specifications

Country of Origin: United States	Barrel Length: 279mm (11in)
Date: 1942	Muzzle Velocity: 335.3m/sec (1100ft/sec)
Calibre: 11.4mm (.45in) M1911	Feed/Magazine: 25-round box magazine
Operation: Delayed blowback	Cyclic Rate: 900rpm
Weight: 4.1kg (10lb)	Range: 120m (394ft)
Overall Length: 820mm (32.3in)	

▲ **United Defense M42**

US Army / Office of Strategic Services

A high-quality potential replacement for the Thompson submachine gun, the M42 fired up to 900 rounds per minute and was adopted by the Office of Strategic Services to supply resistance and covert operations units. Roughly 15,000 were produced from 1942 to 1945.

▲ De Lisle

British Army / No. 3 Commando, Osnabrück, V2 rocket facility, April 1945

The De Lisle carbine incorporated elements of the Mk III SMLE rifle, the Model 1911 pistol and the Thompson submachine gun. Intended as a sniper weapon, it served in small numbers, primarily with Commando units. Its silencing apparatus was quite effective.

Specifications

Country of Origin: United Kingdom	Barrel Length: 210mm (8.26in)
Date: 1943	Muzzle Velocity: 260m/sec (853ft/sec)
Calibre: 11.4mm (.45in) .45 ACP	Feed/Magazine: 7-round detachable box
Operation: Bolt action	magazine
Weight: 3.7kg (8.15lb)	Range: 400m (1312ft)
Overall Length: 960mm (37.79in)	

North Africa: British & Commonwealth Forces
1940–43

The seesaw struggle for supremacy on the African continent was waged across thousands of kilometres of arid desert, and British and Commonwealth forces fought tenaciously to win the final victory over their Axis adversaries.

CONTINUALLY PLAGUED by shortages of supplies and manpower, the British and Commonwealth armed forces in the desert won significant early victories against Mussolini's Italian Army. Outnumbered 10 to one, General Sir Archibald Wavell (1883–1950) authorized an offensive action against the Italians in late 1940. Operation Compass, intended as a five-day raid against Italian bases, turned into a two-month string of Commonwealth victories. Under the command of Lieutenant-General Richard O'Connor (1889–1981), 31,000 troops, 275 tanks and 120 field guns succeeded in forcing a break in Italian lines, routing the enemy.

In eight weeks of fighting, O'Connor's force, which consisted primarily of the 7th Armoured Division and the 4th Indian Infantry Division, killed 3000 Italian soldiers while capturing 115,000 enemy troops, 400 tanks and nearly 1300 artillery pieces. The crowning victory of Operation Compass took place at Beda Fomm, just south of the major Libyan city of Benghazi. The remnants of the Italian Tenth Army were cut off and forced to surrender. O'Connor pleaded for the resources necessary to fight on to the Libyan capital of Tripoli, but Wavell had already turned his focus on the defence of Greece and Crete – primarily at the behest of Prime Minister Winston Churchill.

Within days of the Axis disaster at Beda Fomm, two German divisions, the vanguard of the *Afrika Korps* and what would become the vaunted Panzer Army Afrika in combination with Italian formations, landed at Tripoli. The German commander, Major-General Erwin Rommel (1891–1944), soon engineered a spectacular reversal of fortune, pushing

Commonwealth forces across kilometres of territory and eventually crossing the Egyptian frontier. Rommel's only major setback was the failure to capture the Libyan port of Tobruk, stubbornly defended in the spring of 1941 primarily by soldiers of the Australian 9th Division, who were relieved during Operation Crusader after a 240-day siege. Rommel was plagued by shortages of supplies due to the great distances from bases and the continuing Allied interdiction of shipping and road transport.

During his second North African offensive, Rommel did capture Tobruk in June 1942. By this time, he had achieved fame as the 'Desert Fox', threatening the Egyptian capital of Cairo, Egypt's great port of Alexandria, and the security of the Suez Canal, the lifeline of Commonwealth supply to troops in the Middle East. In October 1942, Axis forces reached their high-water mark. The reinforced British Eighth Army under Lieutenant-General Bernard Montgomery (1887–1976) attacked at El Alamein and drove Rommel westwards. El Alamein is considered the turning point in the Desert War and one of the great Allied victories of World War II.

Meanwhile, Operation Torch, the Allied invasion of North Africa from the west, began on 8 November 1942, with landings at Casablanca, Oran and Algiers. Rommel was fighting on two fronts, and the fate of Axis forces in North Africa was sealed. Hitler recalled Rommel from the African continent, and more than

ANZAC INFANTRY BATTALION, 1941	
Unit	**Strength**
Battalion HQ	
Regimental Aid Post	1
Headquarters Company	1
Signals Platoon	1
Anti-aircraft Platoon	1
Mortar Platoon	1
Pioneer Platoon	1
Administration Platoon	1
Carrier Platoon	1
Rifle Companies	4
Rifle Company HQ	
Platoons	3
Rifle Platoon HQ	
Rifle sections	3
Anti-tank rifle	1
50mm (2in) mortar	1
Rifle Section	
Bren light machine gun	1
Thompson submachine gun	1

▾ Australian Infantry Rifle Section, 1941

Australian troops deployed to the North African desert bore a significant burden during the fighting of the first two years against Erwin Rommel's Panzer Army Afrika. The Australian infantry rifle section was organized in similar fashion to those of other Commonwealth forces and included a rifle group and a gun group. In the rifle group, one automatic weapon, usually a Thompson submachine gun handled by the section leader, supported eight riflemen armed with the Lee-Enfield Mk III. The gun section included a Bren light machine gun and two riflemen.

Rifle Group (section leader, six riflemen), 1 x Thompson SMG, 6 x SMLE rifles

Gun Group (lance-corporal, loader, gunner), 2 x SMLE rifle, 1 x Bren light machine gun

300,000 Axis troops remaining surrendered in Tunisia in May 1943.

Weapons of the Desert War

The British and Commonwealth troops who fought the Germans and Italians in the North African desert came from all areas of the British Empire, particularly Australia, New Zealand and India. The riflemen were equipped with the Mark III Short Magazine Lee-Enfield (SMLE) rifle, the principal rifle of the British Army and all Commonwealth forces for more than half a century.

Among the personal automatic weapons carried in the desert was the Sten Mk II submachine gun, of which nearly two million examples were produced

during World War II. The Sten was constructed of just 47 parts, and these were stamped from steel, then welded or pressed together rapidly. The only machined parts of the weapon were the barrel and the bolt. Firing a 9mm (.35in) cartridge, the Sten was fed by a side-mounted, 32-round magazine and could actually accept captured German ammunition. The weapon could be dismantled quickly for cleaning in the harsh desert environment, but it was sometimes prone to jamming.

The Thompson submachine gun was developed by American inventor John T. Thompson (1860–1940) in 1919 as a means of possibly breaking the stalemate of trench warfare after the heavy bloodshed of World War I. Thompson reasoned that such a weapon could

Specifications

Country of Origin: United Kingdom	Barrel Length: 640mm (25.2in)
Date: 1907	Muzzle Velocity: 634m/sec (2080ft/sec)
Calibre: 7.7mm (.303in)	Feed/Magazine: 10-round box, loaded with
Operation: Bolt action	5-round charger clips
Weight: 3.93kg (8.625lb)	Range: 500m (1640ft)
Overall Length: 1133mm (44.6in)	

▲ **Lee-Enfield Rifle No. 1 Mk III SMLE**

British Eighth Army / 7th Support Group / 1st King's Royal Rifle Corps, Operation Battleaxe, June 1941

The Lee-Enfield Mk III became the primary infantry weapon of Commonwealth forces during World War II. The bolt-action rifle was one of a series of weapons that served through the 1950s with specialized variants still active today.

▲ **Thompson M1**

British Eighth Army / 6th Battalion Durham Light Infantry, El Alamein, November 1942

The American Thompson submachine gun was issued to British and Commonwealth troops early in the Desert War and was later complemented by the Sten Mk II.

Specifications

Country of Origin: United States	Barrel Length: 267mm (10.5in)
Date: 1942	Muzzle Velocity: 280m/sec (920ft/sec)
Calibre: 11.4mm (.45in) M1911	Feed/Magazine: 20- or 30-round box magazine
Operation: Delayed blowback	Cyclic Rate: 700rpm
Weight: 4.74kg (10.45lb) loaded	Range: 120m (394ft)
Overall Length: 813mm (32in)	

provide the firepower to literally sweep enemy soldiers from their trenches. Hence, the moniker 'Trench Broom' was among its many nicknames.

The Thompson did not achieve its greatest fame on the battlefield, but during the Prohibition era of the 1920s and 1930s in the United States. The Thompson became symbolic of the fighting between law enforcement officers and organized crime and was used by both. The weapon fired the 11.4mm (.45in) cartridge and was blowback-operated; it featured the Blish Lock breech-locking system designed by US naval officer John Bell Blish (1860–1921). The Thompson was fed by stick or box magazines of 20 or 30 rounds or by 50- or 100-round drums.

The Thompson was adopted by the US Army in 1938 and made available to British and Commonwealth forces through Lend-Lease. Many examples were placed in the hands of Commando units from Britain and Canada.

As the war progressed, the British Sten and the Australian Owen submachine gun, officially known as the Owen Machine Carbine, began appearing on the battlefield in greater numbers.

Complementing the Vickers Mk I machine gun was the lighter but hefty Vickers-Berthier, a weapon weighing 11.1kg (24.4lb) and firing a 7.7mm

Specifications

Country of Origin: United Kingdom	Barrel Length: 196mm (7.7in)
Date: 1942	Muzzle Velocity: 380m/sec (1247ft/sec)
Calibre: 9mm (.35in) Parabellum	Feed/Magazine: 32-round detachable box
Operation: Blowback	magazine
Weight: 2.95kg (6.5lb)	Cyclic Rate: 500rpm
Overall Length: 762mm (30in)	Range: 70m (230ft)

▲ **Sten Mk II**

South African 2nd Infantry Division / 2nd Infantry Brigade, Tobruk, May 1942

Constructed of only 47 parts, the Sten Mk II submachine gun was stamped and generally pressed together for rapid deployment to Commonwealth forces. The weapon proved popular due to its firepower and ease of disassembly.

Specifications

Country of Origin: United Kingdom	Overall Length: 1156mm (45.5in)
Date: 1932	Barrel Length: 600mm (23.6in)
Calibre: 7.7mm (.303in)	Muzzle Velocity: 745m/sec (2450ft/sec)
Operation: Gas operated	Feed/Magazine: 30-round box magazine
Weight: 11.1kg (24.4lb)	Range: 550m (1805ft)

▲ **Vickers-Berthier**

Western Desert Force / 6th Rajputana Rifles, Egypt, 1940

The Vickers-Berthier was based on a French design of World War I and adopted by the British Indian Army in 1932. It proved heavy and deficient in comparison to the Bren Gun.

Australian troops man foxholes in the hard ground of the Western Desert, 1942. All are armed with the Mk III Short Magazine Lee-Enfield, bayonets fixed.

▲ **Bren Mk II**

British Eighth Army / 51st Highland Division, El Alamein, November 1942

Although a very accurate light machine gun, the Bren's limited magazine capacity could make sustained fire problematic, especially when laying down suppressing fire. However, the Bren proved key to British Army doctrine in World War II and every infantryman was expected to know how to use the section's Bren.

Specifications

Country of Origin: United Kingdom	Barrel Length: 625mm (25in)
Date: 1941	Muzzle Velocity: 730m/sec (2400ft/sec)
Calibre: 7.7mm (.303in)	Feed/Magazine: 30-round box magazine
Operation: Gas operated, air cooled	Cyclic Rate: 500rpm
Weight: 10.25kg (22.5lb)	Range: 1000m (3280ft)
Overall Length: 1150mm (45.25in)	

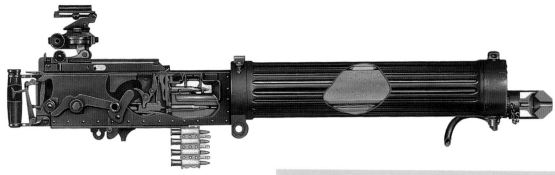

▲ **Vickers Mk I**

British Eighth Army / 10th Armoured Division / 5th Battalion Royal Sussex
Regiment, Tunisia, March 1943

The venerable Vickers Mk I was based on the old Maxim design and had served in
World War I. It fired the same cartridge, the 7.7mm (.303in), as lighter machine
guns and the Lee-Enfield Mk III rifle.

Specifications

Country of Origin: United Kingdom	Barrel Length: 725mm (28.5in)
Date: 1912	Muzzle Velocity: 600m/sec (1970ft/sec)
Calibre: 7.7mm (.303in)	Feed/Magazine: Belt fed
Operation: Recoil, water cooled	Cyclic Rate: 600rpm
Weight: 18kg (40lb)	Range: 2000m (6560ft) + ; later 3000m
Overall Length: 1155mm (40.5in)	(9842ft)

(.303in) cartridge. Based on a French design of the
World War I era, the weapon was licence-built in
Britain as a replacement for the Lewis Gun. The
British Indian Army adopted the Vickers-Berthier in
1932, while the British Army opted for the famous
Bren Gun. The Vickers-Berthier, or VB, was welcome
in the desert for its firepower of 450 to 600 rounds
per minute; however, the weapon was about a
kilogram (2.2lb) heavier than the Bren and was less
portable. As a result, despite the VB's simpler design,
the British Army chose the Bren.

The Vickers Mk I medium machine gun fired the
same cartridge as the lighter Vickers-Berthier, the
7.7mm (.303in) round, but was water-cooled and
significantly heavier at 18kg (40lb), and required a
team of as many as six soldiers to service it. The
Vickers was a veteran of World War I and based on
the venerable Maxim design. Although the British
military establishment had made plans to replace it
between the world wars, the Vickers remained in
service throughout World War II and was not retired
until the late 1960s.

Italian Army
1940–43

**Although its ranks included some elite formations such as the Bersaglieri who fought heroically
in the desert, the Italian Army was badly outclassed early in the Desert War and depended on its
German allies for support and leadership.**

FOLLOWING THE DEBACLE of the Italian Tenth Army
during Operation Compass, Mussolini continued
to send reinforcements to North Africa, and when
Major-General Erwin Rommel (1891–1944) and the
German *Afrika Korps* arrived in Libya, the Germans
were nominally under senior Italian command. Often
the performance of Italian forces during
World War II, and particularly in North Africa, has

been maligned by historians. The Italians suffered
from a pronounced lack of command and control
and proved inexperienced at large-scale military
operations.

Infantry and armoured formations were typically
equipped with small arms of Italian manufacture, and
the quality of many of these weapons has been
criticized, both with reason and also unfairly. Variants

of the Fucile Modello 91 rifle were commonly used by Italian troops during World War II. A veteran of service in World War I, the Modello 1891 was fed by an integral six-round magazine and loaded with an en-bloc clip. It entered service with the Italian Army in 1892 and was originally chambered for a 6.5mm (.256in) rimless cartridge.

However, reports of inadequate performance at both short and long ranges during the Italian expeditions into Africa during the 1930s prompted the government to authorize a new weapon, the Modello 1938, chambered for a more powerful 7.35mm (.29in) cartridge. Problems with

manufacture and supply of the new weapon thwarted the progress and compelled the Italians to revert to 6.5mm (.256in) ammunition and weapons. For a time, the Italian Army deployed a shorter version of the Modello 1891, but by 1941 the longer Carcano M91/41 was in use. It remained slightly shorter than the original Modello 1891. The sojourn of the Modello 1891 is somewhat indicative of the travails of the Italian arms industry of the interwar and World War II period.

The principal light machine gun of the Italian forces from 1940 to 1943 was the Fucile Mitragliatore Breda Modello 30. Although it was

Specifications

Country of Origin: Italy	Barrel Length: 520mm (20.5in)
Date: 1930	Muzzle Velocity: 610m/sec (2000ft/sec)
Calibre: 6.5mm (.256in) M95 and others	Feed/Magazine: 20-round integral box magazine
Operation: Blowback, air cooled	Cyclic Rate: 475rpm
Weight: 10.2kg (22.5lb)	Range: 1000m (3280ft)
Overall Length: 1230mm (48.5in)	

▲ **Fucile Mitragliatore Breda Modello 30**

Italian Tenth Army / 63rd Infantry Division, Sidi Barrani, September 1940

The standard light machine gun of the Italian Army, the Modello 30 developed a reputation for high maintenance and unreliability in combat. Nevertheless, it was deployed with Italian forces for the duration of the war.

▲ **Fucile Modello 91**

64 Infantry Division Catanzaro, Buq Buq, December 1940

The long-serving Modello 91 was the primary shoulder arm of the Italians in World War I. Variants continued in service through World War II despite problems with performance during African campaigns of the 1920s and 1930s.

Specifications

Country of Origin: Italy	Overall Length: 1285mm (50.6in)
Date: 1891	Barrel Length: 780mm (30.7in)
Calibre: 6.5mm (.256in)	Muzzle Velocity: 630m/sec (2067ft/sec)
Operation: Bolt action	Feed/Magazine: 6-round box magazine
Weight: 3.8kg (8.375lb)	Range: 500m (1640ft)

innovative, with a hinged magazine that was opened and filled with 20-round rifle chargers of 6.5mm (.256in) ammunition for reloading, the weapon was less than robust and prone to battlefield damage, which often rendered it useless. The closed-bolt, blowback-operated machine gun also utilized a small mechanism that oiled each cartridge for firing. During combat this process sometimes resulted in the premature 'cooking-off' of a round. The weapon was manufactured by Breda Meccanica Bresciana and is considered inferior to contemporary light machine guns fielded by other armies due to a low rate of fire at 475 rounds per minute, low ammunition capacity, lack of a handle to facilitate changing of barrels, a propensity for jamming, and susceptibility to damage. The early allocation of machine guns to Italian infantry companies was inadequate, with only a single weapon apportioned to a pair of squads, resulting in a maximum of eight Modello 30 guns per company, which was therefore somewhat undergunned. Later, this number was increased to a single gun per squad.

Specifications

Country of Origin: Italy	Barrel Length: Not known
Date: 1915	Muzzle Velocity: 301.82m/sec (990ft/sec)
Calibre: 9mm (.35in)	Feed/Magazine: 25-round detachable box
Operation: Blowback	magazine
Weight: 3.62kg (8lb)	Range: 70m (230ft)
Overall Length: 901.69mm (35.5in)	

▲ **Villar-Perosa OVP M1918**

1st Blackshirt Division 23 Marzo, Bardia, Libya, January 1941

The OVP M1918 submachine gun was an adaptation of an earlier twin-barrelled weapon with a high rate of fire of 900 rounds per minute. It entered service late in World War I and was still in use more than two decades later.

Specifications

Country of Origin: Italy	Barrel Length: 198mm (7.79in)
Date: 1938	Muzzle Velocity: 395m/sec (1295ft/sec)
Calibre: 9mm (.35in)	Feed/Magazine: 10-, 20- or 40-round detachable
Operation: Blowback	box magazine
Weight: 2.72kg (6lb)	Range: 70m (230ft)
Overall Length: 798mm (31.4in)	

▲ **Moschetto Automatico Beretta Modello 38 (MAB 38)**

132 Armoured Division Ariete, Battle of Gazala, May 1942

The successful MAB 38 was a sturdy submachine gun that was originally issued to elite units and compared favourably with its Allied and German counterparts. The weapon fired in either semiautomatic or fully automatic modes with separate triggers.

▶ **Alpine aim**

An Italian mountaintrooper aims a Beretta Modello 1934 pistol during training in the Alps. The Modello 1934 was a reliable handgun, although its 9mm (.35in) short cartridge was underpowered.

Submachine guns

Italian troops deployed a pair of submachine guns, the Villar-Perosa OVP M1918 and the Moschetto Auto Beretta MAB 38. The former was developed during World War I and was an improvement on an earlier version – a twin-barrelled weapon designated the M1915. The M1918 fired a 9mm (.35in) cartridge and was capable of an impressive rate of fire of 900 rounds per minute fed by a top-mounted box magazine with a 25-round capacity. A shoulder stock was added for stability in sustained combat situations.

The Moschetto Automatico Beretta Modello 38 (MAB 38) was a 9mm (.35in) submachine gun manufactured at the Beretta Works in Gardone Valtrompia, Brescia, and firing the same ammunition as Beretta pistols. It was capable of firing a maximum of 500 rounds per minute and was fed by a detachable box magazine of 10, 20 or 40 rounds. This gas-operated submachine gun was capable of semiautomatic or fully automatic firing, with two

triggers. Until 1943, the MAB 38 was primarily issued to elite airborne and Carabineri units and some formations deployed to Africa. It was recognized as a formidable weapon and was sought after by Allied soldiers who faced it in combat. As the war progressed, the weapon was issued to Italian troops fighting with the Allies.

◀ **Fiat Modello 35**

German-Italian Panzer Army / Italian 17th Infantry Division Pavia, Tunisia, 1943

The Fiat-Revelli 35 was a revised version of the Modello 1914, which had equipped the Italian Army during World War I. It proved to be an unreliable weapon, especially in desert conditions.

Specifications

Country of Origin: Italy	Barrel Length: 680mm (26.75in)
Date: 1935	Muzzle Velocity: 790m/sec (2600ft/sec)
Calibre: 8mm (.314in)	Feed/Magazine: 50-round belt
Operation: Gas operated, air cooled	Cyclic Rate: 450rpm
Weight: 19.5kg (43lb)	Range: 2000m (6560ft)
Overall Length: 1270mm (50in)	

Sicily and Italian Campaign
1943–45

The bitter fighting through Sicily and up the boot of Italy was characterized by close-quarters combat in rugged terrain with small arms dealing death from caves, fortified positions and house to house in towns and villages.

IN EARLY JULY 1943, the Allies landed in force on the southern tip of the island of Sicily. Operation Husky launched the Italian campaign, one of the most arduous and prolonged actions of World War II. Within six weeks, the British Eighth Army, commanded by General Sir Bernard Montgomery (1887–1976), had pushed northwards from the southern tip of the island and joined the spearhead of the American Seventh Army, under General George S. Patton Jr. (1885–1945), that had landed to the east at Gela, advanced to the northwest capturing Palermo, and pressed the Axis defenders into a perimeter around the city of Messina in the island's northeast corner.

Although Sicily had been secured by late August, the cooperative Allied offensive had failed to close the trap on the island and allowed thousands of Axis troops to escape to the Italian mainland across the narrow Strait of Messina. German and Italian forces braced for the coming invasion of Italy.

Montgomery's Eighth Army executed Operation Baytown on 3 September 1943, landing in southern Italy, and the US Fifth Army, commanded by General Mark W. Clark (1896–1984), landed at Salerno on 9 September to undertake Operation Avalanche. More than 15 months of costly fighting ensued as the Eighth Army pushed up the east coast along the Adriatic Sea and the Fifth Army doggedly advanced up the west coast near the Tyrrhenian Sea.

The Italian campaign was marked by stubborn German defence, which stiffened following the surrender of Fascist Italy just as Allied forces were poised to invade the country. The Germans constructed a series of lengthy defensive lines stretching for kilometres across the mountainous spine of Italy. The most formidable of these was the Gustav Line. Allied attempts to breach it precipitated the horrendous battle for Monte Cassino and the epic fight for its abbey, as well as the amphibious Allied landing at Anzio, Operation Shingle, that was intended to rapidly seize Rome but instead degenerated into a months-long stalemate.

The first Axis capital to fall into Allied hands, Rome was liberated on 4 June 1944. Two days later, the Allied invasion of Normandy relegated the Italian campaign to a sideshow. Fighting continued in the north of the country until the end of the war in May 1945.

Specifications

Country of Origin: Germany	Barrel Length: 502mm (19.76in)
Date: 1942	Muzzle Velocity: 761m/sec (2500ft/sec)
Calibre: 7.92mm (.312in) Mauser	Feed/Magazine: 20-round detachable box
Operation: Gas operated	magazine
Weight: 4.53kg (9.99lb)	Range: 400m (1312ft) +
Overall Length: 940mm (37in)	

▲ **Fallschirmjägergewehr 42 (FG 42)**

German I Parachute Corps / 1st Parachute Division, Monte Cassino, March 1944

Intended to provide firepower for lightly armed airborne troops, the FG 42 combined elements of a machine gun and a bolt-action rifle and could be considered an early assault rifle.

COLT M1911A1 MILITARY PRODUCTION FIGURES	
Period	Total
1924–39	17,281
1940	4695
1941	34,756
1942	100,266
1943	752,529
1944	134,317
1945	136,000

COLT COMMERCIAL PRODUCTION: MODEL 1911A1		
Serial Numbers	Date	Total
S/N C135000 to C139999	1924	5000
S/N C140000 to 144999	1925	5000
S/N C145000 to C150999	1926	6000
S/N C151000 to C151999	1927	1000
S/N C152000 to C154999	1928	3000
S/N C155000 to C155999	1929	1000
S/N C156000 to C158999	1930	3000
S/N C159000 to C160999	1931	2000
S/N C161000 to C164799	1932	3800
S/N C164800 to C174599	1933	9800
S/N C174600 to C177999	1934	3400
S/N C178000 to C179799	1935	1800
S/N C179800 to C183199	1936	3400
S/N C183200 to C188699	1937	5500
S/N C188700 to C189599	1938	900
S/N C189600 to C198899	1939	9300
S/N C198900 to C199299	1940	400
S/N C199300 to C208799	1941	9500
S/N C208800 to C215018	1942	6219

King of the hill

A few of the elite German *Fallschirmjäger*, or airborne troops, who turned the rubble of the abbey of Monte Cassino into a virtually impregnable redoubt that stood against repeated assaults, were armed with the light Fallschirmjägergewehr 42 (FG 42), developed specifically for the lightly armed and equipped paratroopers. It was first in action during the daring raid by SS troops under the command of Major Otto Skorzeny (1908–75) to rescue Mussolini (1882–1945) from captivity in the Italian Alps in September 1943.

The FG 42 was conceived as a weapon that could provide sustained fire support on the ground, displaying the characteristics of the machine gun with the ease of transport of the basic infantry rifle. Therefore it may truly be classified as an early assault rifle. It weighed only 42kg (9.3lb) and fired the 7.92mm (.312in) cartridge. It was fed by a detachable box magazine of 10 or 20 rounds and was capable of selective semiautomatic or fully automatic firing modes. Intended to supplant the bolt-action Mauser Karabiner 98k rifle and the submachine guns then in wide use, it was designed by Louis Stange and manufactured by Rheinmetall. One complication led to quite low production numbers. Manganese, which was used in making the barrels for the weapon, was in short supply, and after the production of only 2000 guns the limited supply of

▶ **Browning M1911A1**

US VI Corps / 3rd Infantry Division, Anzio, March 1944

One of the most popular small arms of the modern era, the 11.4mm (.45in) Browning M1911A1 pistol set a standard for modern pistols in both design and longevity of service.

Specifications

Country of Origin: United States

Date: 1911

Calibre: 11.4mm (.45in)

Operation: Short recoil

Weight: 1.1kg (2.425lb)

Overall Length: 216mm (8.5in)

Barrel Length: 127mm (5in)

Muzzle Velocity: 262m/sec (860ft/sec)

Feed/Magazine: 7-round magazine

Range: 50m (164ft)

manganese was designated for other projects and other materials were substituted.

Once the FG 42 reached the field, several modifications were requested, including a relocation of the bipod from near the hand guard to the muzzle for greater control, a reduction in the weapon's propensity to overheat by changing the stock from metal to wood, and slanting the handgrip to a nearly vertical position.

When the weapon was in fully automatic mode, the power of the rifle cartridge made it a challenge to maintain control and any degree of accuracy. Later versions reduced the rate of fire from 900 rounds per minute to 750. The muzzle was modified to help with recoil and muzzle flash but this resulted in a much louder report. Due to the great expense of manufacturing the FG 42, only about 7000 were produced from 1943 to 1945.

Browning dominance

The Browning M1911A1 pistol was a common sight on the hips of US Army personnel during the Italian campaign and indeed around the globe during World War II. This robust single-action, semiautomatic pistol fired an 11.4mm (.45in) cartridge and was fed by a seven-round detachable box magazine. It was reputed to have tremendous knockdown capability in the hands of a skilled user and replaced earlier potential standard issue pistols such as the German-made Luger for this reason. The M1911A1 has

▲ **Browning M2HB**

US Fifth Army / 135th Infantry Regiment, Rome, June 1944

The 12.7mm (.5in) Browning M2HB heavy machine gun was an air-cooled variant of the original weapon that entered service in the 1930s. Its proven success on the battlefield has resulted in its remaining in the NATO arsenal.

Specifications

Country of Origin: United States	Barrel Length: 1143mm (45in)
Date: 1933	Muzzle Velocity: 898m/sec (2950ft/sec)
Calibre: 12.7mm (.5in)	Feed/Magazine: 110-round belt
Operation: Short recoil, air cooled	Cyclic Rate: 450–575rpm
Weight: 38.5kg (84lb)	Range: 1800m (5905ft) effective
Overall Length: 1655mm (65in)	

Specifications

Country of Origin: United States	Barrel Length: 266mm (10.5in)
Date: 1921	Muzzle Velocity: 280m/sec (920ft/sec)
Calibre: 11.4mm (.45in) M1911	Feed/Magazine: 18-, 20-, 30-round detachable
Operation: Delayed blowback	box, or 50-, 100-round drum magazine
Weight: 4.88kg (10.75lb)	Cyclic Rate: 800rpm
Overall Length: 857mm (33.75in)	Range: 120m (394ft)

▲ **Thompson 1921**

1st Special Service Force, Monte Majo, January 1944

The Thompson submachine gun was developed in World War I as a means of breaking the stalemate of trench warfare with sustained fire support. It was adopted by the US Army in 1938 and made available to allies through Lend-Lease.

become one of the most famous firearms in modern history and remains popular today with a service life that has extended a full century.

The M1911 Browning pistol was the brainchild of prolific firearms designer John Browning (1855–1926), whose work led to some of the most highly produced firearms of the twentieth century. During his lifetime, Browning worked for his own arms company as well as Colt, Winchester, Remington, Savage and the Belgian company Fabrique Nationale. The M1911 is quite probably his best known design, although others include the Browning Automatic Rifle (BAR) and the 12.7mm (.5in) M2 heavy machine gun.

From 1911 to 1985, the M1911 was the standard issue sidearm for the US military. The handgun was chosen after a series of rigorous field tests, particularly in competition with a rival Savage model. Although officially replaced by the M9 pistol by 1990, it remains in service and is popular with civilian gun enthusiasts. It was officially adopted by the US Army on 29 March 1911, and the US Navy and Marine Corps followed suit two years later. Manufacturing was solely undertaken by Colt until the demand for the weapon grew and the US government's Springfield Armory took up production during World War I.

Combat experience during World War I prompted slight modifications to the original design and resulted in a new designation, M1911A1. The most prominent of these alterations included a shorter trigger, new grip chequering, cutouts behind the trigger, a longer grip safety spur, shorter hammer spur and wider front sight. Several companies produced the M1911A1 during World War II, including Colt, Remington Rand, Union Switch and Signal, Ithaca Gun Company, and Singer. More than 1.9 million were ordered by the US military during the period.

Browning machine guns

Browning's M2 12.7mm (.5in) heavy machine gun was developed during World War I and remains in service today, with more than three million manufactured since its adoption by the US Army in the early 1920s. The HB variant refers to the heavier air-cooled barrel that was introduced in 1933 to offer a lighter, more transportable weapon at 38.5kg (84lb) compared with 55kg (121lb) for the older water-cooled version. The short-recoil-operated M2HB was mounted on a tripod for infantry use, belt-fed and capable of a rate of fire of up to 635 rounds per minute.

Variants of the original Browning M2 machine gun have been mounted aboard fighter and bomber aircraft, tanks and other armoured vehicles, and naval vessels. The weapon's variety of heavy ammunition has proved effective against enemy personnel, light vehicles and aircraft in a multipurpose career. It is second only to the M1911 pistol in length of service with US forces and remains a primary weapon of US and NATO troops in Afghanistan and Iraq.

▲ **Hudson M3A1 with silencer**

US Office of Strategic Services / 2671st Special Recon Battalion,
Naples-Foggia, November 1944

The M3A1 submachine gun was an improved version of the original M3 'Grease Gun' that was capable of further modification with a suppressor. An order for 1000 of these was placed by the OSS.

Specifications

Country of Origin: United States	Overall Length: 762mm (30in)
Date: 1944	Barrel Length: 203mm (8in)
Calibre: 9mm (.35in) or 11.4mm (.45in)	Muzzle Velocity: 275m/sec (900ft/sec)
.45 ACP	Feed/Magazine: 30-round detachable box mag
Operation: Blowback	Cyclic Rate: 450rpm
Weight: 3.7kg (8.15lb)	Range: 50m (164ft)

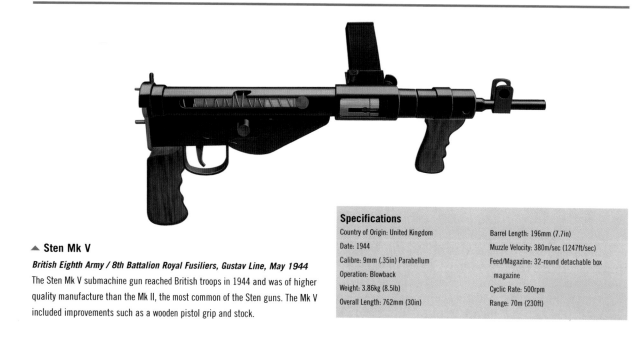

▲ Sten Mk V

British Eighth Army / 8th Battalion Royal Fusiliers, Gustav Line, May 1944

The Sten Mk V submachine gun reached British troops in 1944 and was of higher quality manufacture than the Mk II, the most common of the Sten guns. The Mk V included improvements such as a wooden pistol grip and stock.

Specifications

Country of Origin: United Kingdom	Barrel Length: 196mm (7.7in)
Date: 1944	Muzzle Velocity: 380m/sec (1247ft/sec)
Calibre: 9mm (.35in) Parabellum	Feed/Magazine: 32-round detachable box
Operation: Blowback	magazine
Weight: 3.86kg (8.5lb)	Cyclic Rate: 500rpm
Overall Length: 762mm (30in)	Range: 70m (230ft)

British Army: Normandy to the Rhine 1944–45

From three invasion beaches in Normandy, British and Commonwealth troops slugged their way to the frontier of the Third Reich against stubborn resistance as small-unit engagements often spelled the difference between victory and defeat.

BITTER FIGHTING LAY AHEAD for the British and Commonwealth troops who stormed ashore on Gold, Juno and Sword Beaches on D-Day, 6 June 1944. The liberation of Western Europe would prove to be an arduous task, culminating in the surrender of all German forces the following spring. However, during the weeks following the invasion of Normandy the issue was very much in doubt.

Although the Germans were taken by surprise, they quickly rebounded, organized counterattacks and slowed the Allied pace considerably. The important crossroads and communications centre of Caen, an objective that had been projected for capture on D-Day itself, was not taken for another month. Attempts to break out of the hedgerow country were initially stymied. In mid-July, the successful Operation Goodwood followed the failures of Operation Epsom and Operation Charnwood,

which had cost the British VIII Corps several hundred tanks.

The British Army soldier relied on his rifle, the Short Magazine Lee-Enfield, along with the additional firepower of the Sten series of submachine guns and the infantry machine gun, the Bren. Sustainable fire support was particularly important during airborne operations. Following their deployment by parachute or glider, the airborne troops were typically assigned tasks of seizing and holding key objectives until relieved by heavier units. Due to logistical constraints and the need for rapid movement, airborne units were often equipped with the lightest of weapons.

On D-Day, elements of the 6th Airborne Division executed near-perfect glider landings near the bridge that spanned the Caen Canal north of Sword and Juno beaches. Within minutes, the paras had secured the objective. Their precision operation resulted in Allied control of a key route inland from the invasion beaches. Subsequently, the span was renamed Pegasus Bridge in reference to the mythical winged horse depicted on the airborne unit's shoulder patch.

Arnhem ambition

During the autumn of 1944, Field Marshal Sir Bernard Montgomery (1887–1976) devised a combined airborne and ground assault through the Netherlands to seize key bridges over the Maas, Waal and Neder Rhine Rivers to facilitate a rapid advance across the German frontier and into the Ruhr, the industrial heart of the Reich. Along with the American 101st and 82nd Airborne Divisions, the British 1st Airborne Division would supply the rapid stroke from above, while the veteran XXX Corps would race up a narrow highway to link with the airborne troops, relieve them and hold the corridor open for a major Allied advance.

In the event, the parachute operations were hampered by stubborn German resistance, particularly at Arnhem, where two SS panzer divisions had been located for rest and refitting after

being mauled in Normandy. Only the British 2nd Parachute Battalion under Lieutenant-Colonel John D. Frost (1912–93) reached the bridge across the Rhine at Arnhem. Frost's 745 lightly armed paras were not intended to hold positions for indefinite periods. After several days, Frost was compelled to surrender, and Operation Market-Garden ended in failure, forever to be known by the moniker of 'A Bridge Too Far'.

PIAT potential

When confronted by German armour or engaged in house-to-house fighting, the heaviest weapon available to the men of the 2nd Parachute Battalion was the PIAT (Projector, Infantry, Anti-Tank). The PIAT operated on the same principle as the spigot mortar, utilizing a cocked spring to hurl a bomb tipped with a shaped charge a distance of up to 340m (1115ft). The weapon was front loaded, and the hollow-charge bomb carried explosive filling that weighed 1.1kg (2.5lb).

The origin of the PIAT pre-dates the turn of the twentieth century, and by 1940 it was apparent that older anti-tank rifles were inadequate against the

▲ PIAT

British 6th Airborne Division, Pegasus Bridge, Normandy, June 1944

The PIAT (Projector, Infantry, Anti-Tank) entered service with the British Army in 1943 as an infantry anti-tank weapon. The spring-fired launcher operated in similar fashion to the spigot mortar, igniting propellant in a bomb that carried a hollow charge of 1.1kg (2.5lb).

Specifications

Country of Origin: United Kingdom	Overall Length: 990mm (3ft)
Date: 1942	Muzzle Velocity: 76–137m/sec (250–450ft/sec)
Calibre: 89mm (3.5in)	Feed/Magazine: Front loaded
Operation: Firing spring	Range: 100m (328ft) combat; 340m (1115ft)
Weight: 14.51kg (32lb) launcher;	maximum
1.36kg (3lb) grenade	

increasing armour thickness of German vehicles. Major Millis Jefferis (1899–1963) is credited with reconfiguring prototype weapons and combining the hollow-charge ammunition, perfected in the 1930s, to produce the shoulder-fired weapon that became the functional PIAT. The weapon consisted of a tube with a spring and trigger apparatus and was usually serviced by two soldiers. The spring was quite difficult to cock, particularly in combat conditions, and the PIAT was well known for its hefty recoil that required heavy padding for the shoulder piece.

The PIAT entered service with British and Commonwealth forces in 1943, and 115,000 were produced from 1942 through to the end of the war.

▲ **Reliable rifle**
British troops move warily through a village somewhere in the Netherlands, winter 1944–45. All are armed with the Lee-Enfield Rifle No. 4 Mk I.

Although the weapon was bulky and fairly inaccurate, estimates of its performance in Normandy revealed that approximately seven per cent of the German tanks destroyed had been dispatched by the PIAT.

Sophisticated sniping

Along with improved versions of their standard issue Sten submachine guns and Bren machine guns, British troops in Western Europe also received the Lee-Enfield Rifle No. 4 Mk I and its sniper version, designated the No. 4 Mk I (T). Both prior to the war and as World War II progressed, the need for improvements in rifle performance and utility, not to mention ease of mass production, were noted. As early as 1939, the No. 4 Mk I was issued to some

troops. However, this new version of the ubiquitous Lee-Enfield was not formally adopted by the British military until 1941.

The No. 4 was easily distinguished from the Mk III SMLE, because the former's barrel protruded beyond the end of the stock and was somewhat heavier than that of the Mk III. By 1942, the design had been simplified further with the introduction of an indentation on the bolt track to replace the more complex bolt release catch. This version was produced only in Canada and the United States.

The No. 4 Mk I (T) was configured with the highly accurate standard No. 4 rifle being fitted with a wooden cheek rest and sniper sight. These conversions were produced primarily by the British

▲ Lee-Enfield Rifle No. 4 Mk I

7th Armoured Division / 1st Battalion The Rifle Brigade, Normandy, July 1944

The No. 4 Mk I formally entered service with the British Army in 1941 and provided improvements over earlier versions of the standard issue bolt-action Lee-Enfield rifles.

Specifications

Country of Origin: United Kingdom	Barrel Length: 640mm (25.2in)
Date: 1939	Muzzle Velocity: 751m/sec (2464ft/sec)
Calibre: 7.7mm (.303in) British Service	Feed/Magazine: 10-round detachable box
Operation: Bolt action	magazine
Weight: 4.11kg (9.06lb)	Range: 1000m (3280ft) +
Overall Length: 1128mm (44.43in)	

▲ Lee-Enfield Rifle No. 4 Mk I (T)

2nd Canadian Division / 1st Battalion Royal Winnipeg Rifles, Netherlands, October 1944

The sniper version of the No. 4 Mk I rifle was fitted with a cheek rest and telescopic sight. This weapon served for decades following the end of World War II.

Specifications

Country of Origin: United Kingdom	Barrel Length: 640mm (25.2in)
Date: 1942	Muzzle Velocity: 751m/sec (2464ft/sec)
Calibre: 7.7mm (.303in) British Service	Feed/Magazine: 10-round detachable box
Operation: Bolt action	magazine
Weight: 4.11kg (9.06lb)	Range: 1000m (3280ft) +
Overall Length: 1128mm (44.43in)	

firm of Holland and Holland, while some were retooled in Canada. The sniper variant served with British forces through the 1960s.

New submachine gun

By 1944, the British Army had adopted another submachine gun to complement the supply of Stens already in service. The Patchett Mk 1, like the Sten, fired the 9mm (.35in) Parabellum round and could accept the detachable magazine of the Sten. It could fire at a rate of up to 550 rounds per minute and was

constructed through a higher-quality process than the Sten, which was largely of stamped components due to the exigencies of war.

Named after George Patchett, the chief designer of the Sterling Armaments Company, the Patchett was also known as the Sterling submachine gun and was capable of semiautomatic or fully automatic fire using the blowback, open-bolt system. It was in the hands of some British paras during Operation Market-Garden following rapid trials with just over 100 weapons in use. In fact, it may be said that the

▲ **Sten Mk II**

British Second Army / 2nd Battalion The King's Shropshire Light Infantry, France, August 1944

The mass-produced Sten Mk II equipped thousands of British and Commonwealth troops during World War II. Its reputation for excellent fire support capability was somewhat tarnished by a tendency to jam.

Specifications

Country of Origin: United Kingdom	Barrel Length: 196mm (7.7in)
Date: 1942	Muzzle Velocity: 380m/sec (1247ft/sec)
Calibre: 9mm (.35in) Parabellum	Feed/Magazine: 32-round detachable box
Operation: Blowback	magazine
Weight: 2.95kg (6.5lb)	Cyclic Rate: 500rpm
Overall Length: 762mm (30in)	Range: 70m (230ft)

▲ **Patchett Mk 1**

I British Airborne Corps / 1st Airborne Division / 2nd Parachute Battalion, Arnhem, September 1944

Although largely unproven in combat, a few Patchett submachine guns were issued to airborne troops for Operation Market-Garden. The Patchett eventually replaced the famous Sten Gun.

Specifications

Country of Origin: United Kingdom	Barrel Length: 195mm (7.75in)
Date: 1944	Muzzle Velocity: 395m/sec (1295ft/sec)
Calibre: 9mm (.35in) Parabellum	Feed/Magazine: 32-round detachable box
Operation: Blowback	magazine
Weight: 2.7kg (6lb)	Cyclic Rate: 550rpm
Overall Length: 685mm (27in)	Range: 70m (230ft)

combat experience at Arnhem served as a trial for the weapon as well. The Patchett Mk 1 was assessed as reasonably accurate and capable of withstanding the rigours of prolonged combat with relatively little maintenance.

After the war, the surplus of Sten guns slowed conversion to the Patchett. However, the British Army officially adopted the newer weapon in 1953, and it was in common use until the late 1980s. It has been in service with the armies of more than 40 countries.

▲ Bren Mk II

British Second Army / 6th Airlanding Brigade / 2nd Battalion The Royal Ulster Rifles, Operation Varsity, March 1945

The simplified Bren Mk II infantry machine gun was introduced in 1941 and included a modified bipod, fixed cocking handle and fewer steps in the fabrication of the weapon's wooden components.

Specifications

Country of Origin: United Kingdom	Barrel Length: 625mm (25in)
Date: 1941	Muzzle Velocity: 730m/sec (2400ft/sec)
Calibre: 7.7mm (.303in) British	Feed/Magazine: 30-round box magazine
Operation: Gas operated, air cooled	Cyclic Rate: 500rpm
Weight: 10.25kg (22.5lb)	Range: 1000m (3280ft)
Overall Length: 1150mm (45.25in)	

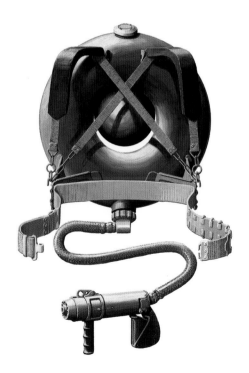

◀ No. 2 Flamethrower

British Second Army / 1st Airborne Division / 2nd Parachute Battalion, Arnhem, September 1944

The No. 2 version of the Mk 1 flamethrower proved the most effective and entered service with the British Army in 1944. Known for its rounded tank and nicknamed the Lifebuoy, the flamethrower was in action at Arnhem during Operation Market-Garden.

Specifications

Country of Origin: United Kingdom	Fuel Capacity: 18.2 litres (4 gallons)
Date: 1943	Duration of Fire: 10 seconds
Weight: 29kg (64lb)	Range: 27–36m (89–118ft)

US Forces
1944–45

Rising from a peacetime strength of scarcely 100,000 soldiers, the US Army developed into a fighting force of millions and supplied essential manpower during the liberation of North Africa, Italy and Western Europe.

ROUGHLY HANDLED DURING its combat debut against battle-hardened German troops at Kasserine Pass in Tunisia in 1943, the US Army gained experience and developed into a potent fighting force that joined its British and Commonwealth allies in successfully pushing northwards through Italy and eastwards across Europe to link up with the Soviet Red Army at the Elbe, splitting Germany in two, in the spring of 1945. The strength of the common 'triangular' US infantry division of World War II neared 20,000 men and included organic infantry, artillery, tank destroyer and support elements.

The infantry regiment consisted of three battalions of combat infantrymen totalling a strength of 600 to 900 troops and included more than 50 Browning M2 12.7mm (.5in) heavy machine guns along with a complement of lighter 7.62mm (.3in) machine guns of Browning design. The infantry company typically was composed of about 200 troops armed with the

▲ **Flushing out a sniper**
US infantrymen armed with M1 carbines attempt to draw fire during the battle for Normandy, July 1944.

standard issue M1 Garand rifle or M1 carbine, two 7.62mm (.3in) machine guns, a single 12.7mm (.5in) machine gun, and 15 Browning Automatic Rifles (BAR) firing the 7.62mm (.3in) rifle cartridge. A platoon of 41 soldiers was upgunned with three BAR men, and a standard squad of 12 soldiers included two men equipped with automatic weapons.

The soldiers of the 4th Infantry Division who landed at Utah Beach on 6 June 1944 actually came ashore in the wrong location; however, Brigadier-General Theodore Roosevelt Jr. (1887–1944), assistant division commander, resolved to 'start the war from here'. Elements of the 4th Division linked up with airborne units behind Utah Beach to begin the fight through hedgerow country, across France and into Germany.

Soldiers of the 1st and 29th Infantry Divisions assaulted Omaha Beach and encountered the stiffest German resistance on D-Day. Some units suffered 70 per cent casualties in the opening minutes of Operation Overlord, their landing craft taken under German machine-gun fire as soon as the ramps were lowered. Individual acts of heroism eventually turned the tide at Omaha Beach, although senior Allied commanders had considered the issue in doubt for

US INFANTRY RIFLE PLATOON, 1944		
Unit	Officers	Men
Headquarters	3	2
Squad 1	2	10
Squad 2	2	10
Squad 3	2	10
Medical Aidman	–	1
Bazooka Team 1	–	3
Bazooka Team 2	–	3
Bazooka Team 3	–	3
Bazooka Team 4	–	3
Bazooka Team 5	–	3

several hours and contemplated the withdrawal of the troops from their tenuous foothold.

Raising the rifle

Those US soldiers wading ashore on D-Day had their rifles wrapped in plastic to prevent fouling by seawater and sand. At times holding them above their heads to avoid the surf, the soldiers sought cover among anti-tank and landing craft obstacles,

▼ US Infantry Rifle Squad

The US Army infantry squad of 1944 was capable of delivering a high volume of small-arms fire. Containing 12 soldiers, the squad was equipped with the M1 Garand rifle, the Browning Automatic Rifle and the M3 submachine gun. Although German units were equipped with highly effective submachine guns throughout the war, the semiautomatic US M1 Garand could fire up to 50 rounds per minute, superior to any other rifle in service, since the shoulder arms of other forces continued to operate on bolt action.

Squad (1 x M3 'Grease Gun', 1 x BAR, 10 x M1 Garand)

hurriedly unwrapping their weapons and returning fire as they could, subsequently advancing across metres of open beach.

M1 Garand

The standard issue rifle of the US Army in World War II was the M1 Garand, a gas-operated rotating-bolt weapon that was actually the first semiautomatic rifle to enter regular service with any army in the world. The M1 Garand was designed by Canadian-born John C. Garand (1888–1974), who had moved to Connecticut with his family as a child. Garand enjoyed shooting and designing firearms and worked to develop a light machine gun. After his machine-gun design was adopted by the US Army, he was employed by the US Bureau of Standards and retained as a consultant with the army's Springfield Armory after World War I. In this capacity, he began to consider a design for a semiautomatic rifle.

For 15 years, Garand worked to perfect his design according to army specifications. By 1934, he had received a patent, and two years later production of the M1 began. It was officially adopted by the US Army in 1936 and entered service the following year. The M1 replaced the bolt-action Springfield Model 1903 and remained in service until the early 1960s, partially replaced by the selective-fire M14.

Through nearly 30 years of manufacture, approximately 6.5 million M1 Garand rifles were produced. The weapon fired the 7.62mm (.3in) cartridge and was fed by an eight-round en-bloc clip through an internal magazine. It was effective up to

402m (1326ft), and in the hands of a skilled rifleman was capable of firing 40 to 50 accurate shots in one minute, by far the highest sustained rate of fire of any standard issue rifle in World War II. A sniper version, the Garand M1C, was also produced.

A smaller and lighter version of the M1 Garand, the M1 carbine, was designed by a group of engineers during a three-year period from 1938 to 1941. Its shorter length made it suitable for issue to support troops, armoured troops, airborne units and some officers. Like the Garand, it was a semiautomatic, gas-operated, rotating-bolt rifle. It fired .30 calibre carbine ammunition from a detachable box magazine of 15 or 30 rounds. The carbine was manufactured in similar numbers to the Garand and remained in service with the US Army from the summer of 1942 into the mid-1970s.

The Greaser

Early in World War II, the automatic weapons available to the individual US soldier consisted of the Thompson submachine gun and the Browning Automatic Rifle. By 1942, it was determined that a more cost-effective and easily produced alternative to the older Thompson was needed. US observers had recognized the merits of such automatic weapons as the German MP 40 and the British Sten and commissioned General Motors designers to come up with a suitable US weapon.

The result was the M3 submachine gun, popularly known as the Grease Gun or simply the Greaser. The M3 and its successor the M3A1 were 11.4mm (.45in)

▲ **M1 carbine**

US Army / 101st Airborne Division / 501st Parachute Infantry Regiment, Normandy, June 1944

The M1 carbine was shorter than the standard M1 Garand rifle and therefore easier to carry and deploy in combat for troops who often operated in confined spaces or were required to perform specialized functions.

Specifications

Country of Origin: United States	Barrel Length: 457mm (18in)
Date: 1942	Muzzle Velocity: 595m/sec (1950ft/sec)
Calibre: 7.62mm (.3in) 0.30 calibre carbine	Feed/Magazine: 15- or 30-round detachable box
Operation: Gas operated	magazine
Weight: 2.5kg (5.47lb)	Range: c.300m (984ft)
Overall Length: 905mm (35.7in)	

▶ Remington M1911 pistol

US Seventh Army / 36th Infantry Division / 141st Infantry Regiment,
Operation Dragoon, Cannes, France, August 1944

The demand for the M1911 pistol was so great that numerous manufacturers
produced the weapon for the US Army. Among these was Remington Rand, which
made more than 900,000 during World War II.

Specifications

Country of Origin: United States	Barrel Length: 127mm (5in)
Date: 1911	Muzzle Velocity: 262m/sec (860ft/sec)
Calibre: 11.4mm (.45in)	Feed/Magazine: 7-round magazine
Operation: Short recoil	Range: 50m (164ft)
Weight: 1.1kg (2.425lb)	
Overall Length: 216mm (8.5in)	

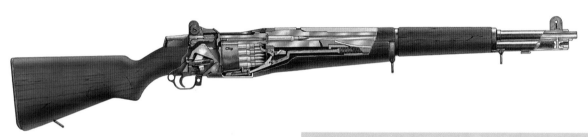

▲ M1 Garand

US First Army / 29th Infantry Division / 116th Regiment, Omaha Beach,
Normandy, June 1944

The M1 Garand was the first semiautomatic shoulder arm to become standard
issue to any army in the world. Its service life spanned four decades.

Specifications

Country of Origin: United States	Overall Length: 1103mm (43.5in)
Date: 1936	Barrel Length: 610mm (24in)
Calibre: 7.62mm (.3in) US .30-06	Muzzle Velocity: 853m/sec (2800ft/sec)
Operation: Gas operated	Feed/Magazine: 8-round internal box magazine
Weight: 4.37kg (9.5lb)	Range: 500m (1640ft) +

▲ Garand M1C

US First Army / 1st Infantry Division / 16th Regiment, Normandy, July 1944

The sniper version of the M1 Garand rifle, the M1C was adopted by the US Army
as its standard issue sniper rifle in June 1944, complementing the Springfield
M1903A4.

Specifications

Country of Origin: United States	Barrel Length: 610mm (24in)
Date: 1944	Muzzle Velocity: 853m/sec (2800ft/sec)
Calibre: 7.62mm (.3in) US .30-06	Feed/Magazine: 8-round internal box
Operation: Gas operated	magazine
Weight: 4.37kg (9.5lb)	Range: 1000m (3280ft) +
Overall Length: 1103mm (43.5in)	

▲ Armoured cover

A US infantry squad take cover behind an M4A3 Sherman tank somewhere in Normandy, July 1944. All are armed with M1 Garand rifles, except the last man, who is carrying a BAR automatic rifle, the squad's heavy firepower.

Specifications

Country of Origin: United States

Date: 1943

Calibre: 7.62mm (.3in) M1906

Operation: Bolt action

Weight: 3.94kg (8.68lb)

Overall Length: 1097mm (43.19in)

Barrel Length: 610mm (24in)

Muzzle Velocity: 853m/sec (2800ft/sec)

Feed/Magazine: 5-round internal box magazine

Range: 1000m (3280ft) +

▲ Springfield M1903A4

US First Army / 9 Infantry Division, Ardennes, December 1944

Intended primarily as a sniper rifle, the old Springfield M1903A4 was fitted with a Weaver 2.5x 330C hunting telescope and incorporated stamped metal parts to expedite production. Other alterations included a modified grip and stock. The rifle entered service in 1943.

blowback, open-bolt automatic weapons with a rate of fire of up to 450 rounds per minute. Due to complications with production, the M3 did not enter service with US frontline troops until late 1944. A relative few were fielded during the weeks-long battles of the Hürtgen Forest and the reduction of the pocket created by the German Ardennes Offensive, popularly known as the Battle of the Bulge. The M3A1 was introduced in December 1944; however, very few of these saw service during World War II. The M3A1 did incorporate several improvements, including a more reliable cocking lever assembly.

Due to the late arrival of the M3, most American squad-level operations were dependent on the

Specifications

Country of Origin: United States	Barrel Length: 203mm (8in)
Date: 1942	Muzzle Velocity: 280m/sec (920ft/sec)
Calibre: 11.4mm (.45in) .45 ACP	Feed/Magazine: 30-round detachable box
Operation: Blowback	magazine
Weight: 4.65kg (10.25lb) loaded	Cyclic Rate: 450rpm
Overall Length: 745mm (29.33in)	Range: 90m (295ft)

▲ **M3 'Grease Gun'**

US Third Army / 28th Infantry Division / 112th Infantry Regiment, Ardennes, December 1944

The M3 submachine gun was developed to replace the Thompson submachine gun but did not enter service with US troops until late 1944. An improved version, the M3A1, was not in service in quantity until the war was over.

Specifications

Country of Origin: United States	Barrel Length: 266mm (10.5in)
Date: 1928	Muzzle Velocity: 280m/sec (920ft/sec)
Calibre: 11.4mm (.45in) M1911	Feed/Magazine: 18-, 20-, 30-round detachable
Operation: Delayed blowback	box magazine
Weight: 4.88kg (10.75lb)	Cyclic Rate: 700rpm
Overall Length: 857mm (33.75in)	Range: 120m (394ft)

▲ **Thompson 1928**

US First Army / 2nd Ranger Battalion, Battle of Hürtgen Forest, September–December 1944

The Thompson submachine gun was designed during World War I and intended to breach enemy trench networks with heavy, mobile fire. Instead, it gained fame during the Prohibition Era of the 1920s. The Thompson 1928 was adopted by the US military in 1938 with modifications to the original design.

Thompson and the BAR for the duration of the war. An assessment of the M3's performance concluded that it was prone to malfunction due to dust, mud and grime build-up and that the single-feed, 30-round magazine was difficult to load manually, particularly under combat conditions.

Another submachine gun, the M2 Hyde-Inland, had competed with the M3 during trials; however, an initial order for more than 160,000 of these 11.4mm (.45in) blowback-operated SMGs was cancelled in the spring of 1943. Although its rate of fire was near 500 rounds per minute and the M2 shared the same ammunition box magazine feed system as the famed Thompson submachine gun, only 400 of these weapons were produced by Marlin Firearms during 1942–43.

▲ M2 Hyde-Inland

US Army / Aberdeen Proving Ground, Maryland, 1944

The M2 Hyde-Inland submachine gun was produced in limited numbers and did not enter service with the US Army. An order was cancelled in favour of the M3 'Grease Gun'.

Specifications

Country of Origin: United States	Barrel Length: 305mm (12in)
Date: 1942	Muzzle Velocity: 292m/sec (960ft/sec)
Calibre: 11.4mm (.45in) .45 ACP	Feed/Magazine: Detachable box magazine
Operation: Blowback	(Thompson)
Weight: 4.19kg (9.24lb)	Cyclic Rate: 500rpm
Overall Length: 813mm (32in)	Range: 50m (164ft)

▲ M9 Bazooka

US Third Army / 106th Infantry Division / 424th Infantry Regiment, central Germany, April 1945

A basic anti-tank weapon, the M9 Bazooka was essentially a tube that fired a shaped-charge warhead at short range and was most effective from the flanks or rear of an enemy armoured vehicle.

Specifications

Country of Origin: United States	Weight: 5.98kg (13.18lb)
Date: 1943	Overall Length: 1545mm (61in)
Calibre: 60mm (2.36in) high-explosive (HE)	Muzzle Velocity: 83m/sec (270ft/sec)
and high-explosive anti-tank (HEAT) warheads	Feed/Magazine: Breech-loader
Operation: Solid rocket motor	Range: 640m (2010ft)

Defending the Reich: German Army
1944–45

The introduction of advanced automatic weapons was too little too late as the German Army, extended to fight on three major fronts, suffered from diminished manpower and resources in the final months of World War II.

BY 1944, THE INFANTRY DIVISIONS of the German Army had been reduced in strength to around 12,500 men, although they retained the same basic structure. The number of heavy machine guns had been reduced somewhat, and senior German commanders reasoned that the introduction of automatic weapons such as the Sturmgewehr 44 assault rifle, capable of a much higher rate of fire than the Karabiner 98k bolt-action weapon, might compensate at least partially for the waning availability of trained and veteran soldiers as casualties mounted.

Inevitably, in the early months of 1945 some divisions had been so drastically reduced in strength that they constituted few more soldiers than a normal regiment or battalion. Following the 1943 reorganization of the infantry squad, the workhorse infantry platoon of the German Army included four squads of 10 soldiers along with a light 50mm (2in) mortar section and a headquarters section of six men, one of them the officer in command.

Out of necessity and also due to the availability of advancing technology, the German Army of World

▲ **Tank killer**
An SS panzergrenadier armed with a Panzerfaust hollow-charge anti-tank weapon waits for an Allied armour attack, Normandy, July 1944.

War II was one of the first to deploy semiautomatic weapons in significant numbers. These included the Sturmgewehr 44 (StG 44) assault rifle, which was capable of semiautomatic and fully automatic firing modes. The StG 44 was the eventual result of a project to develop a *Maschinenkarabiner*, or machine carbine. At one point, Hitler would not sanction any new weapons types, so to disguise the project, it was labelled the MP 43, then the MP 44, where 'MP' stood for *Maschinenpistole*, a type of firearm that already existed. Hitler eventually approved the project and the designation of Sturmgewehr 44 became official when the weapon entered full production.

Storm of fire

The Sturmgewehr 44 is recognizable with its sleek lines and long, curved magazines which held up to 30 rounds of 7.92mm (.312in) ammunition. Many firearms experts conclude that the Sturmgewehr 44 was the world's first actual assault rifle to enter combat. It was capable of firing at a cyclic rate of 500 rounds per minute with a range of up to 300m (984ft). The weapon was gas-operated with a tilting bolt and was designed in the early 1940s. Hitler's

interference delayed production, which did not begin until October 1943, although it might have proceeded months earlier. Nearly 425,000 were manufactured. The majority of the Sturmgewehr 44s produced were sent to the Eastern Front.

Had the Sturmgewehr 44 entered production sooner, it might indeed have altered the course of the war. However, earlier submachine guns, most of them designed by the prolific Hugo Schmeisser (1884–1953), served throughout the conflict. The MP 38 and MP 40 were both high-profile weapons of the German infantry. When captured, they were often placed in service with Allied soldiers who were impressed with their performance.

Walther pistols

Throughout the war, the Walther PP series of pistols was popular with Nazi Party officials, army officers, police units and *Luftwaffe* personnel. The series entered production in 1929 and continues under licence with various companies today. The most popular of the series, the PPK and its variants, followed the original PP pistol into production in 1931. The PPK was carried by Adolf Hitler

Specifications	
Country of Origin: Germany	Overall Length: Not known
Date: 1942	Barrel Length: 590mm (23.23in)
Calibre: N/A	Muzzle Velocity: N/A
Operation: Bolt action	Feed/Magazine: Single shot
Weight: Not known	Range: 125m (410ft)

▲ **Granatbüchse 39**

272nd Infantry Division / 981st Infantry Regiment, Battle of Verrières Ridge, July 1944

The Granatabüchse 39 was a modified anti-tank rifle that could fire anti-personnel or anti-tank grenades. Its threaded launcher was screwed to a rifle barrel.

(1889–1945), who committed suicide while biting down on a cyanide capsule and simultaneously firing a 7.65mm (.301in) bullet from his PPK into the side of his head. It has also become famous as the handgun of choice of fictional superspy James Bond.

The PP series was one of the first semiautomatic double-action pistols to gain wide popularity around the world. The weapons are further distinguished by their exposed hammer and single-column magazine. The PPK was slightly smaller and lighter than the original PP and more easily concealed, thereby increasing its popularity with clandestine operatives and civilian law enforcement personnel.

In 1942, the German Army deployed a variant of its original Panzerbüchse 39 anti-tank rifle. The Granatbüchse 39 was modified to shorten the original barrel of the Panzerbüchse 39, while the

bipod, sling band, carrying sling and handle were moved to different locations on the weapon. A threaded launcher was screwed to the barrel. The Granatbüchse 39 was actually capable of firing three types of grenade: anti-personnel, small anti-tank and large anti-tank. Each was propelled by a blank 7.92mm (.312in) cartridge.

Meanwhile, a new generation of purpose-built anti-tank weapons emerged. The RPzB Panzerschreck was based on the design of a captured American M1 Bazooka and was often manufactured with a blast shield to protect the operator. However, a significant backblast typically betrayed the location of the weapon and drew return fire. The Panzerschreck entered service with the German Army in 1943, and nearly 300,000 were made. Later versions fired a heavy 88mm (3.5in) rocket-propelled round.

▶ Walther PP

Luftwaffe / VIII Fliegerkorps / Jagdgeschwader 27, March 1945

The Walther PP series of semiautomatic double-action pistols entered production in 1929 and remains popular today, having been manufactured in numerous countries. During World War II it was popular with Nazi Party officials.

Specifications

Country of Origin: Germany	Barrel Length: 98mm (3.9in)
Date: 1935	Muzzle Velocity: 256m/sec (840ft/sec)
Calibre: 7.65mm (.301in)	Feed/Magazine: 7-round detachable box
Operation: Straight blowback	magazine
Weight: .665kg (1.46lb)	Range: 30m (98ft)
Overall Length: 170mm (6.7in)	

▲ Gewehr 43

German First Army / 198th Infantry Division, OB West, April 1945

The semiautomatic gas-operated Gewehr 43 was a victim of its own complex engineering and produced in limited numbers late in World War II. A sniper version was highly accurate.

Specifications

Country of Origin: Germany	Barrel Length: 546mm (21.5in)
Date: 1943	Muzzle Velocity: 853.6m/sec (2800ft/sec)
Calibre: 8mm (.314in) IS	Feed/Magazine: 10-round detachable box
Operation: Gas operated	magazine
Weight: 4.1kg (9.7lb)	Range: 500m (1640ft); 800m (2620ft) with
Overall Length: 1130mm (44.49in)	scope

▲ RPzB Panzerschreck

XLVII Panzer Corps / 21st Panzer Division / 125th Panzergrenadier Regiment, Normandy, August 1944

The anti-tank Panzerschreck was fashioned from a captured American M1 Bazooka; however, it was subsequently modified to fire a much more powerful round capable of destroying virtually any Allied armoured vehicle.

Specifications	
Country of Origin: Germany	Overall Length: 1640mm (64.5in)
Date: 1943	Muzzle Velocity: 110m/sec (360ft/sec)
Calibre: 88mm (3.5in) high-explosive (HE)	Feed/Magazine: Breech-loader
and high-explosive anti-tank (HEAT) warheads	Range: 150m (492ft)
Operation: Solid rocket motor	
Weight: 11kg (24.25lb) empty	

Volkssturm: Hitler's Home Guard
1945

As the perimeter of the Third Reich shrank steadily during the last years of World War II, Germany was compelled to enlist old men and boys in the defence of the nation.

HITLER'S LAST LINE OF DEFENCE against the Allies closing in on Germany were the *Volkssturm* formations, which included the old and infirm, the very young and even some women. Boys aged as young as 12 and men in their sixties were called up, given short periods of training and placed in uniform. Their weapons were those that had been in service with the German Army for the duration of the war, such as the Karabiner 98k rifle, the Model 24 hand grenade (a stick grenade known to Allied soldiers as the 'potato masher' due to its construction), the Model 39 and Model 43 hand grenades, the few available MG 34 and MG 42 machine guns, and various submachine guns. Older rifles such as the Gewehr 98 and Gewehr 71 were also issued. There was no standardization of weapons from one *Volkssturm* unit to another.

The basic operational formation of the *Volkssturm* was a battalion of just under 650 troops. Uniforms were often incomplete or unavailable, and those who received training were somtimes led by veterans of World War I or soldiers who had been previously wounded and deemed unfit for further combat duty.

Early in 1945, Germany undertook production of the MP 3008 machine pistol primarily intended to equip *Volkssturm* units with automatic weapons. The MP 3008 was based on captured models of the successful British Sten Gun. It was also known as the 'People's Machine Gun' because of its designation for the *Volkssturm*.

The MP 3008 was a blowback-operated, open-bolt submachine gun that fired up to 450 rounds per minute. It fired the 9mm (.35in) Parabellum cartridge and was fed by a 32-round detachable box magazine. Its production run was short and ceased prior to the end of the war, with only about 10,000 guns actually completed. Undertaken as an emergency solution to the shortage of automatic weapons, the MP 3008 was cheaply produced, with many of its parts stamped from steel plate.

The finish of the weapons was rough. Early versions were made without a handgrip, and the wire stock was welded to the frame. A few examples were actually manufactured with wooden stocks in the final days of production, as supplies of steel were virtually nonexistent.

Prolific Panzerfaust

The anti-tank Panzerfaust is, for many, symbolic of the last days of the Third Reich. Images of middle-aged women training to fire the tube weapon are indicative of the desperation in Germany in 1945. The Panzerfaust was inexpensive to produce, was preloaded and required only one individual to operate it. Therefore, more than six million were manufactured from 1943 to 1945.

The Panzerfaust consisted of a disposable launching tube that fired a 2.9kg (6.4lb) hollow-charge round with .8kg (1.8lb) of high explosive. Range depended on the variant, with a maximum of 100m (328ft). It was the first anti-tank weapon to include a disposable launcher, and its heavy backblast often gave away the concealed position of its operator. As the war progressed, some untrained German soldiers were given only the Panzerfaust and sent into combat. The number of Allied tanks engaged and destroyed by these weapons exceeded 30 per cent of the total losses in Western Europe.

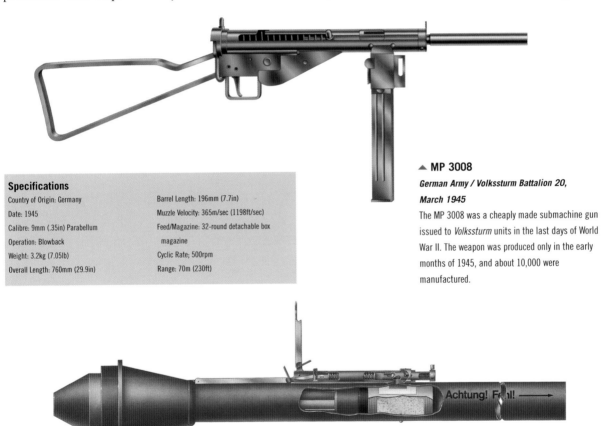

▲ MP 3008

German Army / Volkssturm Battalion 20, March 1945

The MP 3008 was a cheaply made submachine gun issued to *Volkssturm* units in the last days of World War II. The weapon was produced only in the early months of 1945, and about 10,000 were manufactured.

Specifications

Country of Origin: Germany	Barrel Length: 196mm (7.7in)
Date: 1945	Muzzle Velocity: 365m/sec (1198ft/sec)
Calibre: 9mm (.35in) Parabellum	Feed/Magazine: 32-round detachable box
Operation: Blowback	magazine
Weight: 3.2kg (7.05lb)	Cyclic Rate: 500rpm
Overall Length: 760mm (29.9in)	Range: 70m (230ft)

▲ Panzerfaust

German Army / Volkssturm Battalion 301, March 1945

The anti-tank Panzerfaust was fired from a disposable tube and created significant backblast. As more powerful versions emerged during World War II, some were emblazoned with the warning 'Attention! Fire Jet'.

Specifications

Country of Origin: Germany	Overall Length: 1000mm (39.4in)
Date: 1943	Muzzle Velocity: 30m/sec (98ft/sec)
Calibre: 100mm (3.9in)	Feed/Magazine: N/A
Operation: Recoilless gun	Range: 30m (98ft)
Weight: 1.475kg (3.3lb) total	

Chapter 5

World War II: Eastern Front

Hitler's invasion of the Soviet Union on 22 June 1941 opened a two-front war for the German Army and sealed the fate of the Third Reich. The vastness of Russia, the resilience of the peoples of the Soviet Union and harsh winter weather provided the Red Army with the capacity to withstand tremendous losses and achieve ultimate victory four years later. Although German spearheads reached within 19km (12 miles) of the Soviet capital of Moscow, they were denied the prize. Hitler's redirection of his armies towards the south and the oilfields of the Caucasus led to the disaster at Stalingrad and losses from which the *Wehrmacht* could never recover. In the spring of 1945 the emblem of the hammer and sickle flew above the *Reichstag*.

◀ **Machine-gun squad**
Wehrmacht soldiers move carefully through corn fields in southern Russia during Case Blue, the German push towards Stalingrad and the Caucasus, August 1942. The soldier in the foreground is carrying an MG 34 squad machine gun, the standard German infantry support weapon for much of the war.

Introduction

From an uneasy alliance in their cooperative invasion of Poland, Nazi Germany and the Soviet Union became sworn enemies. World War II on the Eastern Front involved more men, machines, equipment, destruction and death than on any other.

Soviet leader Josef Stalin (1878–1953) was astonished when German tanks and troops attacked his country in the predawn hours of 22 June 1941. Repeated warnings had gone unheeded, and in fact Stalin had continued to send shipments of grain and other resources to the Third Reich on a regular basis. More than 160 German divisions assaulted the Soviets without warning on a 1600km (1000-mile) front, and the Red Army was sent reeling from the hammer blows.

Ironically, the Soviets had contributed to their own perilous situation. Since the 1920s, they had secretly facilitated German circumvention of the Versailles Treaty, allowing German troops to train and test new weapons from small arms to tanks on Soviet territory. The Soviets had also entered into a non-aggression pact with the Nazis that provided Stalin with too much assurance that German intentions did not involve eastwards expansion that would extend beyond the agreed upon line of demarcation in a partitioned Poland.

As Hitler's troops advanced, killing and capturing hundreds of thousands of Soviet soldiers and committing countless atrocities, the Red Army also suffered from a shortage of experienced officers. Many of the most senior had been executed during

▲ **Soviet solidity**
Armed with the super-reliable 71-round-drum-magazine PPSh-41 submachine gun, Soviet partisans prepare to move during operations in Belorussia, March 1943.

▲ **MG 30**
A rare photograph showing Axis troops manning a Maschinengewehr Solothurn 1930 (MG 30) somewhere on the Eastern Front.

Stalin's purge of the Red Army officer corps during the mid-1930s.

To compound the problems faced by the Red Army high command, much of the Soviet Union's industrial capacity lay within reach of the German juggernaut. In response, entire factories were dismantled and relocated eastwards, some beyond the Ural mountains. The Soviets drew upon their vast resources in manpower and made good their staggering losses. Then, the winter of 1941 slowed the Germans to a standstill.

The resumption of German offensive operations the following spring offered opportunity for the Red Army. Hitler diverted his main thrust away from Moscow, besieged Leningrad in the north and ordered his spearheads to the south and the oil-rich Caucasus. At Stalingrad on the banks of the Volga River, Soviet forces encircled the German Sixth Army, annihilating it as a fighting force. Stalingrad was the turning point of the war on the Eastern Front, and when the five-month battle for the city ended in February 1943, the Germans had suffered nearly

850,000 killed, wounded or captured. These were casualties that could not be replaced. The Soviet propaganda machine labelled 1944 'The Year of 10 Victories' as a succession of Red Army offensive operations drove the *Wehrmacht* back towards Germany. Repeatedly, Hitler's senior commanders would issue orders to withdraw from hopeless defensive situations only to have the *Führer* countermand the order, demanding that the troops stand their ground and fight to the end. Continuing interference from Hitler prevented the stabilization of the Eastern Front, and Soviet forces were fighting in the suburbs of Berlin by the spring of 1945.

Early in World War II, the Soviet Union depended heavily on military aid from the United States, which shipped millions of tonnes of supplies and equipment through the Lend-Lease programme. Soviet industry did maintain productivity and manufacture improved weapons such as the legendary T-34 medium tank, as well as a number of small arms such as the standard issue semiautomatic SVT-40 rifle and the PPSh-41 submachine gun that carried the Red Army to victory.

Winter War
1939–40

The small but potent Finnish Army fought tenaciously against Red Army aggression during the brief but bitter Winter War. Although the Soviets sustained heavy casualties, the Finns were ultimately overwhelmed.

A TERRITORIAL DISPUTE between Finland and the Soviet Union erupted in war in November 1939, only weeks after World War II had begun and Red Army troops had invaded neighbouring Poland. Anticipating a quick victory, Soviet leader Josef Stalin (1878–1953) failed to comprehend the impact that his purges of the Red Army officer cadre during the mid-1930s would have on later operations. Up to 30,000 Soviet officers, many of them senior commanders, had been imprisoned or murdered to assuage Stalin's paranoia. As a result, when Soviet forces invaded Finland the gallant Finnish Army put up stubborn resistance and inflicted heavy casualties on the Red Army.

Inexperienced Soviet officers executed strategic and tactical blunders that the Finnish Army exploited regularly. The mobile Finnish troops regularly utilized skis for rapid movement in the deep snow and thick forests of their country. Soviet troop and supply columns were often trapped on icy roads and decimated. The result was an embarrassing prolonged war in which the Soviets lost more than 320,000 casualties, more than four times the losses incurred by the Finns.

Soviet victory

In the end, however, the weight of Soviet numerical superiority was too great, the Finns were forced to sue for peace and the war ended on 13 March 1940. Although the Soviets did not achieve the complete subjugation of Finland, they gained more than 10 per cent of the territory that had previously been claimed by the Finns. This included land near the Soviet city of Leningrad and Lake Ladoga, the Karelian Isthmus, islands in the Gulf of Finland and the Rybachy Peninsula. At the same time the Soviets also gained control of significant Finnish natural resources and centres of industry.

◀ **Ski troops**
Ski-mounted Finnish soldiers stop for a break during the Winter War, January 1940. Most Finnish troops were armed with a Finnish version of the Soviet Mosin-Nagant rifle.

Finnish Army
1939–44

The Finnish Army of 1939–40 was small but efficient and well disciplined and exuded a high degree of morale. When the Soviet Union invaded, the Finns fought a vigorous defence.

A S NEGOTIATIONS with the Soviet Union deteriorated in the autumn of 1939, the Finnish Army mobilized nine divisions and four separate brigades totalling slightly more than 200,000 men. In contrast, the Red Army eventually committed 1.2 million soldiers to the fighting in 1939–40. The battalion was the tactical unit most often employed, and for two months the Finns clung to the Mannerheim Line on the Karelian Isthmus while the poorly led Soviets became increasingly frustrated. The Finns themselves, meanwhile, developed a reputation as skilled fighters manoeuvring rapidly on skis across the snowy landscape, attacking Soviet positions and swiftly disappearing before an effective counterstroke could be organized.

Although the Finnish Army was inspired and defending its territory, the army was deficient in heavy weapons, with only 112 anti-tank guns reportedly available and just a handful of armoured vehicles. Nevertheless, in the far north the Finns employed their Motti tactics, fragmenting attacking Soviet divisions and surrounding the weakened elements, then systematically destroying them one at a time. During a series of battles near Suomussalmi from December 1939 to January 1940, the Finns severely mauled the Soviet 44th and 163rd Divisions.

When the Winter War ended in March 1940, the result was an uneasy peace that realistic observers knew would never last. With tensions between Nazi Germany and the Soviet Union growing, the Finns were caught in a vice and eventually drawn into the Continuation War of 1941–44, after which Finland ceded more territory to the Soviet Union but maintained its sovereignty. The Finns did cooperate with Nazi Germany in the planning and execution of Operation Barbarossa, the German invasion of the Soviet Union, and participated somewhat loosely in the 900-day siege of Leningrad.

The Finnish Army of 1939–40 was armed with a number of weapons, including the Mosin-Nagant Model 1891 rifle, many of which had been captured by the Germans and Austro-Hungarians during World War I and then sold to Finland after the war. The bolt-action, internal-magazine-fed Mosin-Nagant had been developed in Belgium prior to becoming the standard issue of the Czarist Army in Russia. It fired a 7.62mm (.3in) cartridge and eventually more than 37 million were manufactured in pre- and post-Soviet Russia and elsewhere. Several Finnish manufacturers subsequently produced variants of the Model 1891, including a carbine and a model with a heavier barrel for greater accuracy

▶ **Lahti L-35**

Finnish Army / 4th Division, Karelian Front, 1940

In overall appearance the Finnish Lahti L-35 pistol was similar to the German Luger; however, its bolt assembly was substantially different. The L-35 functioned well in the harsh Arctic climate of Finland.

Specifications

Country of Origin: Finland	Barrel Length: 107mm (4.21in)
Date: 1935	Muzzle Velocity: 335.3m/sec (1100ft/sec)
Calibre: 9mm (.35in)	Feed/Magazine: 8-round detachable box
Operation: Toggle locked, short recoil	magazine
Weight: 1.2kg (2.6lb)	Range: 50m (164ft)
Overall Length: 245mm (9.65in)	

known as the M24. Prior to the Winter War, the Finns experienced a shortage in small arms and ordered great numbers of rifles from Yugoslavia, Italy, Sweden, Belgium, France and Great Britain.

Designed by Aimo J. Lahti (1896–1970), the Suomi KP-31 ('KP' stands for *Konepistooli*: submachine gun) was a Finnish submachine gun that earned a reputation as an excellent infantry weapon. The original patent was granted in the early 1920s, and the early version was chambered for 7.65mm

(.301in) ammunition, but the standard weapon used the 9mm (.35in) Parabellum cartridge. The KP-31 was fed from a drum magazine of 71 rounds or a box magazine of 20 or 50 rounds. It was capable of semiautomatic or fully automatic fire, and its remarkable rate of fire exceeded 800 rounds per minute. Instances during the Winter War in which small numbers of Finnish troops held off Red Army forces several times their size with the skilful operation of the KP-31 have been documented.

Specifications

Country of Origin: Finland	Barrel Length: 319mm (12.52in)
Date: 1931	Muzzle Velocity: 400m/sec (1310ft/sec)
Calibre: 9mm (.35in) Parabellum	Feed/Magazine: 20- or 50-round detachable box
Operation: Blowback	magazine or 71-round drum magazine
Weight: 4.87kg (10.74lb)	Cyclic Rate: 800–900rpm
Overall Length: 870mm (34.25in)	Range: 100m (328ft) +

▲ **Suomi KP-31**

Finnish Army / Infantry Regiment 16, Suomussalmi, December 1939

The Suomi KP-31 was a blowback-operated submachine gun that proved a formidable adversary during the Winter War. Its high rate of fire and reliability made the KP-31 popular among Finnish troops.

Specifications

Country of Origin: Finland	Barrel Length: 247mm (9.72in)
Date: 1944	Muzzle Velocity: 395m/sec (1300ft/sec)
Calibre: 9mm (.35in) Parabellum	Feed/Magazine: 50-round box magazine or
Operation: Blowback	71-round drum magazine
Weight: 2.8kg (6.17lb)	Cyclic Rate: 650rpm
Overall Length: 825mm (32.48in)	Range: 70m (230ft)

▲ **Konepistooli M44**

Finnish Army / 13th Division, East Karelia, June 1944

A copy of the Soviet PPS-43 submachine gun, the M44 was capable of using the 71-round drum magazine of the KP-31 or a 50-round magazine. It was later modified for the 36-round magazine of the Carl Gustav submachine gun.

Defending the Motherland: Red Army
1941–42

Hard pressed in the early years of what the Soviets called the Great Patriotic War, the Red Army was resurgent. Despite absorbing tremendous losses, the Soviets halted the eastwards advance of German forces.

THE RAPID MOVEMENT of the German *Wehrmacht* across the open terrain of the Russian steppes resulted in the capture of hundreds of thousands of Red Army troops as they were encircled and cut off from retreat. As Soviet troops absorbed heavy losses and fell back, Communist Party commissars often were assigned to smaller units with orders to bolster the morale of the troops with party and patriotic doctrine along with the threat of being shot for desertion or fleeing in the face of the enemy.

As the summer of 1941 extended into winter, German armoured spearheads neared the Soviet capital of Moscow, and officers viewed the onion domes of the city through their binoculars. The citizens of Moscow dug tank traps and built fortifications to defend the city. Resistance stiffened, and Moscow was never occupied by German troops. As the harsh winter weather set in, the Germans found that their mechanized equipment failed to function in sub-zero temperatures. So sure had Hitler been of a quick victory that adequate provision had not been made to supply winter clothing to the troops. Frostbite disabled thousands, and combat efficiency eroded steadily.

Further complicating the situation for the Germans was the tremendous amount of supplies the *Wehrmacht* needed in the East as well as the great distances over which these supplies would have to be transported. While the Germans languished far from home, Soviet forces were augmented with substantial formations from Siberia and other areas untouched by the war. Many of these formations were released for deployment against the Germans after Stalin was assured that war with Japan was not imminent. These troops were to play a key role in the great victory at Stalingrad that followed the German spring and summer offensive of 1942.

When the weather improved sufficiently, Hitler resumed offensive operations and ordered substantial forces southwards toward the Caucasus and its precious oilfields. He further ordered his forces to split, and while a potent thrust continued into the Caucasus, another headed for the city of Stalingrad on the Volga River and a rendezvous with destiny.

Early in World War II the primary shoulder arm of Soviet forces was the venerable Mosin-Nagant Model 1891 bolt-action rifle. With the German invasion, production was stepped up. In 1932, the original

▶ **Tokarev TT30**

Soviet Third Army / 85th Rifle Division, Southwest Front, June 1941

The Tokarev TT30 pistol was intended as a replacement for earlier Nagant revolvers in service with the Red Army. The short-recoil pistol was fed by an eight-round box magazine.

Specifications

Country of Origin: USSR	Barrel Length: 116mm (4.57in)
Date: 1930	Muzzle Velocity: 420m/sec (1380ft/sec)
Calibre: 7.62mm (.3in)	Feed/Magazine: 8-round detachable box
Operation: Short recoil	magazine
Weight: .83kg (1.83lb)	Range: 50m (164ft)
Overall Length: 194mm (7.6in)	

Soviet Rifle Platoon, June 1941

The Soviet rifle platoon of 1941 was a substantial fighting force on paper, consisting of a 50mm (2in) mortar section and four rifle squads, each of 11 soldiers. Two men in each rifle squad were armed with PPD submachine guns. A gunner and loader serviced the single light machine gun available to each squad, the Degtyaryov DP-28, designed in 1927, introduced in 1928 and fed by a 47-round, top-mounted pan magazine.

Platoon HQ (1 Officer, 1 NCO, 1 other rank): 1 x pistol, 1 x SMG, 1 x rifle

Squad 1 (1 NCO, 10 other ranks): 1 x pistol, 2 x SMG, 8 x rifle, 1 x LMG

Squad 2

Squad 3

Squad 4

Mortar Squad (1 NCO, 3 other ranks): 1 x pistol, 3 x rifle

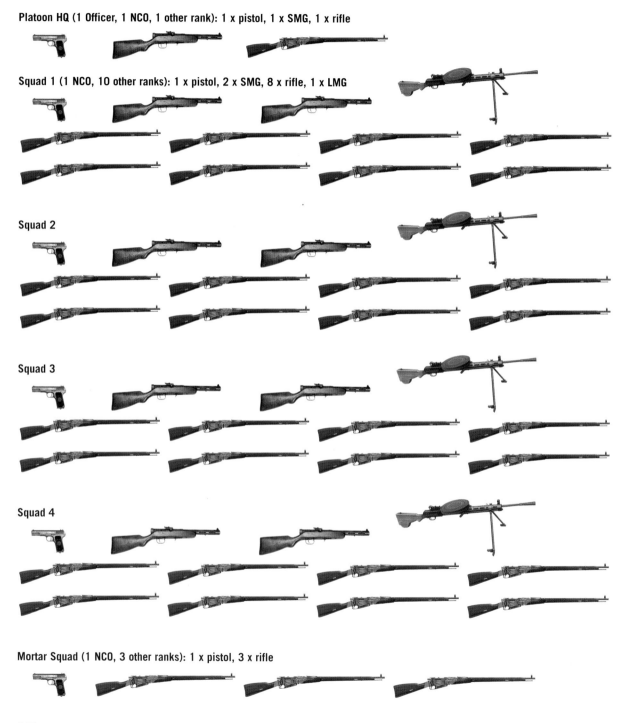

Mosin-Nagant was modified for use by snipers and designated the Model 91/31. Known for its accuracy, the Model 91/31 achieved fame along with Soviet snipers such as Vasily Zaitsev (1915–91), who was renowned as a Hero of the Soviet Union and was reported to have more than 225 kills to his credit. With a telescopic sight fitted above the bolt, the sniper version of the Mosin-Nagant included a longer and more curved bolt to facilitate the shooter's action.

By 1936, the Mosin-Nagant was again modified, this time for more rapid production. The receiver was simplified from an octagonal configuration to a rounded shape, and by the end of the war more than 17 million of the basic Model 91/30 had been manufactured. Known for rugged dependability in harsh conditions and extremes of weather, the Mosin-Nagant production rifles of the war years lacked the finish and overall quality of pre-war rifles due to the need for large numbers to be provided in a relatively short period of time.

Early Soviet submachine gun production borrowed heavily from German designs, as was the case with the PPD-1934/38, a virtual copy of the Bergmann MP 28. The PPD was a blowback, open-bolt weapon that fired the Soviet 7.62mm (.3in) round. It was developed by arms designer Vasily Degtyaryov (1880–1949), and it was fed either by a drum magazine that was copied from the Finnish Suomi KP-31 or a 25-round box magazine. The weapon entered service with the Red Army in 1935 but was soon deemed too expensive for mass production. Although more than 90,000 were manufactured, the cheaper PPSh-41 was already set to replace it by the end of 1941.

Specifications

Country of Origin: Russia	Barrel Length: 802mm (31.6in)
Date: 1891	Muzzle Velocity: 810m/sec (2657ft/sec)
Calibre: 7.62mm (.3in)	Feed/Magazine: 5-round box magazine
Operation: Bolt action	Range: 500m (1640ft); 750m (2460ft) + with
Weight: 4.37kg (9.625lb)	optics
Overall Length: 1305mm (51.4in)	

▲ **Mosin-Nagant Model 1891**

Soviet Eleventh Army / 184th Rifle Division, Northwest Front, June 1941

The Mosin-Nagant rifle was the standard issue weapon of the Soviet Red Army throughout World War II. A product of Belgian design, it has become an icon of Soviet weaponry.

▲ **PPD-1934/38**

Soviet Ninth Army / 5th Cavalry Division, Odessa Special Military District, August 1941

The recognition by Red Army personnel of the potential for the submachine gun on the modern battlefield resulted in the development of the PPD-1934/38, a copy of the German Bergmann MP 28.

Specifications

Country of Origin: USSR	Barrel Length: 269mm (10.60in)
Date: 1934	Muzzle Velocity: 488m/sec (1600ft/sec)
Calibre: 7.62mm (.3in) Soviet	Feed/Magazine: 25-round box magazine or
Operation: Blowback	71-round drum magazine
Weight: 5.69kg (12.54lb) loaded	Cyclic Rate: 800rpm
Overall Length: 780mm (30.71in)	Range: 100m (328ft) +

Designer Georgi Shpagin (1897–1952) developed the PPSh-41 as a blowback, open-bolt submachine gun that was chambered for a 7.62mm (.3in) round and could operate in semiautomatic or automatic firing modes. It was much more cost-effective to produce than its predecessor the PPD 1934/38 and remains in service today.

Following the Red Army encounters with formidable Finnish submachine guns during the Winter War of 1939–40, it became readily apparent that the concentrated, mobile firepower of such weapons could be decisive on the battlefield. In the autumn of 1941, production of the PPSh-41 was undertaken in a number of factories in the Moscow area. During the first five months of 1942, more than 150,000 were manufactured, and as the war progressed more than 3000 per day were being turned out by Soviet production facilities. The simple construction of the PPSh-41 involved 87 components and simple stamping and tooling

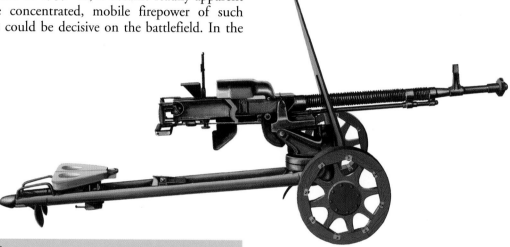

Specifications

Country of Origin: USSR	Barrel Length: 1066mm (42in)
Date: 1938	Muzzle Velocity: 850m/sec (2788ft/sec)
Calibre: 12.7mm (.5in) Soviet	Feed/Magazine: 50-round belt
Operation: Gas operated, air cooled	Cyclic Rate: 550rpm
Weight: 35.5kg (78.5lb)	Range: 2000m (6560ft) +
Overall Length: 1586mm (62.5in)	

▲ **DShK 1938**

Soviet Twentieth Army / 144th Rifle Division, Bryansk Front, October 1941

The heavy DK machine gun was originally fed by a drum magazine. Converted to a belt system as the DShK 1938, it was often mounted on a carriage and served as the primary heavy machine gun of the Red Army in World War II.

Specifications

Country of Origin: USSR	Barrel Length: 266mm (10.5in)
Date: 1941	Muzzle Velocity: 490m/sec (1600ft/sec)
Calibre: 7.62mm (.3in) Soviet	Feed/Magazine: 35-round box magazine or
Operation: Blowback	71-round drum magazine
Weight: 3.64kg (8lb)	Cyclic Rate: 900rpm
Overall Length: 838mm (33in)	Range: 120m (394ft)

▲ **PPSh-41**

Soviet Twentieth Army / 229th Rifle Division, Bryansk Front, December 1941

The PPSh-41 submachine gun was an easily produced and less expensive alternative to the earlier PPD model. More than six million of the highly successful weapon were manufactured during World War II.

Specifications

Country of Origin: USSR

Date: 1942

Calibre: 7.62mm (.3in) Soviet

Operation: Blowback

Weight: 2.95kg (6.5lb)

Overall Length: 907mm (35.7in)

Barrel Length: 273mm (10.7in)

Muzzle Velocity: 500m/sec (1640ft/sec)

Feed/Magazine: 35-round detachable box
  magazine

Cyclic Rate: 650rpm

Range: 100m (328ft) +

▲ PPS-42

Soviet XXIV Tank Corps / 24th Motorized Rifle Brigade, Bryansk Front, July 1942

The inexpensively produced PPS-42 submachine gun proved remarkably robust for its construction and filled a need for rapidly manufactured firepower at the Red Army squad level early in World War II.

Soviet Machine-Gun Platoon, April 1942

The four squads of the Soviet Red Army machine-gun platoon at the time of Operation Barbarossa in 1941 each fielded the DShK 1938 12.7mm (.5in) heavy machine gun with a crew of four. Easily distinguished by its two-wheeled carriage and gun shield, the DShK 1938 performed as an infantry support machine gun as well as an anti-aircraft weapon, similar to Allied counterparts such as the Browning M2. Other elements of the machine-gun platoon were soldiers armed with the Mosin-Nagant Model 1891/30 rifle and Tokarev TT30 sidearms.

Platoon HQ (1 officer): 1 x pistol

MG Squad 1 (1 NCO, 6 other ranks): 2 x pistol, 5 x rifle, 1 x MG

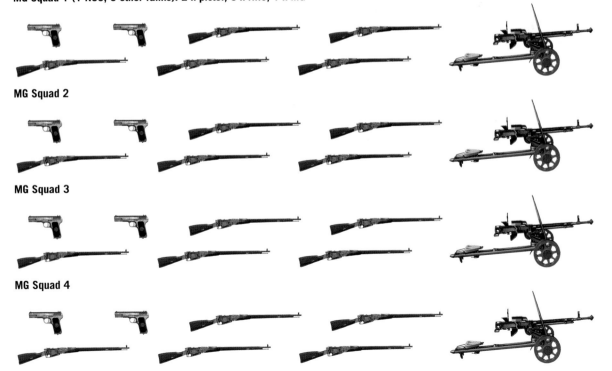

MG Squad 2

MG Squad 3

MG Squad 4

equipment. The machining for a single weapon could be accomplished in just over seven hours.

With tremendous production capacity, more than six million of the PPSh-41 were manufactured by the end of World War II, and the Red Army was eventually able to equip entire divisions with it while also supplying the weapon by air to partisan formations behind German lines. German soldiers also prized the PPSh-41 and pressed captured weapons into service. Conveniently, the Soviet and German 7.62mm (.3in) cartridges were similar, and the weapon could fire either one. In early 1943, yet another submachine gun, the PPS-42, designed by Alexey Sudayev (1912–46),

entered mass production and was even cheaper to produce. By the end of the year, production had increased to 350,000 weapons per month.

The primary Soviet infantry support heavy machine gun of World War II was the DShK 1938, which was developed in the late 1920s. The weapon was often mounted on a two-wheeled carriage and fitted with a shield. Firing a 12.7mm (.5in) round, the machine gun was originally drum fed and designated the DK. A modification to a belt-feed system resulted in the DShK 1938 designation. The weapon's rate of fire was 550 rounds per minute, and it served in an anti-aircraft role as well.

▲ PTRS-41

Soviet Third Shock Army / 54th Rifle Brigade, Kalinin Front, March 1942

Heavier than the PTRD-41, the PTRS-41 anti-tank rifle was fed by a five-round magazine and was easier to transport, having a detachable barrel. It fired a powerful round with a steel or tungsten core.

Specifications

Country of Origin: USSR	Overall Length: 2100mm (83in)
Date: 1941	Barrel Length: 1219mm (47in)
Calibre: 14.5mm (.57in)	Muzzle Velocity: 1114m/sec (3655ft/sec)
Operation: Gas operated	Feed/Magazine: 5-round magazine
Weight: 20.3kg (46lb)	Range: 800m (2620ft)

▲ PTRD-41

Soviet Ninth Shock Army / Southern Front, June 1942

The PTRD-41 anti-tank rifle entered service with the Red Army in 1941, a time when most armies had opted for rocket- or spring-fired weapons to combat enemy armour. Later, Soviet troops used the PTRD-41 against entrenched infantry.

Specifications

Country of Origin: USSR	Overall Length: 2020mm (79.5in)
Date: 1941	Barrel Length: 1350mm (53.14in)
Calibre: 14.5mm (.57in)	Muzzle Velocity: 1114m/sec (3655ft/sec)
Operation: Single fire	Feed/Magazine: Single shot
Weight: 17.3kg (38.1lb)	Range: 1000m (3280ft)

Soviet Anti-tank Rifle Squad, 1942

The Soviet anti-tank rifle squad of 1942 included three examples of the PTRS-41, capable of firing up to five steel- or tungsten-cored rounds without reloading, or a similar number of the single-shot PTRD-41. The anti-tank platoon consisted of three squads, totalling nine anti-tank rifles and 24 soldiers. The anti-tank rifles themselves were late in developing within the Soviet Union since Red Army commanders initially believed that early German tanks were too heavily armoured to be penetrated by such weapons. The rifles were also developed at a time when other armies were favouring rocket- or spring-propelled anti-tank weapons.

Squad (8 soldiers): 3 x PTRS-41 or PTRD-41

Germany and Allies
1941–42

Hitler's unbroken string of victories in the East came to an end in the autumn of 1942 as the Red Army and unfavourable weather halted the eastward march of the *Wehrmacht*.

WHEN HITLER launched Operation Barbarossa in June 1941, the German war machine had gained an aura of invincibility. From the Arctic Circle to the North African desert, Axis forces had the ascendancy. The *Führer* and his generals were afflicted with that most dangerous of military maladies – victory disease.

War with the Soviet Union was a gamble regardless of the apparent prowess of the German armed forces. Hitler was aware that fighting would one day resume in the West, creating a second front that had always been seen as the potential undoing of German military ambitions. Nevertheless, he was sure of a

quick victory and opined that the Soviet Union was in decay. Germany needed only to 'kick the door in and the whole house will come down!'

The German high command did have reason for optimism. The *Führer* appeared to be the master of the calculated risk. Besides, the German armed forces were the best trained and disciplined in the world and their equipment was of the highest quality.

The Germans and their allies, the Romanians, Hungarians, a contingent of Italian troops, and even a division of volunteers from Fascist Spain, failed to consider the vastness of the Soviet Union from the northern tundra to the steppes and the Crimea. They

◀ **Star Model B**

Spanish Blue Division / 250th Reconnaissance Battalion, Volkhov River, 1942

The Star Model B was a Spanish copy of the Colt Model 1911 pistol chambered for the 9mm (.35in) Parabellum cartridge. The pistol was carried on the Eastern Front by Spanish volunteers.

Specifications

Country of Origin: Spain	Overall Length: 215mm (8.46in)
Date: 1924	Barrel Length: 122mm (4.8in)
Calibre: 9mm (.35in) Parabellum	Muzzle Velocity: Not known
Operation: Short recoil	Feed/Magazine: Not known
Weight: 1.1kg (2.4lb)	Range: Not known

GERMAN INFANTRY BATTALION, *CIRCA* 1941–42		
Unit	Officers	Men
Battalion Headquarters	5	27
Communications Platoon		22
Battalion Train		32
Machine Gun Company	5	197
Company HQ	1	14
Battle Train		14
Rations Train		3
Mortar Platoon	1	61
Three Machine Gun Platoons, each	1	35
Three Rifle Companies, each	4	187
Company HQ	1	12
Battle Train		17
Rations and Baggage Trains		7
Anti-tank Rifle Section		7
Three Rifle Platoons, each		
Platoon HQ	1	5
Light Mortar Section		3
Four Rifle Squads, each		10
Total Strength of 861 all ranks	22	839

encircling and annihilating entire Soviet armies. However, they failed to win the decisive victory that would compel Stalin to sue for peace. Fighting literally at the gates of Moscow, the Germans were frustrated in their attempts to capture the Soviet capital. The price was horrific as the Red Army sustained more than a million casualties in several weeks of heavy fighting from October 1941 to January 1942.

Among the German small arms that were responsible for such grim Soviet losses was the outstanding Maschinengewehr 34, or MG 34, the mainstay of the German Army infantry support weapons since the beginning of the war. With a rate of fire of up to 900 rounds per minute and an easy exchange of barrels in combat, the MG 34 was both feared and respected by Allied soldiers. However, its precision manufacturing process was costly, particularly during wartime, and prompted German designers to seek an alternative that could be more rapidly and inexpensively produced.

Applying similar mass production techniques to those that had been used with the MP 38 submachine gun, the Germans developed the Maschinengewehr 42, or MG 42. The MG 42 was light and easily maintained and capable of producing an astonishing rate of fire of 1550 rounds per minute. Its distinctive report was similar to a ripping or shredding sound and is remembered to this day by Allied veterans who faced it in combat. Its 7.92mm (.312in) ammunition was fed from a 50-round belt, and the weapon was fired from a tripod or bipod mounting.

failed to comprehend the extent of Soviet resources in terms of manpower and machines. They failed to prepare for the cruel winter climate should their sensitive timetable stretch beyond the seasons of favourable weather.

The German advance across Russia in the summer of 1941 wreaked havoc on the Red Army, killing and capturing more than a million men. At times covering more than 160km (100 miles) in a single day, German spearheads pushed deep into Russia,

▲ **vz. 24**

Romanian Army / 11th Infantry Division, Odessa, August 1941

A rifle manufactured in Czechoslovakia shortly after the end of World War I, the vz. 24 was similar in design to the German Gewehr 98. However, it is not considered an identical copy, with a shorter barrel and other modifications.

Specifications

Country of Origin: Czechoslovakia
Date: 1938
Calibre: 7.92mm (.312in) Mauser M98
Operation: Bolt action
Weight: 4.2kg (9.2lb)

Overall Length: 1110mm (43.7in)
Barrel Length: 590mm (23.23in)
Muzzle Velocity: 760m/sec (2493ft/sec)
Feed/Magazine: 5-round integral box magazine
Range: 500m (1640ft) + with iron sights

▶ **Walther P38**

German Eighteenth Army / 21st Infantry Division, Army Group North,
June 1941

The Walther P38 was one of a family of handguns that has been acknowledged as among the best pistols of the twentieth century. Always in short supply, it was nevertheless adopted in the 1930s as the official sidearm of the German Army.

Specifications

Country of Origin: Germany	Barrel Length: 127mm (5in)
Date: 1938	Muzzle Velocity: 350m/sec (1150ft/sec)
Calibre: 9mm (.35in) Parabellum	Feed/Magazine: 8-round detachable box
Operation: Short recoil	magazine
Weight: .96kg (2.11lb)	Range: 30m (98ft)
Overall Length: 213mm (8.38in)	

▲ **Karabiner 98k sniper rifle**

German Eleventh Army / 2nd SS Brigade, Army Group North, July 1942

Fitted with a precision telescopic sight, the sniper version of the standard issue German infantry rifle was extremely accurate up to 1000m (3280ft) in the hands of a skilled operator.

Specifications

Country of Origin: Germany	Overall Length: 1110mm (43.7in)
Date: 1935	Barrel Length: 600mm (23.62in)
Calibre: 7.92mm (.312in) Mauser M98	Muzzle Velocity: 745m/sec (2444ft/sec)
Operation: Bolt action	Feed/Magazine: 5-round integral box magazine
Weight: 3.9kg (8.6lb)	Range: 1000m (3280ft) +

Specifications

Country of Origin: Germany	Barrel Length: 1085mm (42.7in)
Date: 1939	Muzzle Velocity: 1265m/sec (4150ft/sec)
Calibre: 7.92mm (.312in)	Feed/Magazine: Single shot
Operation: Bolt action	Range: 300m (984ft) against 25mm (.98in)
Weight: 11.6kg (25.57lb)	armour
Overall Length: 1620mm (63.8in)	

▲ **Panzerbüchse 39**

German Fourth Army / 331st Infantry Division, Army Group Centre, May 1942

The Panzerbüchse 39 anti-tank rifle was not highly effective against Soviet tanks; however, with the introduction of ammunition with a tungsten core, the unusually long weapon remained in service.

The MG 42 entered service on the Eastern Front and in North Africa in 1942, and more than 400,000 were produced during the war with the highest number per year at 212,000 in 1944. Its crew of six included a commander, gunner, bipod or tripod bearer, and three others who carried ammunition and spare barrels.

Like its predecessors the MP 38 and MP 40, the MP 41 submachine gun that emerged on the Eastern Front was conceived to provide the individual soldier with substantial firepower. It was intended to be carried by the crewmen of armoured vehicles, airborne troops and the commanders of small ground units, particularly at squad and platoon level. However, the MP 41 was never deployed by the German Army and was utilized mainly by SS and police units. The MP 41 was essentially the same weapon as the MP 40 with a wooden stock and selective-fire option. It fired the 9mm (.35in) Parabellum cartridge at a rate of up to 550 rounds per minute. One impediment to its wide acceptance was a legal battle over patent rights.

Specifications

Country of Origin: Germany	Barrel Length: 250mm (9.8mm)
Date: 1941	Muzzle Velocity: 381m/sec (1250ft/sec)
Calibre: 9mm (.35in) Parabellum	Feed/Magazine: 32-round box magazine
Operation: Blowback	Cyclic Rate: 500rpm
Weight: 3.87kg (8.5lb)	Range: 150-200m (492-656ft)
Overall Length: 860mm (33.8in)	

▲ **Maschinenpistole 41 (MP 41)**

307th Police Abteilung (Motorized), Army Group Centre, June 1942

The MP 41 was originally designed as a new infantry submachine gun but was instead deployed with police and SS units. Essentially the same weapon as the MP 40, it was manufactured with a wooden stock.

Specifications

Country of Origin: Germany	Barrel Length: 535mm (21in)
Date: 1942	Muzzle Velocity: 800m/sec (2650ft/sec)
Calibre: 7.92mm (.312in) Mauser	Feed/Magazine: 50-round belt
Operation: Short recoil, air cooled	Cyclic Rate: 1200rpm
Weight: 11.5kg (25.35lb)	Range: 3000m (9842ft) +
Overall Length: 1220mm (48in)	

▲ **Maschinengewehr 42 (MG 42)**

German Fourth Army / 331st Infantry Division, Army Group Centre, May 1942

The MG 42 was renowned for its high rate of fire and ease of transport. It was simpler to manufacture in large quantities than its predecessor, the MG 34, which also remained in production until the end of the war.

Stalingrad
AUGUST 1942 – JANUARY 1943

Hitler's dream of conquest in the East came to ruin as the German Sixth Army was surrounded and utterly destroyed by the Soviets at Stalingrad, signalling the beginning of the end for Nazi Germany.

STALINGRAD, THE INDUSTRIAL CITY on the Volga that bore the name of the Soviet leader himself, was not necessarily a primary objective of the German advance into Russia – except in the mind of Adolf Hitler (1889–1945). Although Stalingrad was an important centre of manufacturing, its capture did not spell the difference between victory and defeat for Germany; however, Hitler was determined to capture the city.

As German offensive operations commenced in the spring of 1942, Hitler directed a powerful thrust towards the Caucasus and detailed a portion of that force, primarily the Sixth Army under General Friedrich Paulus (1890–1957), to capture Stalingrad. Fighting raged for months as the Germans took most of the city but then found themselves surrounded. Paulus requested permission to break out of the trap, but Hitler refused.

Luftwaffe chief Hermann Göring (1893–1946) asserted that he could keep the beleaguered Sixth Army supplied by air, but German planes were able to deliver only a fraction of the supplies needed to maintain the Germans in Stalingrad in fighting condition. An effort to relieve the city on the ground

was turned back, and the fate of the Sixth Army was sealed. Expecting Paulus to fight to the last man, Hitler promoted him to field marshal, aware that no German commander of such high rank had ever been taken alive. Instead, Paulus surrendered to the Red Army and went into captivity with more than 90,000 of his soldiers. The disaster at Stalingrad cost the Germans a total of more than 700,000 casualties.

The privation, death and destruction at Stalingrad reduced the city to a shambles, and German soldiers who experienced the fighting in the shattered streets or from house to house called the horrific experience *Rattenkrieg*, the war of the rats. While the threat of the sniper was constant, another hidden peril lay around the corner or through the next door. Along with the Tokarev, Mosin-Nagant or Karabiner 98k sniper rifle, the submachine gun reigned in the rubble of Stalingrad.

The Soviet PPSh-41 and the German Maschinenpistole 40, or MP 40, were commonly in use during the battle for Stalingrad. The PPSh-41 had been designed for mass production with a minimum of components, stamped from steel and

Specifications

Country of Origin: USSR	Barrel Length: 266mm (10.5in)
Date: 1941	Muzzle Velocity: 490m/sec (1600ft/sec)
Calibre: 7.62mm (.3in) Soviet	Feed/Magazine: 35-round box magazine or
Operation: Blowback	71-round drum magazine
Weight: 3.64kg (8lb)	Cyclic Rate: 900rpm
Overall Length: 838mm (33in)	Range: 120m (394ft)

▲ **PPSh-41**

Soviet Sixty-Second Army / 284th Rifle Division, Stalingrad Front, September 1942

The mass-produced PPSh-41 submachine gun included a barrel lined with chrome to reduce wear. Its drum magazines could hold up to 71 rounds of ammunition.

assembled within a matter of hours to equip formations of the Red Army as large as divisions.

Like the PPSh-41, the open-bolt, blowback-operated MP 40 was mass produced, and during World War II more than a million of the MP 40 family were built. The weapon fired the 9mm (.35in) Parabellum cartridge and was capable of a cyclic rate of fire of 500 rounds per minute. Automatic-fire mode was the single option with the MP 40, although the rate of fire, which might be considered low, allowed an accomplished user to squeeze off single shots with careful manipulation of the trigger. The weapon was fed by a 32-round detachable box magazine or a 64-round dual-magazine configuration.

The MP 40 was one of a long line of submachine guns that stretched back more than 20 years. It followed the MP 38 and came about primarily due to the need for more rapid production, taking advantage of stamped parts. It combined the elements of guns from several design concerns, but its principal proponent was Heinrich Vollmer (1885–1961), who had also been instrumental in the development of the ubiquitous MG 34 infantry machine gun.

The MP 40 was intended for issue to squad or platoon leaders of the German Army, while the lion's share of the weapons was to go to airborne troops and those who operated in confined spaces such as armoured vehicle crews. However, during the Battle of Stalingrad the Germans encountered entire squads or platoons of Red Army troops equipped with the PPSh-41 and were overmatched in terms of firepower. As the war on the Eastern Front

▲ Tokarev SVT-40

Soviet Sixty-Second Army / 35th Guards Rifle Division, Stalingrad Front, September 1942

Based on a design by Fedor Tokarev (1871–1968), the SVT-40 assault rifle entered production in the spring of 1940 following the termination of its predecessor, the SVT-38. The weapon was fed by a 10-round box magazine, and more than 1.5 million were manufactured during World War II.

Specifications

Country of Origin: USSR	Barrel Length: 610mm (25in)
Date: 1940	Muzzle Velocity: 840m/sec (2755ft/sec)
Calibre: 7.62mm (.3in)	Feed/Magazine: 10-round detachable box
Operation: Gas operated	magazine
Weight: 3.9kg (8.6lb)	Range: 500m (1640ft) +
Overall Length: 1226mm (48.27in)	

Specifications

Country of Origin: USSR	Barrel Length: 605mm (23.8in)
Date: 1927	Muzzle Velocity: 840m/sec (2756ft/sec)
Calibre: 7.62mm (.3in) Soviet	Feed/Magazine: 47-round pan magazine
Operation: Gas operated, air cooled	Cyclic Rate: 500–600rpm
Weight: 9.12kg (20.1lb)	Range: 2000m (6560ft)
Overall Length: 1290mm (50.8in)	

▲ Degtyaryov DP-28

Soviet Sixty-Second Army / 244th Rifle Division, Stalingrad Front, November 1942

The primary Soviet infantry light machine gun of World War II, the DP-28 was fed by a 47-round pan magazine mounted on the top of the weapon. It was capable of firing up to 600 rounds per minute.

progressed, it became common for the *Wehrmacht* to equip larger units in the same fashion as the Soviets, with the full firepower of multiple submachine guns.

The MP 40 was generally considered a reliable weapon, and US and British soldiers who captured MP 40s in the West often pressed them into service. Still, there were problems at times with the 32-round magazine. Soldiers often grasped the magazine with one hand to stabilize the weapon and caused the feed to malfunction, particularly when debris had got into the chamber. The forward-folding stock allowed the weapon to be carried more easily but did not hold up well in prolonged use.

German troops used the *Flammenwerfer* (flamethrower) to eliminate pockets of resistance within Stalingrad, spraying flames into houses and sewers. The Flammenwerfer 35 equipped the German forces early in the war, and this was followed by the Flammenwerfer 41 with side-by-side fuel tanks and a range of 25–30m (82–98ft). The Flammenwerfer 41 was modified so that the trigger and muzzle sections were similar to the infantry rifle in an effort to avoid drawing concentrated enemy fire to the operator.

Specifications

Country of Origin: Germany	630mm (24.75in) stock folded
Date: 1940	Barrel Length: 248mm (9.75in)
Calibre: 9mm (.35in) Parabellum	Muzzle Velocity: 395m/sec (1300ft/sec)
Operation: Blowback	Feed/Magazine: 32-round box magazine
Weight: 3.97kg (8.75lb)	Cyclic Rate: 500rpm
Overall Length: 832mm (32.75in) stock extended;	Range: 70m (230ft)

▲ **Maschinenpistole 40 (MP 40)**

Army Group B / German Sixth Army / 44th Infantry Division, September 1942

The MP 40 was simple to manufacture and remarkably robust, even in the harsh winter weather of the Eastern Front. Its long service life extended into the 1990s.

Specifications

Country of Origin: Germany	Fuel Capacity: 11.8 litres (2.6 gallons)
Date: 1941	Duration of Fire: 10 seconds
Weight: 35.8kg (79lb)	Range: 25–30m (82–98ft)

▶ **Flammenwerfer 41**

Army Group B / German Sixth Army / 389th Pioneer Battalion, September 1942

The deadly flamethrower was employed at Stalingrad by the Germans to clear houses, strongpoints and even sewers of tenacious Red Army soldiers. Spewing fuel mixed with propellant, the weapon not only burned victims but consumed available oxygen in confined spaces.

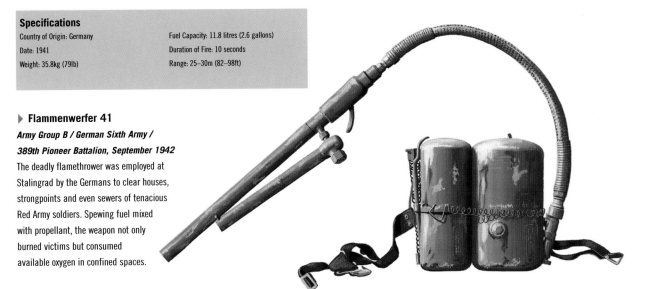

Eastern Front
1943–45

With the disastrous defeat at Stalingrad, German fortunes in the East were irretrievably reversed. The Red Army gained strength with renewed industrial capacity and fresh divisions of infantry transferred from beyond the Urals to fight the Nazis.

WORLD WAR II on the Eastern Front was a prolonged and brutal affair. Hitler had told the German people that land in the East would provide *Lebensraum*, or living space. However, by 1943 it was apparent that the *Wehrmacht* was destined to defend the borders of the Reich itself as overwhelming numbers of Red Army troops led by capable commanders such as Marshals Georgi Zhukov (1896–1974), Konstantin Rokossovsky (1896–1968) and Ivan Konev (1897–1973) drove the Germans from Russian soil and liberated most of Eastern Europe, which remained under Soviet domination for the next half-century.

As the Red Army advanced on all fronts, Stalin promoted mistrust and competition among his top commanders in order to prevent their gaining too much regard among the Soviet people or threatening his own iron grip on the Red Army and the nation. Two long years after the turning point at Stalingrad, the Red Army had raised the siege of Leningrad in the north, liberated the Ukrainian capital of Kiev and killed or captured hundreds of thousands of German troops. The battle for Berlin itself lasted from mid-April 1945 to early May, and when the end came Hitler had already committed suicide in his bunker beneath the shattered city.

▲ **Soviet sniper**
Armed with a Mosin-Nagant 1891/31 rifle equipped with a x4 PE telescopic sight, a Red Army sniper poses in full winter camouflage during the winter of 1942–43.

From Kursk to Berlin: Red Army 1943–45

The Red Army rose like the proverbial phoenix from the ashes of defeat of 1941, becoming the largest and arguably the most powerful land army in the world by the end of World War II.

BY THE SUMMER OF 1943, the Soviets had seized the initiative on the Eastern Front, driving the *Wehrmacht* westwards across hundreds of kilometres of territory. Near the city of Kursk, 450km (280 miles) south of Moscow, the Red Army had advanced in force, creating a large salient, or bulge. The Germans recognized an opportunity to trap thousands of Soviet troops and tanks inside the salient and to shorten their defensive lines by eliminating it.

In July, the Germans attacked. The largest armoured battle in history followed. In the south, the Germans pushed towards the town of Prokhorovka where a wild melee of armour and panzergrenadiers and Red Army troops firing automatic weapons erupted. When the Soviets committed their armoured reserves to the fight, Hitler acknowledged that the offensive was a failure and halted further operations.

As mentioned earlier, the Soviets remember 1944 as 'The Year of 10 Victories', commemorating the

◀ **Tula-Tokarev TT33**

Soviet Thirty-Third Army / 144th Rifle Division, Eastern Front, July 1943

A reliable and sturdy weapon, the 7.62mm (.3in) TT33 pistol was patterned after the earlier TT30, of which more than two million were manufactured. The TT33 was the result of an altered frame, barrel and trigger.

Specifications

Country of Origin: USSR	Barrel Length: 116mm (4.57in)
Date: 1933	Muzzle Velocity: 415m/sec (1362ft/sec)
Calibre: 7.62mm (.3in) Soviet	Feed/Magazine: 8-round detachable box
Operation: Short recoil	magazine
Weight: .83kg (1.83lb)	Range: 30m (98ft)
Overall Length: 194mm (7.6in)	

▲ **Mosin-Nagant M1938 carbine**

Soviet Tenth Army / 330th Rifle Division, Eastern Front, July 1943

The short-barrelled carbine version of the Mosin-Nagant M91/30 rifle, the M1938 was developed and tested in 1938, but did not enter production until 1939. It was not designed to take a bayonet.

Specifications

Country of Origin: USSR	Overall Length: 1020mm (40in)
Date: 1938	Barrel Length: 510mm (20in)
Calibre: 7.62mm (.3in)	Muzzle Velocity: 800m/sec (2625ft/sec)
Operation: Bolt action	Feed/Magazine: 5-round box magazine
Weight: 3.45kg (7.62lb)	Range: 500m (1640ft)

SOVIET RIFLE BRIGADE PERSONNEL & EQUIPMENT, 1943	
Personnel type/Equipment item	Strength
Officers	58
NCOs	193
Other ranks	677
Submachine guns	126
Bolt-action rifles	220
Semiautomatic rifles	403
Light machine guns	36
Medium machine guns	12
Heavy machine guns	0
Anti-tank rifles	8
Anti-tank mortars	7
50mm (2in) mortars	12
82mm (3.2in) mortars	0
120mm (4.7in) mortars	0
45mm (1.8in) anti-tank guns	0
76mm (3in) guns	0
Horses	89

against German Panzerfaust and Panzerschreck teams and mopping up pockets of resistance. In the hands of a number of these Red Army soldiers was the Tokarev SVT-40 assault rifle. A gas-operated, short-stroke piston rifle with a tilting bolt, the SVT-40 was based on a design undertaken by Fedor Tokarev (1871–1968) in about 1930. Tokarev had previously worked on a recoil-operated semiautomatic rifle and abandoned that effort.

The SVT-40 was the successor to an earlier model, the SVT-38, and fired the Soviet 7.62mm (.3in) cartridge. Fed by a 10-round detachable box magazine, it entered production at the Tula Arsenal in the summer of 1939. More than 1.5 million were manufactured during the course of the war. About 150,000 examples of the SVT-38 had been manufactured and issued to troops during the Winter War with Finland in 1939–40. Contrary to most Soviet small-arms designs, the SVT-38 was well built with precision machining.

By the summer of 1941, however, the SVT-40 had been authorized for distribution to Red Army troops and incorporated some improvements to the previous

succession of offensive operations that carried the Red Army to the gates of Berlin by the spring of 1945. Two of these actions stand out among the others. Early in the year, an offensive finally lifted the siege of Leningrad, which had dragged on for 900 days and cost the lives of more than a million civilians. At mid-year, Operation Bagration utterly destroyed German Army Group Centre and drove the last German troops from Russian soil before the Red Army advanced into Germany.

In January 1945, the Soviet offensive along the rivers Vistula and Oder opened the drive to Berlin through East Prussia and Silesia. By mid-April, Zhukov's 1st Belorussian Front and Konev's 1st Ukrainian Front were pressing into the suburbs of the city. On 2 May, Red Army troops captured the Reich Chancellery and raised their flag above the defeated city. Victory had come at a tremendous price with estimates of Soviet military and civilian deaths at 20 million.

As Soviet armour rumbled through the streets of Berlin, infantry supported the tanks, protecting

▶ **Guards soldier**
Armed with a PPS-43 submachine gun, a corporal from the 1st Ukrainian Front pauses during the advance through suburban Berlin, April 1945.

▲ Tokarev AVT-40

Soviet Eleventh Guards Army / 5th Guards Motor Rifle Division, Kursk Front, July 1943

The Tokarev AVT-40 was a fully automatic version of the SVT-40 semiautomatic rifle. Its 10-round magazine limited the supply of ammunition available to the weapon, and it proved unstable in combat.

Specifications

Country of Origin: USSR
Date: 1940
Calibre: 7.62mm (.3in)
Operation: Gas-operated short-stroke piston
Weight: 3.9kg (8.6lb)
Overall Length: 1226mm (48.27in)
Barrel Length: 610mm (25in)
Muzzle Velocity: 840m/sec (2756ft/sec)
Feed/Magazine: 10-round detachable box magazine
Range: 500m (1640ft)

Specifications

Country of Origin: USSR
Date: 1943
Calibre: 7.62mm (.3in) Soviet
Operation: Blowback
Weight: 3.36kg (7.4lb)
Overall Length: 820mm (32.3in)
Barrel Length: 254mm (10in)
Muzzle Velocity: 500m/sec (1640ft/sec)
Feed/Magazine: 35-round detachable box magazine
Cyclic Rate: 650rpm
Range: 100m (328ft) +

▲ PPS-43

Soviet Eleventh Guards Army / 31st Guards Rifle Division, Orel Offensive, August 1943

The PPS-43 submachine gun was a modified version of the earlier PPS-42; it was designed and produced in the city of Leningrad while under siege. Remarkably, the weapon was a success and served with Soviet forces for years.

▲ SKS carbine

Soviet First Guards Tank Army / 12th Motor Rifle Brigade, 1st Belorussian Front, March 1945

The SKS carbine did not appear in combat until 1945 as a shorter rifle for troops who operated in vehicles and other close-quarters situations. A semiautomatic weapon, its ammunition supply was limited by a 10-round box magazine.

Specifications

Country of Origin: USSR
Date: 1945
Calibre: 7.62mm (.3in)
Operation: Gas-operated short-stroke piston
Weight: 3.85kg (8.49lb)
Overall Length: 1021mm (40.2in)
Barrel Length: 521mm (20.5in)
Muzzle Velocity: 735m/sec (2411ft/sec)
Feed/Magazine: 10-round integral box magazine
Range: 400m (1312ft)

weapon, particularly a modified magazine release and a hand guard made of a single piece. It was also easier to manufacture and lighter than the SVT-38. When German forces invaded the Soviet Union, substantial numbers of the SVT-40 were already in service and helped eventually to turn the tide of the war on the Eastern Front.

In 1943, the Soviets introduced the Goryunov SG-43 medium machine gun, finally intending to replace the old Model 1910 Maxim Guns still in service. Like other Soviet machine guns, the SG-43 was often mounted on a wheeled carriage, although a tripod option was available. This gas-operated weapon fired the 7.62mm (.3in) cartridge at a rate of up to 700 rounds per minute, and it was fed by ammunition belts of 200 or 250 rounds. It had a range of 1000m (3280ft). After World War II, the SG-43 was exported to several nations of the Communist Bloc. The SG-43 was difficult to load, and its barrel was cumbersome to change in the field.

Specifications

Country of Origin: USSR

Date: 1943

Calibre: 7.62mm (.3in) Soviet

Operation: Gas operated, air cooled

Weight: 13.6kg (29.98lb)

Overall Length: 1120mm (44.1in)

Barrel Length: 719mm (28.3in)

Muzzle Velocity: 850m/sec (2788ft/sec)

Feed/Magazine: 200- or 250-round belt

Cyclic Rate: 500–700rpm

Range: 1000m (3280ft)

▲ **Goryunov SG-43**

Soviet Fifteenth Army / 238th Rifle Division, 2nd Belorussian Front, June 1944

The SG-43 medium machine gun entered service with the Red Army in 1943 as a replacement for the venerable Model 1910 Maxim Gun. The SG-43 was often placed on a two-wheeled carriage or mounted on a tripod.

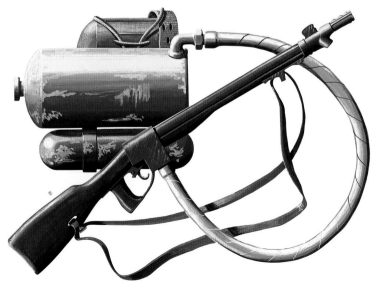

Specifications

Country of Origin: USSR

Date: 1943

Weight: 22.7kg (50lb)

Fuel Capacity: 9 litres (5 gallons)

Duration of Fire: 8–10 seconds

Range: 23–27m (75–89ft)

◄ **ROKS-3**

Soviet Fifteenth Army / 64th Engineer Brigade, June 1944

The ROKS-3 flamethrower was a wartime expedient version of the ROKS-2. It was designed for mass production, and performance was improved with the introduction of thicker fuel, increasing its range.

Retreat and Defeat: German Army 1943–45

Götterdämmerung for the Third Reich began on the Eastern Front in 1943. Defeats at Stalingrad and Kursk were followed by relentless Red Army offensive action, and despite temporary setbacks the Soviets crushed German resistance.

THE GERMANS COMMITTED tremendous numbers of *Wehrmacht* and SS troops and enormous amounts of weapons large and small to the maelstrom of World War II on the Eastern Front. Among these were legions of their finest tanks, the Mark V Panther and Mark VI Tiger; their most fanatical armoured and infantry formations in the SS divisions; thousands of their reliable 88mm (3.5in) anti-aircraft guns that had proved deadly in the anti-tank role; and the first assault rifles to see action. None of these had stabilized, let alone reversed, the situation in the East by the end of 1943.

German defeats at Stalingrad and in the great tank battle of Kursk placed momentum solidly on the side of the Red Army, although from time to time the Germans did mount successful counterattacks. These, however, were only temporary, pyrrhic victories. None were sustainable due to a lack of troops and materiel to exploit any progress. The German armed forces were being bled white by the Red Army.

During 1944, the Soviets advanced steadily towards the German frontier. By the spring of 1945, they had marched into Warsaw, Prague and Vienna, liberating the capitals and major cities of Eastern Europe and forcing the Germans to press old men of the *Volkssturm* and boys of the Hitler Youth into the defence of the Fatherland.

As the Red Army moved inexorably westwards, Hitler became delusional, ordering phantom armies or formations that had long been decimated in the crucible of combat to counterattack. His generals often petitioned the *Führer* to withdraw from exposed positions in order to prevent further needless loss of life and resources; however, Hitler ordered his troops invariably to stand fast. These orders were sometimes ignored and troops pulled out despite the *Führer*'s decrees.

In the south, thousands of German and Romanian troops were trapped in the Crimea and rendered useless for months. Hitler ordered the garrison of Sevastopol to fight to the last shell; however, such an effort was unrealistic due to the rapid movement of Soviet forces. The Axis troops who could be evacuated were taken by sea to the Romanian city of Constanta on the Black Sea coast. Approximately 100,000 German and Romanian soldiers were lost in the fighting.

With deficiencies in manpower and equipment at critical levels, German forces in the East were sometimes organized into 'fire brigades' whose purpose was to rapidly move to areas of Soviet breakthroughs

▶ **Walther PPK**

Army Group B / German Fifteenth Army / 84th Infantry Division, June 1944

The double-action PPK was smaller than other Walther pistols of the PP series and originally intended for police work. It was easily concealed and could be drawn and fired rapidly.

Specifications

Country of Origin: Germany	Barrel Length: 80mm (3.15in)
Date: 1931	Muzzle Velocity: 290m/sec (950ft/sec)
Calibre: 7.65mm (.301in)	Feed/Magazine: 7-round detachable box
Operation: Blowback	magazine
Weight: .59kg (1.3lb)	Range: 30m (98ft)
Overall Length: 148mm (5.8in)	

▲ **Squad action**

A German squad armed primarily with with Kar 98 rifles advances warily somewhere in northern Germany, early 1945.

and attempt to contain breaches in German lines. Such a strategy was born of necessity but wore the Germans down through painful attrition.

The Battle of Berlin began in earnest in mid-April 1945 and was concluded during the first week of May as Red Army troops took control of the German capital following weeks of artillery bombardment and fighting that was characterized by bloody, close-quarters shoot-outs from street to street and house to house. The Germans made the Soviets pay dearly for their conquest of Berlin. In the two weeks of fighting that preceded the city's capture the Soviets suffered more than 360,000 killed, wounded and missing. The Germans lost at least 125,000 dead during the period, and more than 20,000 of these were civilians. By the time Berlin fell, most high-ranking Nazis had committed suicide or attempted to flee towards the Western Allies in fear of Soviet reprisals against them.

Wartime weapons evolution

The war on the Eastern Front had become a proving ground for advancing small-arms technology. The rifle, assault rifle, submachine gun, infantry support machine gun and anti-tank weapons were evaluated, modified, discarded or simplified for mass production. The firepower of the individual soldier was substantially augmented, and German innovation was largely responsible for the evolution of infantry weapons.

The majority of the 425,000 Sturmgewehr 44 assault rifles manufactured during the war were sent to the Eastern Front. Many firearms experts consider the Sturmgewehr 44 to be the first assault rifle to enter combat, but its development was slowed by interference from Hitler, and its continuation was in doubt for a time. As alluded to above, earlier incarnations of the assault rifle – first designated the Maschinenkarabiner 42 (Mkb 42), then the Maschinenpistole 43 (MP 43) – were quietly continued, eventually becoming the Sturmgewehr 44, literally translated as Storm Rifle 44.

Actually, it was reported that Hitler named the Sturmgewehr 44 after test-firing the weapon he had opposed. During a conference, Hitler had questioned several commanders from the Eastern Front as to their most pressing needs. One of them replied that more of the new automatic rifles they had received would be beneficial. The *Führer* was shocked to learn of its covert development but later acquiesced. The Sturmgewehr 44 went on to revolutionize individual small arms around the world, inspiring a generation of new weapons.

German forays into the development of semiautomatic rifles were less successful. The highly accurate, gas-operated Gewehr 43 rifle was designed by the Walther firm and showed some promise although it was slow and costly to produce. German soldiers were impressed with the Soviet Tokarev SVT-40 semiautomatic rifle, another gas-operated weapon, which they encountered during Operation Barbarossa. Walther studied captured examples of the SVT-40 and developed a gas operating system similar to that of the Soviet weapon.

The high manufacturing cost of the Gewehr 43, particularly when it entered production in the autumn of 1943 and Germany was experiencing serious shortages of raw materials, limited the availability of the weapon. It was issued to a relative few German troops in the final two years of the war.

Production of the Gewehr 43 and its predecessor, the Gewehr 41, totalled slightly more than 400,000 including over 50,000 units of a sniper version that was fitted with a telescopic sight.

While both automatic and semiautomatic rifles were effective combat weapons, German industrial capacity failed to produce enough of them to stave off defeat in World War II. The same may be said of other German weaponry that appeared during the war. Small arms, armoured vehicles and tanks, jet aircraft and rockets were products of the German industrial base. However, the mismanagement of these projects, their general lack of support from high-ranking Nazis, or their sheer expense prevented a tipping of the balance of power towards the Axis.

Specifications

Country of Origin: Germany	Barrel Length: 418mm (16.5in)
Date: 1943	Muzzle Velocity: 700m/sec (2300ft/sec)
Calibre: 7.92mm (.312in) Kurz	Feed/Magazine: 30-round detachable box
Operation: Gas operated	magazine
Weight: 5.1kg (11.24lb)	Cyclic Rate: 550–600rpm
Overall Length: 940mm (37in)	Range: c.300m (984ft)

▲ Maschinenpistole 43 (MP 43)

Army Group Centre / First Panzer Army / 20th SS (Estonian) Grenadier Division, March 1945

The MP 43 was essentially the same weapon as the famed Sturmgewehr 44, the *Maschinenpistole* designation being given to the project that produced the StG 44 to avoid Hitler's disapproval of the weapon's development.

▲ Sturmgewehr 44 (StG 44)

Army Group Centre / German Seventeenth Army / 6th Volksgrenadier Division, March 1945

The Sturmgewehr 44 may be considered the first true assault rifle to enter combat. It served as the basis for a generation of future infantry automatic weapons around the world.

Specifications

Country of Origin: Germany	Barrel Length: 418mm (16.5in)
Date: 1944	Muzzle Velocity: 700m/sec (2300ft/sec)
Calibre: 7.92mm (.312in) Kurz	Feed/Magazine: 30-round detachable box
Operation: Gas operated	magazine
Weight: 5.1kg (11.24lb)	Cyclic Rate: 550–600rpm
Overall Length: 940mm (37in)	Range: c.400m (1312ft)

Chapter 6

World War II: Pacific Theatre

Japanese expansion throughout Asia and the Pacific was driven by the rise of militarism in Japan as well as by shortages of land and raw materials that could sustain a growing population. Since the early twentieth century, Japan had gained preeminent status in Asia, its military steadily increasing in strength along the model of Western powers. By the 1930s, the Japanese Army had conquered vast territories in northern China, and conflict with the only nation strong enough to oppose continuing expansion in the region, the United States, loomed. By the time the US declared war on Japan following the 7 December 1941 attack on Pearl Harbor, the Japanese soldier was well trained and equipped with modern weapons, many of which had been made to high standards of precision in Japan.

◀ **Tommy Gun**
A US Marine of the 1st Marine Division draws a bead on a Japanese sniper with his Thompson submachine gun, Wana Ridge, Okinawa, 1945. His companion is armed with a Browning Automatic Rifle (BAR) squad support weapon.

Introduction

World War II in the Pacific spanned the jungles of Southeast Asia, the vastness of China, the Arctic reaches of the Aleutians, and remote tropical islands. While fighting men endured tremendous hardships, their small arms were subjected to the harshest of conditions.

O N SUNDAY 7 DECEMBER 1941, Japanese attacks against the US Pacific Fleet anchorage at Pearl Harbor and other installations on the island of Oahu and across Asia were launched within hours of one another. The aim was to seize the initiative in the Pacific with the intent of expanding the empire and maintaining control over significant territory occupied through mandate, treaty or military action during the previous half-century. Japanese propagandists had mounted a continuing effort to promote 'Asia for Asians'. Their creation of the Greater East Asia Co-Prosperity Sphere was political posturing that advocated the removal of Western influence from Asia and the Pacific. In truth, 'Asia for Asians' meant Asia for exploitation and domination by Japan.

Onslaught of the Rising Sun

The Japanese Army had been active in China since 1931, and following the outbreak of hostilities the well-disciplined force reeled off an unbroken string of victories. Hong Kong fell on Christmas Day 1941, and the Japanese tide rolled into the spring of 1942. In the Philippines, US and Filipino forces under the command of General Douglas MacArthur (1880–1964) were pushed into a defensive perimeter on the Bataan peninsula and then to the island fortress of Corregidor. In May 1942, Corregidor capitulated, and more than 100,000 were taken prisoner.

On the Malay peninsula, the Japanese drove relentlessly towards the British bastion of Singapore, swiftly outflanking and defeating British and Commonwealth troops. On 15 February 1942, Singapore fell, and 120,000 soldiers under the command of Lieutenant-General Arthur Percival (1887–1966) were captured. The Japanese occupied Burma and threatened India, the jewel in the crown of the British Empire, with invasion.

In the Pacific and Indian Oceans, the Imperial Japanese Navy appeared invincible. Three days after Pearl Harbor, naval aircraft sank the British battleship *Prince of Wales* and the battlecruiser *Repulse*, sent to the Orient to bolster the defences of Singapore and

the Malay peninsula. Admiral Isoroku Yamamoto (1884–1943), architect of the attack on Pearl Harbor, had warned the Japanese military establishment, 'For six months, I will run wild in the Pacific. After that, I make no guarantees.'

Yamamoto was correct almost to the day in his prediction. By June 1942, scarcely a month after the debacle in the Philippines, the US Navy denied the Japanese bid to capture Midway Atoll, a scant 1770km (1100 miles) from Hawaii. The victory at Midway was the turning point of the war in the Pacific and virtually erased Japanese superiority in aircraft carriers, planes and trained pilots. However, the island road to Tokyo would be long and costly. Victory at sea would necessarily be accompanied by victory on land.

Jungle fighting and island hopping

In August 1942, US forces landed on the island of Guadalcanal in the Solomons chain. Six months of bitter fighting followed before the Japanese withdrew from the island. Commonwealth troops held the line in the China–Burma–India Theatre and in New Guinea. The Allies assumed the offensive to the south in 1943, and General MacArthur triumphantly returned to the Philippines in the autumn of 1944. US Marines and Army troops stormed ashore and fought horrific battles on small, previously obscure islands such as Tarawa, Saipan, Peleliu, Iwo Jima and Okinawa during an island-hopping campaign that carried the war across the expanse of the Pacific to the doorstep of the Japanese home islands.

Invasion of the home islands

In early 1945, Allied war planners contemplated the costliest operation of the war, an invasion of Japan itself. Estimates of Allied casualties ran into the hundreds of thousands. However, the invasion proved unnecessary with the dropping of atomic bombs on the cities of Hiroshima and Nagasaki. Ironically, a war that had been fought on land with a plethora of small arms was ultimately ended with the most destructive weapon yet seen in human history.

▲ **Jungle fighters**
US Marines pose for a photo in the jungle of Bougainville, Solomon Islands, 1943. Most are armed with M1 Garand rifles, although a few are carrying the M1903 Springfield and M1 carbine, both popular with troops involved in jungle warfare.

The Japanese troops that fought the Allies across the Pacific and on the Asian continent were equipped with an assortment of small arms including the Type 38 and Type 99 Arisaka rifles, the Type 11 and Type 96 light machine guns, the Type 1, Type 3 and Type 92 heavy machine guns, and the Type 100 submachine gun. Generally these weapons were of quality manufacture until late in the war when concentrated US bombing had taken its toll on Japan's industrial capacity and submarines of the US Navy had choked the lifeline of supplies and raw materials for Japanese factories, crippling the war effort and finally helping to bring the Empire of the Rising Sun to its knees.

Imperial Japanese Army
1941–45

The Japanese Empire began to modernize its military and look to expand throughout Asia as resources were scarce for its growing population. The primary tool of that expansion was a military machine that rivalled the great powers of the West.

THE JAPANESE SOLDIER who conquered vast areas of the Asian continent and the Pacific stood approximately 1.6m (5ft 3in) tall. He was imbued with the belief that the Japanese were a superior people and that service to the emperor, particularly service resulting in his death in battle, was glorious. He was trained to follow the Code of Bushido, stressing that it was his duty to fight to the death. Surrender was not an option.

In 1943, the US military published a report titled *Some Basic Tactics of the Japanese*. Its content reveals the perception of the American commanders who faced the Japanese enemy. 'From almost every fighting front in the Pacific there have come reports that it has been necessary to completely wipe out all Japanese opposition before the objective could be attained. The following…taken from a British source [is] illustrative of some basic Japanese tactics. "When I received my mobilization orders, I had already sacrificed my life for my country…you must not expect me to return alive…." The last blood smeared page of a diary captured in Burma has "Three cheers for the Emperor" scrawled across it.'

Fanatical fighters

In keeping with Bushido, the Japanese soldier sacrificed himself without hesitation, fighting to the death rather than bringing dishonour upon himself and his family. At Tarawa in the Gilbert Islands, only 17 of the 3000-man garrison were taken alive following the bloody 76-hour fight with US Marines for control of the atoll. At Saipan in the Marianas, only 900 of an estimated 31,000 Japanese defenders surrendered during the fighting in mid-1944.

For some historians, the impetus behind the wave of atrocities that were perpetrated by Japanese troops against Allied prisoners of war is rooted in strict adherence to the Bushido code. Since the Japanese were unwilling to surrender themselves, it seemed plausible to them that Allied prisoners should be held to the same standard and treated harshly for their dishonourable conduct. Incidents of summary executions and forced labour as well as the infamous Bataan Death March are indicative of such behaviour.

The Japanese soldier displayed great courage and endurance during World War II, covering extreme

▶ **94 Shiki Kenju (Type 94)**

Imperial Guards Division / 4th Konoye Regiment, Muar, Malaya,
January 1942

Firing a weak 8mm (.314in) round, the Type 94 pistol was intended for use by vehicle crews and officers. It was designed for mass production and as a more compact pistol than the earlier Type 14.

Specifications

Country of Origin: Japan	Barrel Length: 96mm (3.78in)
Date: 1934	Muzzle Velocity: 305m/sec (1000ft/sec)
Calibre: 8mm (.314in)	Feed/Magazine: 6-round box magazine
Operation: Not known	Range: Not known
Weight: .688kg (1.52lb)	
Overall Length: 183mm (7.2in)	

distances on foot while carrying a pack of weapons, ammunition, food and personal items that often weighed in excess of 27kg (60lb). Rapid manoeuvre, concealment and ambush were identified as Japanese strengths by the American authors of the *Tactics* report; however, when it seemed that the situation called for desperate measures, the Banzai charge characterized the defence of a Pacific island. Hundreds of Japanese soldiers, sometimes fortified with sake, Japanese rice wine, hurled themselves at entrenched US Marines with utter disregard for personal safety. The results were predictable, but the soldier of Nippon had remained true to his creed.

When war broke out between Japan and the United States, the Imperial Japanese Army numbered 1.7 million men in 51 divisions. As the war progressed, the number of men under arms swelled to 5.5 million.

As fortunes were reversed, great numbers of these troops were isolated on Pacific islands, bypassed in the Allied island-hopping offensive or cut off from resupply on the Asian mainland. In fact, the Japanese lifeline of essential war materiel was choked by interdiction from American submarines, resulting in an erosion of the combat efficiency of the Japanese soldier on all fronts.

Specifications*

Country of Origin: Japan	Barrel Length: 657mm (25.87in)
Date: 1939	Muzzle Velocity: 730m/sec (2394ft/sec)
Calibre: 7.7mm (.303in) Arisaka	Feed/Magazine: N/A
Operation: Bolt action	Range (Grenade): 100m (328ft)
Weight: 3.7kg (8.16lb)	* Of rifle without grenade
Overall Length: 1120mm (44.1in)	

▲ **Type 99 rifle with Type 2 grenade launcher**

1st Independent Anti-Tank Battalion, Bukit Timah, Singapore, February 1942

A grenade launcher was available for both the Type 99 and Type 38 bolt-action rifles. The effective range of the grenade was about 100m (328ft).

▲ **Type 99 rifle**

9th Infantry Brigade, Batu Pahat, Johore, Malaya, January 1942

The Type 99 rifle was developed as a heavier-calibre shoulder arm to replace the Type 38. However, war with the United States prevented full implementation and the two rifles were common during World War II.

Specifications

Country of Origin: Japan	Barrel Length: 657mm (25.87in)
Date: 1939	Muzzle Velocity: 730m/sec (2394ft/sec)
Calibre: 7.7mm (.303in) Arisaka	Feed/Magazine: 5-round internal box magazine,
Operation: Bolt action	stripper-clip-loaded
Weight: 3.7kg (8.16lb)	Range: 500m (1640ft)
Overall Length: 1120mm (44.1in)	

By 1945, Japan had succumbed to the weight of US and Commonwealth arms. However, a handful of individual soldiers, refusing to believe that their country would surrender, held out in the jungles of the Philippines and other locations across the Pacific, abandoning their posts only when former comrades or commanding officers coaxed them into the open in the 1970s.

Japanese small arms

The Imperial Japanese Army fielded two prominent bolt-action rifles during World War II, the Arisaka Type 38 and Type 99. These were identified according to the 38th year of the Meiji period and the year 2099 of the Japanese calendar respectively. Colonel Nariakira Arisaka (1852–1915) headed the commission established to develop modern shoulder

Specifications

Country of Origin: Japan	Overall Length: 966mm (38.03in)
Date: 1911	Barrel Length: 487mm (19.17in)
Calibre: 6.5mm (.256in) Arisaka	Muzzle Velocity: 685m/sec (2246.8ft/sec)
Operation: Bolt action	Feed/Magazine: 5-round internal magazine
Weight: 3.3kg (7.28lb)	Range: 400m (1312ft)

▲ **Type 44**

38th Infantry Division / 38th Engineer Battalion, Guadalcanal, November 1942

A compact version of the Type 38 rifle, this carbine is also referred to as the Type 44 cavalry rifle. It fired an identical cartridge but was equipped with a needle-style bayonet.

Specifications

Country of Origin: Japan	Barrel Length: 589mm (23.2in)
Date: 1941	Muzzle Velocity: 770m/sec (2500ft/sec)
Calibre: 7.7mm (.303in) Arisaka	Feed/Magazine: 30-round metallic feed trays
Operation: Gas operated	Cyclic Rate: 450rpm
Weight: 31.8kg (70.1lb)	Range: 1400m (4593ft)
Overall Length: 1077mm (42.4in)	

▲ **Type 1**

16th Infantry Division, Luzon, Philippines, April 1942

The Type 1 heavy machine gun, a scaled-down version of the Type 92, was introduced in 1941 and became a primary weapon of Japanese infantry units during World War II.

arms for the Japanese military, and both rifles are commonly known as Arisakas. Both were also heavily influenced by the German Mauser design.

The Type 38 fired a 6.5mm (.256in) cartridge, and practical experience in the Sino-Japanese wars of the 1930s indicated the need for a higher-calibre weapon. The Type 99 was intended to replace the Type 38; however, this was never accomplished and both served throughout World War II. More than

3.5 million examples of the Type 99 were built from 1939 to 1945 at nine arsenals, seven of which were located in Japan with one in Mukden, China, and another at Jinsen in Korea.

Fed by a five-round internal box magazine that was loaded from stripper clips, the Type 99 fired a heavier 7.7mm (.303in) cartridge and was notable for its monopod, which was intended to steady the weapon for firing, and an anti-aircraft sight. The

Specifications

Country of Origin: Japan

Date: 1936

Calibre: 6.5mm (.256in) Arisaka

Operation: Gas operated, air cooled

Weight: 9kg (20lb)

Overall Length: 1055mm (41.5in)

Barrel Length: 555mm (21.75in)

Muzzle Velocity: 730m/sec (2300ft/sec)

Feed/Magazine: 30-round box magazine

Cyclic Rate: 450–500rpm

Range: 1000m (3280ft)

▲ **Type 96**

Sixteenth Army, Java, March 1942

Intended to replace the Type 11 light machine gun, the Type 96 was also based on the French Hotchkiss design. The hopper feed of the Type 11 was replaced with a 30-round box magazine.

▲ **Type 97 sniper rifle**

39th Brigade, New Britain, New Guinea, April 1944

An adaptation of the Type 38 infantry rifle, the Type 97 sniper rifle fired the same weak 6.5mm (.256in) round. Its low muzzle flash made detection of concealed snipers difficult.

Specifications

Country of Origin: Japan

Date: 1937

Calibre: 6.5mm (.256in) Arisaka

Operation: Bolt action

Weight: 3.95kg (8.7lb)

Overall Length: 1280mm (50.7in)

Barrel Length: 797mm (31.4in)

Muzzle Velocity: 762.1m/sec (2500ft/sec)

Feed/Magazine: 5-round internal magazine,
 stripper-clip-loaded

Range: 800m (2620ft)

Type 99 was also the first rifle to be equipped with a chrome-lined barrel for easier cleaning. Each weapon was marked on the barrel with the chrysanthemum, identifying the rifle as the property of Emperor Hirohito (1901–89), and many of those that were surrendered by the end of World War II had their emblems defaced in order to preserve the emperor's honour. Contrary to some reports of the poor quality of the Type 99, those built prior to and during the early years of the war were of good quality and performance. Similar to the experience with German rifles, as shortages of materials and the exigencies of war pressed Japanese industrial capacity, quality declined substantially.

▲ Type 100

62nd Infantry Division, Okinawa, April 1945

The only Japanese submachine gun of World War II, the Type 100 was inferior to Western counterparts with a weak 8mm (.314in) round and low rate of fire.

Specifications

Country of Origin: Japan	Barrel Length: 228mm (9in)
Date: 1942	Muzzle Velocity: 335m/sec (1100ft/sec)
Calibre: 8mm (.314in) Nambu	Feed/Magazine: 30-round box magazine
Operation: Blowback	Cyclic Rate: 450rpm (1942); 800rpm (1944)
Weight: 3.83kg (8.44lb)	Range: 70m (230ft)
Overall Length: 890mm (35in)	

▲ Type 92

Thirty-Second Army / 44th Independent Mixed Brigade, Okinawa, April 1945

Differing mainly in its heavier 7.7mm (.303in) cartridge from its predecessor, the Type 3, the Type 92 was nicknamed the Woodpecker by Allied troops.

Specifications

Country of Origin: Japan	Barrel Length: 700mm (27.5in)
Date: 1932	Muzzle Velocity: 715m/sec (2350ft/sec)
Calibre: 7.7mm (.303in)	Feed/Magazine: 30-round metal strip
Operation: Gas operated, air cooled	Cyclic Rate: 450rpm
Weight: 55kg (122lb)	Range: 2000m (6560ft)
Overall Length: 1160mm (45in)	

Therefore, late-war rifles have been noted for inferior performance.

Japanese machine guns

French design heavily influenced the development of Japanese machine guns during the 1920s and 1930s. The air-cooled, gas-operated Type 11 fired a 6.5mm (.256in) cartridge identical to that of the Type 38 rifle from an open hopper magazine that was loaded with five-round clips. Although this arrangement enhanced the rate of fire, the open magazine allowed debris to accumulate in the hopper and receiver, causing frequent jamming.

By 1936, prolific designer Kijiro Nambu (1869–1949) had introduced the Type 96, firing the same cartridge from a 30-round detachable box magazine with a rate of fire of up to 500 rounds per minute. When the jamming problem persisted,

▼ Japanese Machine-Gun Company, 1942

The standard Japanese machine-gun platoon included four Type 92 heavy machine guns firing the 7.7mm (.303in) round, each with a crew of three men. However, in the field it was noted that many of these platoons included only two weapons. Japanese machine-gun companies consisted of three platoons of four guns, totalling 12 weapons, or four platoons of two guns each, totalling eight. The Type 92 machine gun was often transported affixed to its tripod for rapid deployment in combat.

Platoon 1 (2 x Type 92)

Platoon 3 (2 x Type 92)

Platoon 2 (2 x Type 92)

Platoon 4 (2 x Type 92)

▲ Type 97 anti-tank rifle

2nd Mixed Brigade, Iwo Jima, March 1945

Packing a tremendous recoil, the Type 97 anti-tank rifle was inaccurate. It was lightweight and easily transportable, firing a 20mm (.79in) round from a seven-round magazine.

Specifications

Country of Origin: Japan	Barrel Length: 1200mm (47.2in)
Date: 1937	Muzzle Velocity: 750m/sec (2460ft/sec)
Calibre: 20mm (.79in)	Feed/Magazine: 7-round detachable box
Operation: Gas operated	magazine
Weight: 59kg (130lb)	Range: 350m (1148ft) against 30mm (1.18in)
Overall Length: 2060mm (81.1in)	armour; 700m (2296ft) against 20mm (.79in)
	armour

Nambu offered the solution of oiling the rounds; however, this only compounded the issue.

Both the Type 11 and the Type 96, which served throughout World War II, were based on the French air-cooled Hotchkiss of pre-World War I vintage, while the Type 96 incorporated some elements of the Czech ZB vz.26. The top-mounted box magazine of the Type 96 reduced the weight of the weapon, while finned gun barrels eased changing in combat conditions. The Type 96 was also fitted with a bipod and a mounting for a bayonet.

The Type 99 light machine gun was introduced in 1939 and closely resembled the Type 96. The oiling mechanism was removed, and the Type 99 also fired the heavier 7.7mm (.303in) cartridge. It was capable of firing up to 700 rounds per minute, and an airborne version was produced with a detachable stock. Like the Type 96, the Type 99 could take a telescopic sight.

Heavy machine gun

The primary heavy machine gun of the Imperial Japanese Army was the Type 92, again based on a French Hotchkiss modified by Kijiro Nambu. It was recognized by its unique tripod that included extended legs for ease of carry and quick combat deployment. An updated version of the earlier Type 3 that was produced under licence as a copy of the Hotchkiss Model 1914, the Type 92 heavy machine gun was introduced in 1932 and fired the 7.7mm (.303in) cartridge from a 30-round metal strip at up to 450 rounds per minute. The low number of rounds per strip reduced the rate of fire substantially.

Allied soldiers who encountered the Type 92 nicknamed it the Woodpecker due to the distinctive clicking sound of its report. Oiled cartridges created jamming issues for this weapon as well. A smaller and lighter version of the Type 92, the Type 1, was introduced in 1941 and often used as an anti-aircraft weapon. It was tripod-mounted and, like the Type 3, readily identifiable with its prominent cooling rings.

The compact, semiautomatic Type 94 Shiki Kenju pistol was designed by Nambu as a mass production replacement for the larger Type 14. Intended for use by air crews, armoured troops and officers, it fired an 8mm (.314in) cartridge and was fed by a six-round detachable box magazine. More than 70,000 of these pistols were manufactured between 1934 and 1945.

▶ Model 93

Fourteenth Army, Luzon, Philippines, February 1945

The Model 93 flamethrower was used by the Kwantung Army in China but failed to operate efficiently in cold weather. The improved Model 100 entered service in 1940.

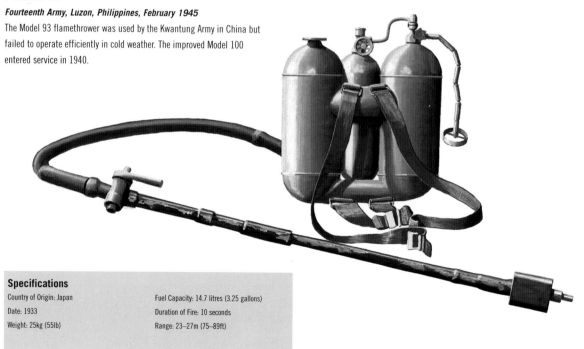

Specifications

Country of Origin: Japan	Fuel Capacity: 14.7 litres (3.25 gallons)
Date: 1933	Duration of Fire: 10 seconds
Weight: 25kg (55lb)	Range: 23–27m (75–89ft)

Allied Forces: Burma and New Guinea
1942–44

Months of difficult jungle fighting taxed the endurance of the Japanese and Allied soldiers in New Guinea and in Burma on the Asian mainland. Along with fighting one another, the soldiers were plagued by disease and torrential rains.

THE FIRST JAPANESE REVERSAL of World War II on land at Guadalcanal was accomplished while Allied troops, primarily Australian and American under the command of General Douglas MacArthur (1880–1964), were fighting the enemy in the jungles and along the unforgiving Kokoda Track on the island of New Guinea. Initially defending Port Moresby at the southeastern tip of the island, the Allies assumed the offensive and executed a series of amphibious landings and overland campaigns that eventually killed thousands of Japanese troops in combat while strangling enemy resupply efforts and leaving survivors to subsist on starvation rations.

Meanwhile, the British Fourteenth Army under Lieutenant-General William Slim (1891–1970) and American and Chinese forces under Lieutenant-General Joseph Stilwell (1883–1946) mounted a resurgent campaign in Burma, denying the Japanese follow-up territorial gains beyond their high-water mark of 1942 and winning victories at Myitkyina, Imphal and Kohima. In the China–Burma–India Theatre, the British Chindits of Brigadier Orde Wingate (1903–44) and the American 5307th Composite Unit, better known as Merrill's Marauders and commanded by Brigadier-General Frank Merrill (1903–55), conducted long-range penetration operations behind Japanese lines, disrupting communications and keeping enemy forces off balance during prolonged jungle fighting across great distances.

Jungle weapons

The rigours of combat in the unforgiving jungles of Burma and New Guinea took their toll on both men and equipment. Heavy rain, searing heat and prolonged periods in the field caused weapons to fail or to be abandoned altogether.

In response to the need for a lighter, shortened version of the Lee-Enfield rifles in widespread use, the No. 5 Jungle Carbine was deployed in 1944 to elements of the British Army. The No. 5 was an adaptation of the shortened Lee-Enfield No. 4 that was originally intended for airborne troops. The No. 5 was 100mm

▲ **Lewis Gun**

9th Australian Division / 15th Australian Infantry Battalion (Queensland), New Guinea campaign, March 1943

The Lewis Gun was pressed into prolonged service during World War II to supplement low Allied inventories of the Bren and other light machine guns. The Lewis was innovative during World War I, employing a gas-operated system.

Specifications

Country of Origin: United States	Barrel Length: 665mm (26.25in)
Date: 1914	Muzzle Velocity: 600m/sec (1970ft/sec)
Calibre: 7.7mm (.303in)	Feed/Magazine: Magazine feed
Operation: Gas operated, air cooled	Cyclic Rate: 550rpm
Weight: 11.8kg (26lb)	Range: 1000m (3280ft)
Overall Length: 965mm (38in)	

ANZAC INFANTRY BATTALION, 1944 (TROPICAL)	
Unit	**Strength**
Battalion HQ	
Regimental Aid Post	1
Headquarters Company	1
Signals Platoon	1
Machine-Gun Platoon	1
Mortar Platoon	1
Pioneer Platoon	1
Administration Platoon	1
Tank-attack Platoon	1
Rifle Companies	4
Rifle Company HQ	
Rifle Platoons	3
Rifle Platoon HQ	
Rifle Sections	3
PIAT (projector, infantry, anti-tank)	1
50mm (2in) mortar	1
Rifle Section	
Bren light machine gun	1
Owen/Austen submachine gun	2
Sniper rifle	1

(3.9in) shorter and a kilogram (2.2lb) lighter than the No. 4, and this was accomplished by drilling out the bolt knob, reducing woodwork and reworking the barrel and receiver. A rubber buttplate and a flash suppressor helped to absorb the substantial recoil from the 7.7mm (.303in) round and to conceal the firer from detection by the enemy.

Although it was capable of a rate of fire of up to 30 rounds per minute, the No. 5 had problems with accuracy. It was plagued by what soldiers termed a 'wandering zero', meaning that the weapon could not be sighted and counted on to fire accurately to the same point at a later time. The No. 5 was fed by a 10-round magazine loaded from five-round charger clips, and more than 300,000 examples of this model were produced between 1944 and 1947.

The venerable Lewis

A relic of World War I, the air-cooled Lewis Gun was gas-operated and fired the 7.7mm (.303in) British cartridge from a top-mounted drum magazine of 47 or 97 rounds at a rate of up to 600 rounds per minute. Although the original design was American, it was perfected by the British and produced from 1913 to 1953. While the British Army had begun replacing the Lewis Gun with the updated Bren, many examples of the older model were still in service during the early months of the Pacific War. Early shortages of machine guns resulted in the reissuing of nearly 60,000 surplus Lewis Guns to regular army units and the British Home Guard, while a large number were also supplied to Britain by the United States through the Lend-Lease programme.

Individual automatic weapons were relatively scarce during the jungle war, and the innovative Charlton Automatic Rifle designed by New Zealand

Specifications

Country of Origin: New Zealand	Overall Length: 1150mm (44.5in)
Date: 1941	Barrel Length: Not known
Calibre: 7.7mm (.303in)	Muzzle Velocity: 744m/sec (2440ft/sec)
Operation: Gas operated	Feed/Magazine: 10- or 30-round magazine
Weight: 7.3kg (16lb)	Range: 910m (2985ft)

▲ **Charlton Automatic Rifle**

3rd New Zealand Division / Vella Lavella, Solomon Islands, September 1943

The Charlton Automatic Rifle was intended to supplement the Allied light machine guns in service in the Pacific War. The weapon was an adapted version of older Lee-Enfield and Lee-Metford rifles.

▲ ANZAC invasion

Operating with USMC support, infantry from the 3rd New Zealand Division land on the island of Vella Lavella in the Solomon Islands, September 1943. Most are armed with SMLE rifles, while their landing craft are fitted with Lewis machine guns.

inventor Philip Charlton (1902–78) was a semiautomatic version of the Lee-Enfield and Lee-Metford rifles to supplement the meagre supply of Bren and Lewis light machine guns. Most of the rifles converted by Charlton were early models that dated from the turn of the twentieth century. Firing the 7.7mm (.303in) cartridge, the Charlton was fed by a 10-round magazine or larger 30-round magazine that also worked with the Bren Gun. Two versions of the Charlton were manufactured. The New Zealand version included a bipod and forward pistol grip. The Australian version was lighter and did not incorporate either of these features.

The Austen submachine gun was an Australian adaptation of the British Sten. Firing the 9mm

(.35in) cartridge, the Austen entered service with Australian forces in 1942, and slightly fewer than 20,000 were produced by the end of World War II. The blowback-operated weapon was capable of firing up to 500 rounds per minute from a 28-round side-mounted box magazine that was compatible with the Sten Gun. The Austen, however, never achieved the popularity among Australian soldiers of another model, the 9mm (.35in) Owen, which was fed by a 33-round top-mounted box magazine. The Owen was considered a more reliable weapon, and more than 50,000 were manufactured from 1941 to 1945. Designed by inventor Evelyn Ernest Owen (1915–49), the blowback-operated Owen was the only weapon of its type developed in Australia and used in World War II. It reached service with the Australian Army in 1943 and fired the 9mm (.35in) Parabellum cartridge fed by a 32-round detachable magazine. About 50,000 Owen submachine guns were produced during World War II, and while a few reached Australian troops in the desert, the majority of were supplied to troops fighting the Japanese in the jungles of the Southwest Pacific.

▲ **Austen**

Australian First Army / 4th Division, Lae, New Guinea, 1944

The Austen was an Australian adaptation of the British Sten Gun with a foregrip. An improved model, the M2, and a suppressed variant were introduced later. Its manufacturing process included several diecasting steps.

Specifications

Country of Origin: Australia	Barrel Length: 196mm (7.75in)
Date: 1942	Muzzle Velocity: 380m/sec (1246ft/sec)
Calibre: 9mm (.35in) Parabellum	Feed/Magazine: 28-round detachable box
Operation: Blowback	magazine
Weight: 3.98kg (8.75lb)	Cyclic Rate: 500rpm
Overall Length: 845mm (33.25in)	Range: 50m (164ft)

Specifications

Country of Origin: Australia	Barrel Length: 247mm (9.75in)
Date: 1941	Muzzle Velocity: 380m/sec (1247ft/sec)
Calibre: 9mm (.35in) Parabellum	Feed/Magazine: 33-round detachable box
Operation: Blowback	magazine
Weight: 4.21kg (9.28lb)	Cyclic Rate: 700rpm
Overall Length: 813mm (32in)	Range: 70m (230ft)

▲ **Owen Machine Carbine**

5th Australian Division, New Britain, April 1945

The Owen Machine Carbine, commonly called the Owen Gun, was developed and manufactured in Australia, reaching frontline troops by early 1943. The majority of the 50,000 Owen Guns manufactured were deployed in the Pacific.

Specifications

Country of Origin: United Kingdom

Date: 1942

Calibre: 9mm (.35in) Parabellum

Operation: Blowback

Weight: 2.95kg (6.5lb)

Overall Length: 762mm (30in)

Barrel Length: 196mm (7.7in)

Muzzle Velocity: 380m/sec (1247ft/sec)

Feed/Magazine: 32-round detachable box
   magazine

Cyclic Rate: 500rpm

Range: 70m (230ft)

▲ Sten Mk II

Australian 7th Division, Battle of Buna-Gona, New Guinea, January 1943

Unsuited to rough conditions, the Sten had a poor reputation among Australian soldiers, due to its tendency to either jam when used in jungle conditions or to fire off uncontrollably.

Specifications

Country of Origin: United Kingdom

Date: 1907

Calibre: 7.7mm (.303in)

Operation: Bolt action

Weight: 3.93kg (8.625lb)

Overall Length: 1133mm (44.6in)

Barrel Length: 640mm (25.2in)

Muzzle Velocity: 634m/sec (2080ft/sec)

Feed/Magazine: 10-round box, loaded with
   5-round charger clips

Range: 500m (1640ft)

▲ Lee-Enfield Rifle No. 1 Mk III SMLE

British Fourteenth Army / 7th Indian Infantry Division, Battle of the Admin Box, Arakan, Burma, February 1944

The Lee-Enfield Mk III became the primary infantry weapon of Commonwealth forces during World War II. The bolt-action rifle was one of a long-serving series of weapons, with specialized variants still active today.

▲ Rifle No. 5 Mk I (Jungle Carbine)

British Fourteenth Army / 2nd Battalion Royal Norfolk Regiment, Mandalay, Burma, December 1944

Known unofficially as the Jungle Carbine, the No. 5 was abandoned in 1947. The 7.7mm (.303in) round gave it a fearsome recoil.

Specifications

Country of Origin: United Kingdom

Date: 1944

Calibre: 7.7mm (.303in) British Service

Operation: Bolt action

Weight: 3.24kg (7.14lb)

Overall Length: 1000mm (39.37in)

Barrel Length: 478mm (18.7in)

Muzzle Velocity: 610m/sec (2000ft/sec)

Feed/Magazine: 10-round detachable box
   magazine

Range: 1000m (3280ft)

US Forces: Island Hopping
1942–45

The US Marine Corps bore the brunt of the brutal fighting that characterized the war in the Central Pacific. Amphibious landings on hotly contested beaches resulted in heavy casualties.

A S DOZENS OF LANDING CRAFT carrying troops of the US 2nd Marine Division churned towards the beaches of Tarawa Atoll in the Gilbert Islands on 20 November 1943, many of them encountered an unforeseen obstacle – a lengthy coral reef that only the few tracked landing craft available could traverse. The Marines in flat-bottom landing craft were forced to disembark and wade up to 500m (546 yards) to the beaches, all the while enduring heavy Japanese machine-gun and rifle fire.

Despite the early difficulties and the prospect that a Japanese counterattack might push the Marines into the sea, Tarawa was declared secure after 76 hours of heavy fighting. The Marines and elements of the US Army's 27th Division blasted the Japanese out of concrete bunkers, reinforced pillboxes and other strongpoints, taking only a handful of prisoners.

Tarawa was the first of a series of amphibious landings across the Central Pacific that were undertaken simultaneously with the Allied thrust northwards from Australia to New Guinea and the Philippines. Marine planners learned significant lessons from the Tarawa operation, in which more than 1000 Marines were killed and 2100 wounded.

▲ **Jungle firepower**
Surrounded by thick jungle foliage, US Marines man a Browning M1917A1 heavy machine gun as the Japanese mount a counterattack against the American advance on Cape Gloucester on the island of New Britain, January 1944.

More accurate reconnaissance of invasion beaches could avoid problems such as those encountered at the reef, while more tracked landing craft would be needed for future operations. Aerial and naval bombardment that had been counted on to soften up the Japanese defences had been proved largely ineffective, and adjustments were made to achieve plunging fire against enemy concrete emplacements.

The island road

Despite the tactical adjustments made following the capture of Tarawa, the Marines' trek towards Tokyo was fiercely contested island by island. When Marines of the 3rd, 4th and 5th Divisions landed on Iwo Jima in February 1945, they encountered a labyrinth of Japanese bunkers and reinforced gun emplacements, each of which was either reduced with direct fire or satchel explosives or sealed with its occupants inside. The interlocking fields of fire of Japanese machine guns and continuing artillery and mortar fire caused heavy casualties among the Marines, eventually killing more than 6800 and wounding over 19,000.

On 23 February 1945, four days into the assault on Iwo Jima, a Marine patrol reached the summit of 170m (556ft) Mount Suribachi and planted the US

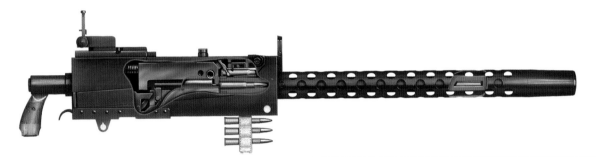

▲ Browning M1919A4

USMC / 1st Tank Battalion, Guadalcanal, September 1942

The Browning M1919A4 machine gun provided effective infantry fire support and was light enough for rapid displacement under combat conditions. It was an adaptation of the Browning Model 1917.

Specifications

Country of Origin: United States	Barrel Length: 610mm (24in)
Date: 1936	Muzzle Velocity: 853m/sec (2800ft/sec)
Calibre: 7.62mm (.3in) Browning	Feed/Magazine: 250-round belt
Operation: Recoil, air cooled	Cyclic Rate: 400–600rpm
Weight: 14kg (31lb)	Range: 2000m (6560ft) +
Overall Length: 1041mm (41in)	

Specifications

Country of Origin: United States	Barrel Length: 266mm (10.5in)
Date: 1941	Muzzle Velocity: 280m/sec (920ft/sec)
Calibre: 11.4mm (.45in) M1911	Feed/Magazine: 12- or 25-round box magazine
Operation: Delayed blowback	Cyclic Rate: 500rpm
Weight: 2.89kg (6.37lb)	Range: 120m (394ft)
Overall Length: 787mm (31in)	

▲ Reising Model 55

USMC / 1st Marine Division / 1st Parachute Battalion, Battle of Edson's Ridge, Guadalcanal, September 1942

.A compact, lightweight semiautomatic carbine that has sometimes been described as a submachine gun, the Reising Model 55 was developed in 1940 and produced until the end of World War II. It entered service to supplement the supply of Thompson submachine guns and was manufactured with a folding stock.

flag atop the extinct volcano, creating the most famous photographic image of the Pacific War. Still, more than a month of bitter combat lay ahead. One area of strong resistance came to be known as the Meat Grinder. Individual Japanese soldiers dug spider holes and popped up to fire on advancing Marines. Fanatical groups of enemy soldiers flung themselves at American lines and died by the score.

The heavy losses sustained at Iwo Jima and the prolonged, costly invasion of Okinawa, a scant 547km (340 miles) from the mainland of Japan, during which more than 12,000 Americans died and 39,000 were wounded, influenced the decision by President Harry Truman (1884–1972) to drop atomic bombs on the Japanese cities of Hiroshima

and Nagasaki. The end of the war came quickly, with Japan formally surrendering in early September 1945, and an invasion of the Japanese home islands that would have cost both sides horrendous casualties was avoided. The decisive factor in the Allied victory in the Pacific, however, was not the atomic bomb. It was the perseverance of Allied fighting men and the capabilities of the small arms they carried.

Forward firepower

A major contributing factor to the inexorable advance of the US Marines across the Central Pacific was the quality of their small arms. The M1 Garand was arguably the finest standard issue rifle of the war for a simple reason. While its contemporaries in other

▲ M1 Garand

USMC / 1st Marine Regiment, Guadalcanal, October 1942

The semiautomatic M1 Garand rifle gave US Marines a combat advantage with sustained-fire capability. Often Japanese formations were unable to hold their positions with bolt-action rifles that laid down a much slower rate of fire.

Specifications

Country of Origin: United States	Overall Length: 1103mm (43.5in)
Date: 1936	Barrel Length: 610mm (24in)
Calibre: 7.62mm (.3in) US .30-06	Muzzle Velocity: 853m/sec (2800ft/sec)
Operation: Gas operated	Feed/Magazine: 8-round internal box magazine
Weight: 4.37kg (9.5lb)	Range: 500m (1640ft) +

▲ M1 carbine

USMC / 3rd Division, Guam, August 1944

The M1 carbine proved to be a handy, compact weapon for operations in the jungle, although some soldiers complained of its lack of stopping power in protracted operations where heavy fire needed to be brought to bear on fixed or defended positions.

Specifications

Country of Origin: United States	Barrel Length: 457mm (18in)
Date: 1942	Muzzle Velocity: 595m/sec (1950ft/sec)
Calibre: 7.62mm (.3in) Carbine	Feed/Magazine: 15- or 30-round detachable box
Operation: Gas operated	magazine
Weight: 2.5kg (5.47lb)	Range: c.300m (984ft)
Overall Length: 905mm (35.7in)	

Allied and Axis armies were bolt-action weapons, the gas-operated, rotating-bolt M1 was semiautomatic, feeding 7.62mm (.3in) cartridges to the firing chamber from an eight-round en-bloc clip and allowing the American soldier and Marine to produce a rate of fire of up to 50 accurate shots per minute at a range of some 300m (984ft).

The sustained fire of the M1 at the squad level proved potent in close-quarter fighting, sometimes overwhelming Japanese troops armed with the bolt-action Type 38 or Type 99 Arisaka rifles. The penetration of the .30-06 Springfield rifle round also provided plenty of stopping power. In contrast to the success of their massed Banzai charges while fighting against the Chinese in the 1930s, the Japanese encountered a much more formidable wall of fire from the US Marine shouldering the M1 Garand. The rifle was actually in production from 1936 to 1963, and approximately 6.5 million were manufactured during the period. The M1 was the first semiautomatic rifle to become standard issue in any army.

THE 'E' SERIES MARINE BATTALION, *CIRCA* 1943–44		
Unit	Officers	Men
Headquarters Company	12	125
Battalion Headquarters Section	9	22
US Navy Medical Detachment	2	32
Intelligence Section		12
Supply Section		6
Communications Platoon	1	39
Company Headquarters		14
Weapons Company	8	220
Company Headquarters	3	38
Mortar Platoon	2	56
Three Machine-Gun Platoons, each	1	42
Three Rifle Companies, each	6	190
Company HQ	2	26
Weapons Platoon		
Platoon HQ	1	3
Mortar Section		16
Machine-Gun Section		19
Three Rifle Platoons, each		
Platoon HQ	1	6
Three Rifle Squads, each		12
Total Strength of 953 all ranks	38	915

US Marine Rifle Squad, May 1944

The standard rifle squad of the US Marine Corps in 1944 was a potent self-contained unit with 13 riflemen. Organized in three fire teams, the sub-units included one man armed with the semiautomatic Browning Automatic Rifle (BAR), while three carried the semiautomatic M1 Garand rifle. The squad leader was often issued the M1 carbine, while at times he might be equipped with a Thompson or M3A1 submachine gun. Infantry support machine guns were regularly deployed from the battalion level for additional fire support.

Squad Leader (1 x M1 carbine)

Fire Team 1 (3 x M1 Garand, 1 x BAR) Fire Team 2 **Fire Team 3**

The M1 carbine was a versatile semiautomatic rifle issued to lighter troops such as airborne units and the crews of vehicles and tanks, and some officers. Firing a 7.62mm (.3in) carbine round, it actually shared only one common part, a buttplate screw, with the M1 Garand rifle. The M1 carbine was also intended to give rear-echelon troops a heavier weapon than the standard issue pistols of the World War II period.

Designed by a trio of US Army engineers, the M1 carbine entered service in the summer of 1942 and was in common circulation until the 1970s. It was fed by a 15- or 30-round box magazine, and the selective fire, fully automatic M2 variant was capable of firing up to 900 rounds per minute. While the weapon was praised for its light weight and handy size, its firepower came into question when in the hands of frontline troops who reported that it sometimes failed to knock down an approaching enemy soldier. In fairness, the M1 carbine was not originally intended as a frontline weapon, although it found its way to the front on many occasions and was extensively utilized throughout the Korean and Vietnam conflicts.

Semiautomatic firepower at the Marine fire-team level was regularly supplied by the World War I-vintage Browning Automatic Rifle (BAR) and the Thompson submachine gun. Later in the war, the M3 and M3A1 submachine guns – light, mass-produced 11.4mm (.45in) weapons – began to appear. Nicknamed the Grease Gun, the M3 and M3A1 entered service in 1944 and never fully replaced the earlier weapons.

Browning MGs

Two strongly performing machine guns that helped turn the tide of the Pacific War were the Browning Model 1919A4 and the Browning M2HB. These weapons and similar contemporary models were responsible in large part for holding the line against Japanese pressure at Guadalcanal and then decimating furious Banzai charges to break the back of enemy resistance during later operations on islands such as Saipan and Iwo Jima.

The M1919A4 was in widespread use with US (and NATO) military organizations for more than half a century. During World War II, its versatility as an infantry, anti-aircraft and aircraft-mounted machine gun was noted. The weapon was an improvement to the earlier Model 1917 design by John Browning and was produced until the end of World War II in 1945. This short-recoil machine gun was capable of firing up to 600 rounds of 7.62mm (.3in) ammunition per minute and was fed by a 250-round belt.

Although it could be operated by as few as two men, an optimal M1919A4 crew comprised four: a gunner, an assistant gunner and a pair of ammunition carriers. Present at the platoon level, the machine gun gave company commanders the option to deploy heavier firepower at a lower tactical level more

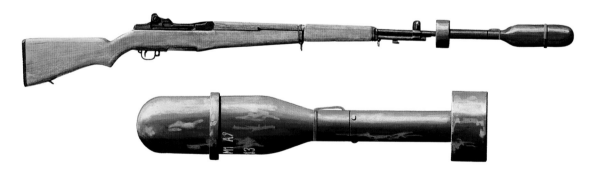

▲ **M1 Garand with M11A2 rifle grenade**

US Army / 40th Infantry Division, New Britain, June 1944

A potent rifle-grenade-launcher model of the M1 Garand was available during World War II. While few variants of the standard infantry rifle other than the sniper version saw action, this was an exception.

Specifications*

Country of Origin: United States	Barrel Length: 610mm (24in)
Date: 1936	Muzzle Velocity: 853m/sec (2800ft/sec)
Calibre: 7.62mm (.3in) US .30-06	Feed/Magazine: N/A
Operation: Gas operated	Range (Grenade): 100m (328ft)
Weight: 4.37kg (9.5lb)	* Of rifle without grenade
Overall Length: 1103mm (43.5in)	

rapidly. The M1919A4 was air-cooled. It was mounted on a tripod and weighed a relatively light 14kg (31lb), allowing the gun to fulfil its combat mission of heavier sustained fire support combined with light weight and ease of movement.

The M2HB machine gun was a heavy 12.7mm (.5in) weapon, and since it entered production in 1921 more than three million have been produced. The weapon has undergone a series of modifications

through the years and remains a standard heavy machine gun of NATO armed forces today. The original M2 design included a water-cooling jacket; however, a subsequent variant eliminated the water-cooling system for an air-cooled configuration. This caused the barrel to overheat rapidly during prolonged firing and generated the need for a thicker barrel. This resulted in the HB, or heavy barrel, designation, introduced in 1933.

▲ Thompson 1928

USMC / 1st Marine Regiment / 2nd Battalion, Okinawa, May 1945

The first Thompson submachine gun widely adopted for military service, the 1928 differed little from the earlier 1921, although it employed a simplified delayed-blowback operation.

Specifications

Country of Origin: United States	Barrel Length: 266mm (10.5in)
Date: 1928	Muzzle Velocity: 280m/sec (920ft/sec)
Calibre: 11.4mm (.45in) M1911	Feed/Magazine: 18-, 20-, 30-round detachable
Operation: Delayed blowback	box magazine
Weight: 4.88kg (10.75lb)	Cyclic Rate: 700rpm
Overall Length: 857mm (33.75in)	Range: 120m (394ft)

▲ M3A1 'Grease Gun'

US Army / 37th Infantry Division, Battle for Manila, February 1945

The M3A1 'Grease Gun', an improved version of the M3, did not enter service in large numbers before the end of World War II. The M3A1's removable stock was equipped with a built-in magazine-loading tool.

Specifications

Country of Origin: United States	Barrel Length: 203mm (8in)
Date: 1944	Muzzle Velocity: 280m/sec (920ft/sec)
Calibre: 11.4mm (.45in) .45 ACP	Feed/Magazine: 30-round detachable box
Operation: Blowback	magazine
Weight: 3.61kg (7.95lb)	Cyclic Rate: 450rpm
Overall Length: 745mm (29.33in)	Range: 90m (295ft)

During World War II the belt-fed M2HB was capable of a cyclic rate of fire of up to 575 rounds per minute and could fire a range of ammunition types. As an infantry support weapon, it was either fired from a tripod or mounted on trucks, halftracks and tanks. It proved extremely effective against enemy troop concentrations, and its heavy round was capable of penetrating light armoured vehicles as well as shooting down low-flying enemy aircraft.

Many heavy weapons battalions of the US Army and formations of the US Marine Corps were issued at least one Browning M2HB. While the weapon was superior to any machine gun fielded by the Japanese, it was not in widespread use in the Pacific due to the difficulties inherent in jungle fighting and the weight of the weapon at roughly 58kg (128lb) including the tripod. Even so, it was sometimes deployed in a static, defensive role.

Fire breather

Island fighting was a nasty business, and often the only method of clearing Japanese soldiers from honeycombed caverns and bunkers was with the flamethrower. It was a fearsome weapon, and the US Marines became particularly adept with it on Iwo Jima. The M2-2 portable flamethrower was introduced by the United States military in 1943 as an improvement to the M1 and M1A1 designs of earlier in the war. It was recognized by its three tanks (two of gasoline fuel and one of nitrogen propellant),

▲ **Semiautomatic**

Armed with an M1 carbine, a US Marine awaits the signal to move out in the battle to recapture Guam from the Japanese, July 1944.

prominent nozzle, and dual handgrips. The M2-2 could spout roughly 2.27 litres (4 pints) of flame per second to an effective distance of 20m (65.5ft) with a burn time of about 47 seconds.

▲ **M1918A2 Browning Automatic Rifle (BAR)**

USMC / 3rd Division / 24th Regiment, Iwo Jima, March 1945

The Browning Automatic Rifle provided semiautomatic fire support to the lowest operational unit of the Marine infantry, the fire team. Although it was a heavy item and its bipod was of questionable value, the BAR was a primary infantry weapon throughout World War II.

Specifications

Country of Origin: United States	Barrel Length: 610mm (24in)
Date: 1938	Muzzle Velocity: 860m/sec (2822ft/sec)
Calibre: 7.62mm (.3in)	Feed/Magazine: 20-round straight box magazine
Operation: Gas operated, tilting breech block	Cyclic Rate: 500–650rpm
Weight: 8.8kg (19lb)	Range: 1000–1500m (3280–4921ft)
Overall Length: 1215mm (47.8in)	

Although it was an effective weapon, particularly at close range, and could kill by burning and by consuming available oxygen in an enclosed space, it was hazardous for a single soldier to operate since enemy troops targeted those with the packs visible.

The advent of the flamethrowing tank rendered the portable flamethrower functionally obsolescent, although some of these devices were deployed during the Korean and Vietnam Wars.

▲ Browning M2HB

US Army / 11th Airborne Division 'Angels' / 152nd Airborne Antiaircraft Battalion, Leyte, December 1944

The Browning M2HB heavy machine gun was devastating against Japanese personnel and light vehicles. Due to its weight, the weapon was often deployed in a defensive role in the Pacific.

Specifications

Country of Origin: United States	Barrel Length: 1143mm (45in)
Date: 1933	Muzzle Velocity: 898m/sec (2950ft/sec)
Calibre: 12.7mm (.5in)	Feed/Magazine: 110-round belt
Operation: Short recoil, air cooled	Cyclic Rate: 450–575rpm
Weight: 38.5kg (84lb)	Range: 1800m (5905ft) effective
Overall Length: 1655mm (65in)	

◀ M2-2

USMC / 3rd Division / 21st Regiment, Iwo Jima, March 1945

The flamethrower was a feared weapon that was quite effective against Japanese strongpoints and soldiers sequestered in caves. However, its range was limited and Marines that operated it accepted especially hazardous duty.

Specifications

Country of Origin: United States	Fuel Capacity: 18.2 litres (4 gallons)
Date: 1943	Duration of Fire: 8–9 seconds
Weight: 30.8kg (68lb) filled	Range: 20–40m (65.5–132ft)

Volume Two:
1945–Present

Introduction

The invention of firearms placed long-range killing power in the hands of anyone with access to a weapon. Maximum effectiveness is difficult to achieve, however, and requires good tactics as well as marksmanship.

THE TERM 'SMALL ARMS' was coined long ago to describe firearms that could be carried by a single person, i.e., gunpowder weapons lighter than artillery. Over the years, distinct types of small arms began to appear, each optimized to a particular role. The line between artillery and small arms was blurred when firearms heavy enough to be classed as support weapons began to appear. Light enough to move with infantry but more potent than standard personal weapons, battlefield support weapons greatly increased the firepower of an infantry force.

The invention of personal automatic weapons was another profound leap forward. Where previously, group action was necessary to provide intense firepower, now a single individual could target multiple opponents or deliver suppressing fire into an area. The increasing frequency of urban combat

during World War II was another influence on the development of small arms and infantry support weapons. Whereas previously most engagements were at relatively long ranges of several hundred metres, which required accurate aimed rifle fire, urban battles were characterised by vicious short-range firefights. German troops armed with bolt-action rifles found themselves outgunned in such engagements by Red Army soldiers armed with submachine guns. Swapping rifles for submachine guns would have been an effective counter for urban combat, but in longer-

▼ **Sniper team**
Snipers from the US 82nd Airborne Division provide security from a rooftop for Afghan forces in Dey Yak, Afghanistan, 2007. The sniper on the right is armed with a Mk.14 Mod EBR, an updated version of the M14. His companion is armed with an M40A1 fitted with an AN/PVS-10 day-and-night vision sniper scope.

range engagements the rifle was still the weapon of choice. The answer was an intermediate weapon, smaller, lighter and faster firing than the traditional battle rifle, but still retaining good accuracy out to a respectable range, and reasonable penetrating power. Thus was born the assault rifle, and with it came a change in emphasis from groups of riflemen trained to a high standard of marksmanship towards smaller units capable of delivering intense firepower within their local vicinity.

A group of militia or gunmen will normally fight as individuals with whatever weapons they can get, but formal military forces are organised in a way that optimises the effectiveness of their weapons. Various approaches have been tried in order to obtain maximum combat effectiveness, and the success of one does not necessarily mean another is wrong.

Typically, an infantry squad consists mainly of riflemen armed with a basic personal weapon; usually an assault rifle. The squad will normally contain a support weapon of some kind. This may be a general-purpose machinegun (GPMG) or a lighter squad support weapon. GPMGs tend to be chambered for battle rifle calibres; their ammunition is not compatible with the lighter cartridges used in assault weapons. However, GPMGs are powerful and offer good sustained firepower, out to ranges that lighter weapons cannot effectively reach.

Squad (or light) support weapons are sometimes little more than a variant of the standard infantry rifle, which has the advantage that magazines can be shared and any soldier can take over the support weapon. Mobility is better, too, since the weapon is lighter. However, a light support weapon does not have the hitting power or the sustained firepower of a GPMG.

Other weapons are generally used for supporting purposes. Handguns are carried as sidearms, shotguns are primarily used for security (and sometimes counter-ambush) applications, and an infantry force may be supported by grenade launchers and/or personnel armed with extremely accurate and often high-powered precision rifles.

Other approaches have been used, and successfully. For example, Chinese forces in the Korean conflict made extensive use of massed submachine guns in the assault role, while the British Army long considered marksmanship with a semi-automatic rifle more effective than automatic suppressive fire.

In the final analysis, although the capabilities of a weapon are important, what really matters is the user. Good tactics and skilled marksmanship can overcome the limitations of a mediocre weapon system, while a truly great weapon cannot make a rabble fight any better. It is when training, tactics and fighting spirit are combined with an effective weapon that great things are achieved.

▶ **Girl soldiers**

Armed with M1 carbines, female volunteers of the People's Self-Defense Force of the village of Kien Dien north of Saigon, patrol the hamlet's perimeter to discourage Viet Cong infiltration, 1967. More than 6.5 million M1 carbines of various models were manufactured, and the weapon was used widely during World War II, the Korean War, the Indochina war, Algerian War and Vietnam War.

Chapter 7

Korean War, 1950–53

At the end of World War II, Korea was
partitioned along an arbitrary line based on the positions of
Western and Soviet forces operating against the Japanese in
the region. These areas grew into very different nations and,
in 1950, Communist North Korea invaded South Korea. This
invasion drew in forces from many nations, but notably the
United States, to defend South Korea. International forces
pushed deep into North Korea before Chinese intervention
brought the conflict to a stalemate. The war was fought
for the most part with World War II-era tactics
and weapons, which were available to both
sides in huge numbers.

◀ **Taking a breather**
A soldier from the US 32nd Regimental Combat Team, 7th Infantry Division, rests following the capture of
a Chinese bunker along the slope of Hill 902 north of Ip-Tong. He is armed with an M1 carbine. Next to
him lies an abandoned Soviet-made DP light machine gun.

Introduction

After World War II ended, there was a feeling in some quarters that large conventional forces had become obsolete. Any future major conflict would surely involve a nuclear exchange, which might make war unthinkable.

HOWEVER, AT THE SAME TIME the divisions between the Communist East and the democratic West were deepening, leading to the armed standoff of the Cold War. The Korean conflict of 1950–53 was the first major armed clash of the new, post-war world. Like many later conflicts, each side was backed by East or West, turning the whole conflict into a proxy war between democracy and communism.

The war proceeded through fairly distinct phases, and was greatly influenced by external factors. Initially the North Korean forces were vastly superior to their South Korean opponents, who in particular lacked the ability to stop armoured assaults by Russian-supplied T34 tanks. These were the same excellent vehicles that defeated the Panzer divisions of the *Wehrmacht* a few years previously, and although Western tank design had advanced sufficiently that they might not be effective against European/US forces, the T34 was entirely capable of overrunning anything South Korea could put in its path.

International response

As North Korean forces advanced rapidly southwards, an international response began. Led by American forces redeployed from Japan, troops from

▲ **Machine-gun squad**
A machine-gun squad armed with a Browning M1919A6 from the US 2nd Infantry Division keeps watch north of the Chongchon River, 1952.

▲ **Firefight**
Soldiers from the 3rd Battalion, Royal Australian Regiment, armed with SMLE No. III rifles exchange fire with North Korean forces, 1951.

many nations began landing in South Korea to help defend the unoccupied portions of the country. This intervention was sanctioned by the United Nations (UN), and ultimately resulted in what amounted to a war between the UN and North Korea plus North Korea's Communist backers.

The international response was just in time to prevent the complete conquest of South Korea, but for a period the UN forces struggled to hold a relatively small perimeter around the port of Pusan in the south of the country. A counter-offensive was needed, but a conventional attack would be costly. At this point, recent US experience of amphibious warfare in the Pacific theatre came to the fore.

The deadlock was broken by an ambitious amphibious operation and simultaneous land offensive. Amphibious forces landed at Inchon, close to the South Korean capital of Seoul. Taking the capital cut the supply lines to North Korean forces

fighting in the south of the country, and greatly assisted the breakout from the Pusan perimeter.

Push north

With their supply lines cut, the North Korean forces in the south collapsed quickly, and UN troops were able to push into North Korea almost as far as the Yalu River. Chinese intervention at this point brought tens of thousands of troops into the fight on the Northern side, driving the UN back down the country. A defensive line was established at the 38th Parallel, more or less where the original demarcation line had been, and from 1951–53 the conflict took on the character of World War I static warfare.

After months of artillery bombardment and savage fighting over fortified positions, little had been achieved by either side and a ceasefire came into effect in July 1953. Tensions still run high between North and South Korea, however.

North Korean forces
1950–53

North Korea had prepared for war, and could deploy forces that were both better equipped and more experienced than their opponents.

THE FORCES OF NORTH KOREA could draw upon large numbers of personnel who had fought in World War II alongside Soviet troops. Others had participated in the recent Chinese Civil War. Although the North Korean People's Army (NKPA) was by no means composed entirely of such veterans, it was, overall, an experienced and confident force. It was also highly politicized, with Communist fervour being especially prevalent among those who had fought alongside Mao Zedong in China.

The NKPA had around 150 T34 tanks of Soviet origin. Although North Korean crews were perhaps not up to the standard of their Soviet or European counterparts, this armoured force was a formidable one in any theatre of war, and especially so against an opponent who lacked the weapons and training to counter an armoured assault. The armoured force, along with the rest of the army, had received training from Soviet advisors since the end of World War II in 1945 and had a good grasp of how to make use of its mobility and firepower.

The majority of the North Korean forces were arrayed as eight full-strength infantry divisions, each of which was supported by 122mm (4.8in) towed artillery pieces and 76mm (3in) self-propelled guns. Additional forces included two half-strength divisions and a motorcycle reconnaissance formation. Other formations were held back in reserve or deployed for rear-area security.

Invasion tactics

The withdrawal of US troops from the Korean peninsula in July 1949 created an opportunity for North Korea to invade. A period of increasing tension ensued, with raids launched across the border, before the NKPA finally launched its offensive in June 1950. The attack came as a complete surprise to the UN troops, catching many units understrength due to troops being on leave. Korea's mountainous terrain funnelled the invasion into predictable routes, but with the South Korean forces caught by surprise there was no real opportunity to exploit this advantage. The main thrust was directed down the west coast, needing to cover a fairly short distance to reach Seoul. Offensives were also launched in the central mountains and along the west coast.

The North Korean armoured brigade was used as a spearhead for assaults as resistance developed. The

◀ **Nambu Pistol Model 14**

North Korean People's Army / 109th Armoured Regiment, 1950

The Japanese Nambu pistol was a poor, unreliable weapon firing a weak cartridge. Its weaknesses were not much of a liability, however, since handguns were more status symbols and discipline tools than combat weapons.

Specifications

Country of Origin: Japan	Overall Length: 227mm (8.93in)
Date: 1906	Barrel Length: 121mm (4.76in)
Calibre: 8mm (.314in) Nambu	Muzzle Velocity: 335m/sec (1100ft/sec)
Operation: Short recoil	Feed/Magazine: 8-round detachable box
Weight: .9kg (1.98lb)	magazine
	Range: 30m (98ft)

tactics were simple but effective: a tank force would punch through the enemy position and rally at a safe distance on the far side. An unsupported attack of this sort might bring about disaster against an enemy that possessed good anti-armour weapons, but the South Koreans did not. Their positions were thrown into chaos by the armoured attack, then units were prevented from retreating by the tanks' presence in their rear.

Exploiting chaos

Meanwhile, NKPA infantry forces attacked the disorganized positions from the front and passed around the flanks, crushing resistance with an attack from all sides. The demoralized South Korean army could do little to prevent defeat in these circumstances, and it was not until international forces arrived with the training and equipment to stop the T34s that the situation was stabilized.

Chinese Infantry Section

The idea of the three-cell infantry section (i.e. a small combat unit made up of three sub-units capable of functioning semi-independently) seems to have arisen in China in the 1930s. The weapons available to the People's Volunteer Army (the name given to Chinese forces operating in Korea) were not uniform, though there was a distinct move towards entire battalions armed with versions of the Soviet PPSh-41 submachine gun. A theoretical Chinese infantry section consisted of three 'cells' or squads, each of three men, all armed with PPSh-41 or Chinese copies. The section was commanded by an NCO who was armed the same as his men. Sometimes a four-man machine-gun team was added to a section, but this depended upon the availability of support weapons.

Cell 1

Cell 2

Cell 3

▲ **Type 56 (SKS) rifle**

North Korean People's Army / 12th Division, 1951

The SKS was one of the first weapons chambered for the 7.62x39mm M43 round later used in the AK-47 and RPD.

Specifications

Country of Origin: China/USSR	Overall Length:1021mm (40.2in)
Date: 1945	Barrel Length: 521mm (20.5in)
Calibre: 7.62mm (.3in)	Muzzle Velocity: 735m/sec (2411ft/sec)
Operation: Gas short-stroke piston	Feed/Magazine: 10-round integral box magazine
Weight: 3.85kg (8.49lb)	Range: 400m (1312ft)

Although the North Korean armoured brigade represented the most potent force in the NKPA arsenal, the offensive's success owed much to the fighting power of its infantry forces. These were primarily equipped with weapons of Soviet origin. Mosin-Nagant bolt-action rifles and more modern SVT-40 semi-automatic rifles were common infantry weapons, along with a version of the Soviet SKS carbine, the Chinese designated Type 56. The SKS used a lighter 7.62x39mm round, rather than 7.62x54mm of the Mosin-Nagant and SVT-40 battle rifles.

North Korean troops also made good use of the Soviet PPSh-41 submachine gun, which delivered high firepower along with great reliability. Its accuracy and effective range were somewhat better than those of the typical submachine gun, so North Korean troops were not significantly disadvantaged in more open terrain.

Other equipment came from a variety of sources, including weapons left behind by the Japanese, who had occupied Korea for several decades. Most support weapons were of Russian origin, but some equipment did come from China. However, China had only recently been unified at the end of the Chinese Civil War, and its arms industry was just beginning to develop. Many Chinese weapons of the time were copies of Soviet equipment.

Specifications

Country of Origin: USSR

Date: 1941

Calibre: 7.62mm (.3in) Soviet

Operation: Blowback

Weight: 3.64kg (8lb)

Overall Length: 838mm (33in)

Barrel Length: 266mm (10.5in)

Muzzle Velocity: 490m/sec (1600ft/sec)

Feed/Magazine: 35-round box magazine or
  71-round drum magazine

Range: 120m (394ft)

▲ PPSh-41

North Korean People's Army / 7th Division, 1952

Soviet-supplied PPSh-41 submachine guns were used in Korea under their own name, and alongside license-built versions such as the Chinese Type 50 and North Korean Type 49.

Specifications

Country of Origin: USSR

Date: 1940

Calibre: 7.62mm (.3in)

Operation: Gas

Weight: 3.9kg (8.6lb)

Overall Length: 1226mm (48.27in)

Barrel Length: 610mm (25in)

Muzzle Velocity: 840m/sec (2755ft/sec)

Feed/Magazine: 10-round detachable box
  magazine

Range: 500m (1640ft) +

▲ Tokarev SVT-40

North Korean People's Army / 6th Division, 1951

The SVT-40 used the same 7.62x54mm ammunition as the proven Mosin-Nagant rifle, and its 10-round internal magazine could even be loaded using the same 10-round stripper clips. It was an effective combat weapon, though eclipsed by the new first-generation assault rifles then emerging.

Specifications

Country of Origin: USSR	Barrel Length: 719mm (28.3in)
Date: 1943	Muzzle Velocity: 850m/sec (2788ft/sec)
Calibre: 7.62mm (.3in) Soviet	Feed/Magazine: 250-round belt
Operation: Gas, air-cooled	Cyclic Rate: 650rpm
Weight: 13.6kg (29.98lb)	Range: 1000m (3280ft)
Overall Length: 1120mm (44.1in)	

▲ **Goryunov SGM**

North Korean People's Army / 4th Infantry Division

Firing the same 7.62x54mm ammunition as the SVT-40, the Goryunov machine gun served in a variety of roles on tripod or wheeled mounts. A licensed version was manufactured in China.

US forces
1950–53

The first US troops deployed to Korea from Japan, where they had been undertaking occupation duties. They were unprepared for a major war.

AT THE MOMENT OF INVASION, South Korea's military was armed mainly with obsolete US equipment. Half of its eight divisions were badly understrength, and none had adequate anti-tank weapons. Those formations that were at establishment were deployed forward near the 38th Parallel and took the brunt of the initial assault, being rapidly reduced to ineffectiveness. The remainder had to function in a chaotic situation where defensive lines were overrun faster than they could be established.

Morale plummeted and many soldiers defected to the North Korean side. As the remnant of the South Korean army was driven south, US forces began landing to give assistance. Bombing missions against North Korean targets were launched, but had no immediate effect on the conflict. Nor did the first US troops to arrive. The 24th Infantry Division, followed by two more divisions, arrived from Japan via Pusan and began moving north to confront the advancing North Koreans. However, these troops had come from 'soft' occupation duties and were not combat-ready. The US intervention force was roughly handled by the North Koreans, and forced to retire towards Pusan. Particularly demoralizing was the difficulty in stopping the Koreans' T34s. Despite a series of determined stands the US force was pushed all the way back to the Naktong River, where it managed to hang on to lines that became known as the Pusan Perimeter. Into this small area came reinforcements from the United States and the rest of the world, eventually enabling a counter-offensive to be made.

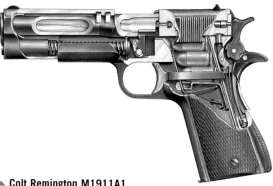

▲ **Colt Remington M1911A1**

US Army / Task Force Smith, Osan, 1950

The M1911A1 was the standard-issue sidearm for US officers and vehicle crews. Firing a hard-hitting .45 ACP round, it was an effective tool for last-ditch self-defence.

Specifications

Country of Origin: United States	Barrell Length: 127mm (5.03in)
Date: 1911	Muzzle Velocity: 255m/sec (835ft/sec)
Calibre: 11.43mm (.45in)	Feed/Magazine: 7-round detachable box
Operation: Recoil	magazine
Weight: 1.105kg (2.436lb)	Range: 100m (328ft)
Overall Length: 210mm (8.25in)	

For a time the perimeter was under severe threat, and was only narrowly saved from collapsing. However, the NKPA was operating at the end of a long supply line and UN strength around Pusan was growing. North Korean attacks became less effective as time went on and in September 1950 the NKPA failed in its last major effort to break through.

UN forces broke out of the Pusan perimeter with the assistance of an amphibious operation to retake Seoul via landings at Inchon. This was an incredibly daring operation, conducted in very difficult conditions. After the landings, Seoul was retaken in bitter street fighting, where submachine guns such as the Thompson M1A1 and fast-firing semi-automatic rifles showed their worth.

With mobility restored to the campaign, and assisted by forces of tanks and other armoured vehicles landed at Pusan, UN forces drove rapidly up the country and seemed within reach of total victory when China intervened. Lacking armoured forces, the Chinese used infantry tactics to overwhelm their UN opponents.

The 'human wave' assaults used by the Chinese People's Volunteer Army (PVA) were not suicide attacks as such, though they did result in heavy casualties. They were launched as a series of waves, with personnel expected to press forward as best they could. If an assault failed the survivors would go to ground and provide forward covering fire as the next wave advanced, then join it and begin moving forward again.

Against such attacks, firepower was the only effective defence. The primary US infantry weapon was the M1 Garand, an excellent semi-automatic rifle using an eight-round internal magazine. Some troops were armed instead with the M1 carbine, an entirely different weapon despite its similar designation. The

▶ **Smith & Wesson M1917 .45 revolver**

US Marine Corps / 1st US Marine Division, Inchon, 1950

Although semi-automatic pistols had become prevalent as military sidearms, some units were issued with revolvers firing the same round.

Specifications

Country of Origin: United States	Overall Length: 298mm (11.75in)
Date: 1917	Barrel Length: 185mm (7.3in)
Calibre: 11.4mm (.45in)	Muzzle Velocity: 198m/sec (650ft/sec)
Operation: Revolver	Feed/Magazine: 6-round cylinder
Weight: 1.08kg (2.4lb)	Range: 20m (66ft)

Specifications

Country of Origin: United States

Date: 1942

Calibre: 7.62mm (.3in) Carbine

Operation: Gas

Weight: 2.5kg (5.47lb)

Overall Length: 905mm (35.7in)

Barrel Length: 457mm (18in)

Muzzle Velocity: 595m/sec (1950ft/sec)

Feed/Magazine: 15- or 30-round detachable box magazine

Range: c.300m (984ft)

▲ M1A1 carbine

US Eighth Army / 2nd Infantry Division / 38th Infantry Regiment, 1951

The M1A1 carbine was a lightweight weapon intended for officers and non-combat specialists. It was prone to malfunction in very cold conditions.

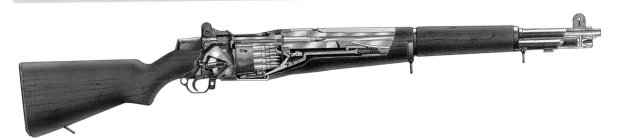

▲ M1 Garand

US Eighth Army / 24th Infantry Division, Pusan, 1950

The M1 Garand offered the US infantryman hard-hitting long-range firepower. One of the finest weapons of World War II, it remained an excellent rifle in the 1950s.

Specifications

Country of Origin: United States

Date: 1936

Calibre: 7.62mm (.3in) US .30-06

Operation: Gas

Weight: 4.37kg (9.5lb)

Overall Length: 1103mm (43.5in)

Barrel Length: 610mm (24in)

Muzzle Velocity: 853m/sec (2800ft/sec)

Feed/Magazine: 8-round internal box magazine

Range: 500m (1640ft) +

Specifications

Country of Origin: United States

Date: 1903

Calibre: 7.62mm (.3in)

Operation: Bolt action

Weight: 3.9kg (8.63lb)

Overall Length: 1115mm (43.9in)

Barrel Length: 610mm (24in)

Muzzle Velocity: 823m/sec (2700ft/sec)

Feed/Magazine: 5-round stripper clip, box magazine

Range: 750m (2460ft)

▲ Springfield M1903A4 sniper rifle

US Marine Corps / 1st US Marine Division, Inchon, 1950

Developed in 1943, the sniper version of the veteran Springfield bolt-action rifle saw action in every theatre during World War II and again in the Korean War, especially with US Marine units. It had an effective range of about 750m (2460ft), with the main limit on long-range accuracy coming from its very low power telescopic sight (2.5x).

M1 GARAND MANUFACTURE		
Manufacturer	Serial	Quantity
Springfield		
	4,200,001–4,399,999	1,999,998
	5,000,000–5,000,500	499
	5,278,246–5,488,246	210,000
	5,793,848–6,099,905	306,057
International Harvester		
	4,440,000–4,660,000	260,000
	5,000,501–5,278,245	277,744
Harrington & Richardson		
	4,660,001–4,800,000	139,999
	5,488,247–5,793,847	306,600

Post-World War II production totals: (approx.):
Springfield Armory: 661,747 (from 1952–56)
Harrington & Richardson Arms: 428,600 (from 1953–56)
International Harvester Corporation: 337,623 (from 1953–56)

M1 carbine fired a pistol-calibre round and was effective only at short range, though its fully-automatic M2 variant was useful at close quarters.

US forces also made use of the Thompson submachine gun, whose powerful .45 ACP round was highly lethal in close-quarters combat. The primary support weapon was the Browning M1919, which started life as a water-cooled weapon (M1917) in the trenches of World War I. By 1950 it had matured into a robust and reliable support weapon that could be deployed in the field or aboard almost any vehicle.

Close assault role

The Communist forces gradually moved more and more away from rifles and towards entire units equipped with submachine guns for the close assault role. Coupled with a willingness to accept massive casualties and a tactic of trying to break UN positions by concentrating on the poorly equipped South Korean forces wherever possible, this emphasis led to a clash of UN firepower versus dogged Communist aggression.

The Chinese intervention eventually resulted in stalemate along the 38th Parallel for many months. In this static phase of the war, snipers and skilled marksmen with accurate rifles were highly effective. There were still bitter close-quarters fights, however, as one side or the other tried to capture a strategic location and break the enemy's line.

The Korean War did not last long enough for major changes in US weaponry to take place; it was

Specifications

Country of Origin: United States
Date: 1936
Calibre: 7.62mm (.3in) Browning
Operation: Recoil, air-cooled
Weight: 15.05kg (33lb)
Overall Length: 1041mm (41in)

Barrel Length: 610mm (24in)
Muzzle Velocity: 853m/sec (2800ft/sec)
Feed/Magazine: 250-round belt
Cyclic Rate: 400–600rpm
Range: 2000m (6560ft) +

▲ **M1919A4 Browning**

US Eighth Army / 1st Cavalry Division, 1951

In addition to its infantry support role, the .30-calibre M1919, or 'thirty-cal', was used aboard a variety of armoured and soft-skinned vehicles.

fought with World War II-era equipment. Yet the character of the war changed several times, ranging from defensive positional warfare through mobile armoured operations and amphibious landings to street fighting. The flexibility of US equipment and combat doctrine was tested to its limits during the three years of involvement in the Korean conflict.

▶ **Sniper response**
US Marines move warily through an urban landscape somewhere in Korea. The Marine in the foreground is aiming an M1 carbine, while his comrades are both armed with M1 Garand rifles.

Commonwealth forces
1950–53

Although many nations assisted with the UN effort in Korea, by far the largest non-US contribution came from Britain and the Commonwealth.

DESPITE ALSO HAVING TO DEAL with insurgencies in Malaysia and Africa, Britain and the Commonwealth responded to the Korean crisis by making a major commitment of troops. Most nations that sent assistance contributed infantry formations ranging in size from a company to a brigade; few possessed the sealift capability to deploy large combined-arms forces. Britain and the Commonwealth had both the manpower and the means to transport it. The Commonwealth contribution included two British and one Canadian infantry brigades plus infantry battalions from Australia, plus an armoured brigade and artillery formations from Britain and New Zealand. The British naval contribution was also very significant.

By combining Commonwealth troops from different nations it became possible to field a complete division. Many British and Commonwealth forces fought as part of the 1st Commonwealth Division, which was formed in 1951, though some units were detached. For example, 41 Royal Marine

Commando was attached to the 1st US Marine Division at the time of the battle of Chosin Reservoir in late 1950. The Commonwealth forces had recent wartime experience in a variety of terrains and proved highly competent in both large-scale set-piece battles and the more confused fighting that resulted when Chinese forces launched a wave attack on dispersed positions.

Like the US contingent, the Commonwealth forces arrived in Korea equipped largely with the weapons they had possessed at the end of World War II. Unlike the US Army, who had gone over to semi-automatic rifles as their main infantry weapon, British and Commonwealth troops were primarily armed with bolt-action Lee-Enfield rifles. A tradition of rapid aimed fire and good marksmanship made these weapons deadly in medium- to long-range engagements but when attempting to repel a close assault they were less effective.

British and many commonwealth troops used the Sten submachine gun in Korea. Although trials were at that time underway to find a replacement for the cheap and crude Sten, its successor (the Sterling submachine gun) would not be available in time for the conflict. Stens were effective at close range but their rounds reportedly lost velocity fast over distance, adversely affecting the weapon's already fairly poor accuracy and caused stopping power to drop off sharply.

Some Commonwealth nations used their own indigenous equipment, such as the Australian Owen submachine gun, but much equipment was common across the various contingents. The standard support

weapon was the Bren gun, whose accuracy allowed it to be used for sharpshooting as well as suppressive fire. The Bren used the same .303-calibre round as the infantry's rifles, simplifying ammunition supply.

▲ Webley Mk IV revolver

1st Commonwealth Division / King's Royal Irish Hussars, Han River, 1951

Dating back to the beginning of the century, the Webley Mk IV fired a .455 round that made it one of the most powerful military handguns ever fielded. The Webley was not completely replaced in British Army service by the Browning Hi-Power until 1963.

Specifications

Country of Origin: United Kingdom	Overall Length: 279mm (11in)
Date: 1899	Barrel Length: 152mm (6in)
Calibre: 11.55mm (.455in)	Muzzle Velocity: 198m/sec (650ft/sec)
Operation: Revolver	Feed/Magazine: 6-round cylinder
Weight: 1.5kg (3.3lb)	Range: 20m (66ft)

▲ Lee-Enfield Rifle No. 4 Mk I

1st Commonwealth Division / 1st Battalion, The Gloucestershire Regiment

The Lee-Enfield rifle had proven its worth in half a century of conflict, though not long after the end of the conflict it was phased out in favour of the semi-automatic FN-FAL.

Specifications

Country of Origin: United Kingdom	Barrel Length: 640mm (25.2in)
Date: 1939	Muzzle Velocity: 751m/sec (2464ft/sec)
Calibre: 7.7mm (.303in) British Service	Feed/Magazine: 10-round detachable box magazine
Operation: Bolt action	
Weight: 4.11kg (9.06lb)	Range: 1000m (3280ft) +
Overall Length: 1128mm (44.43in)	

▲ De Lisle silent carbine

British/Commonwealth Special Forces

Developed to shoot a .45 ACP round almost silently, the De Lisle carbine was available in limited numbers to British special operations units.

Specifications

Country of Origin: United Kingdom	Barrel Length: 210mm (8.26in)
Date: 1943	Muzzle Velocity: 260m/sec (853ft/sec)
Calibre: 11.4mm (.45in)	Feed/Magazine: 7-round detachable box magazine
Operation: Bolt action	
Weight: 3.7kg (8.15lb)	Range: 400m (1312ft)
Overall Length: 960mm (37.79in)	

Full-bore rifles such as the Lee-Enfield are known as 'battle rifles' as opposed to the new generation of 'assault rifles' that were then emerging. Assault rifles use an intermediate round of lower power, trading hitting power and long-range accuracy for volume of fire and lightness.

The Commonwealth battle rifles were most effective in open engagements, but when facing Chinese troops armed with submachine guns at close range they were disadvantaged. A variety of weapons were nicknamed 'burp guns' by the US and Commonwealth forces in Korea. The term was applied to any fast-firing submachine gun. Most commonly this was a Soviet-made PPSh-41 or one of the Chinese or North Korean copies. These were less accurate and well-made than the Soviet originals, but retained the extremely high rate of fire. Both sides tried to play to their strengths; the Commonwealth forces trying to break up an assault by marksmanship, artillery fire and air support, and the Communists trying to get close enough to take advantage of their massive firepower.

Commonwealth Rifle Platoon

British and Commonwealth forces entered the Korean conflict with much the same organization and equipment that they had in World War II. Organization varied in practice, and few units were ever up to their 'paper' strength. A rifle platoon would consist of a HQ squad and three rifle squads, each containing a Bren LMG.

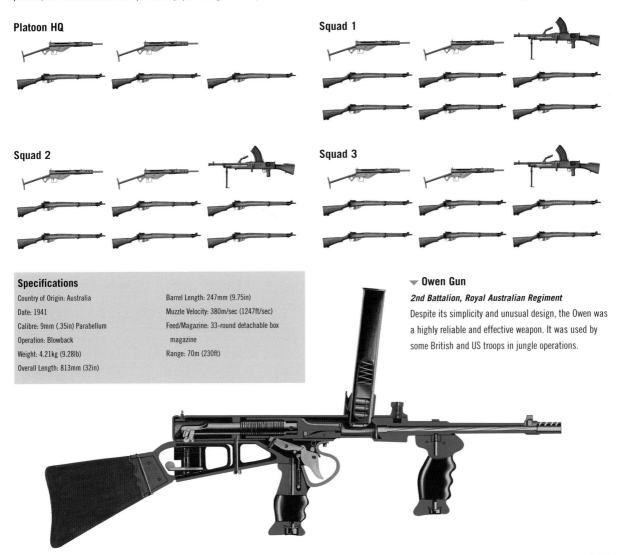

Platoon HQ

Squad 1

Squad 2

Squad 3

Specifications

Country of Origin: Australia

Date: 1941

Calibre: 9mm (.35in) Parabellum

Operation: Blowback

Weight: 4.21kg (9.28lb)

Overall Length: 813mm (32in)

Barrel Length: 247mm (9.75in)

Muzzle Velocity: 380m/sec (1247ft/sec)

Feed/Magazine: 33-round detachable box magazine

Range: 70m (230ft)

▼ Owen Gun

2nd Battalion, Royal Australian Regiment

Despite its simplicity and unusual design, the Owen was a highly reliable and effective weapon. It was used by some British and US troops in jungle operations.

Chapter 8

Wars in Asia, 1947–89

Asia was the scene for enormous upheaval in
the years after World War II. Shifts in the worldwide power
balance and the weakening of traditional colonial powers in
the region coincided with the emergence of a newly unified
China. Thus began a clash of ideologies: independence
versus colonialism, Communism versus democracy.
Many conflicts saw extensive use of irregular forces and
asymmetric warfare techniques, countering the firepower of
the major armies with new tactics designed to nullify
their strengths. Wars in Asia thus tended to become
drawn-out affairs where a decisive victory
was seemingly impossible to achieve.

◀ **Weapons training**
A US Army advisor instructs a class of Army of the Republic of Vietnam (ARVN) soldiers in the workings
and construction of an M16 assault rifle.

Introduction

In the years immediately after World War II, conflicts in Asia demonstrated the truism that victory cannot be achieved solely by military means.

T HE DEFEATS SUFFERED BY THE NETHERLANDS, Britain and France at the hands of the Axis powers early in World War II had lasting political implications worldwide. Not only did the colonial powers see a drastic reduction in their ability to deploy forces to their overseas possessions, but there was a shift in perception among the people of those areas. Independence movements began to emerge, and in some cases the pro-independence factions were willing to fight for their freedom.

The changed political climate also created opportunities for others to expand their influence. China, newly unified under a Communist regime,

▲ **M79 grenade launcher**
A soldier from the Army of the Republic of Vietnam (ARVN) crouches with his M79 grenade launcher. The M79 proved to be an ideal squad support weapon during the Vietnam War.

was willing and able to move into the power vacuum created by weakened Western powers. Thus emerged a complex politico-military situation in Asia, as the colonial powers sought to retain their hold on their possessions and other Western powers wanted to prevent the spread of Communism.

The Chinese Civil War produced large numbers of combat veterans and also political evangelists who were keen to spread Communism. This 'outreach' suited the purposes of the Chinese government, as it spread their influence wider. The war also displaced large numbers of people, who settled in areas such as Malaysia. There, they often lived in poverty in marginal areas. Deprivation made them receptive to the words of anyone who might be able to make things better.

Chinese influence was not a major factor in the Indonesian Revolution, which began in 1945, but displaced Chinese people and Communist Party officials played a major part in the Malayan Emergency which followed soon afterward. Meanwhile, France was drawn into a long conflict in what was then Indochina, beginning in 1946.

Indochina

French defeat in Indochina permitted the creation of a Communist state in North Vietnam, and the avowed intention of this state was to unify the whole of Vietnam under its rule. This objective, in turn, drew in the United States in an effort to prevent the spread of Communism. The conflicts in Malaysia, Indonesia and Indochina had involved colonial powers with a traditional interest in the region, but in Vietnam the Americans had a different goal.

The region had never been an American possession and the USA was not trying to make it one. The intent was to support the democratic state of South Vietnam and enable it to repel Communist encroachment. Perhaps there were echoes of Korea, where a Communist takeover had been prevented, but Vietnam was a different prospect. Indeed, the two sides were in many ways fighting quite different wars.

▲ **Dien Bien Phu**
French legionnaires take a break during a patrol in northern Indochina during the fighting around Dien Bien Phu, 1954. All are armed with the French-made MAT 49 submachine gun, a versatile and hardy weapon that saw more than 30 years of service.

The USA and her allies sought a conventional military victory and were undeniably successful in military terms, but the North Vietnamese were applying the lessons of the Chinese Civil War and the Indochina conflict, and were fighting for a political victory. Thus, although undefeated in the field, the US was eventually forced to withdraw and leave South Vietnam to its fate.

Red Army in Afghanistan

The Soviet invasion of Afghanistan in 1979 resulted in a similar story. Although able to take control of the governmental structure and the key cities, the Soviet Union was unable to deal effectively with the insurgent groups that operated in the vast countryside of Afghanistan. Ambushes and raids took a steady toll on the Soviet occupation force and while huge reserves of manpower were available to replace casualties, the war ended up costing far too much and achieving far too little to be viable.

Ultimately, the Soviet Union was forced to withdraw from Afghanistan. Like the other conflicts in this chapter, the war could have been won if the Soviets were willing to pay the price. It was, however, simply not worth it. This has become a characteristic of modern warfare for insurgent groups – they may not be able to win in military terms, but if they can push up the price of continued involvement, a conventional army may decide to cut its losses and withdraw.

Malayan Emergency
1948–60

The conflict in Malaya was quite unlike the war the British Army had just fought, and required a wholly different strategy.

THE CHINESE CIVIL WAR displaced large numbers of people, many of whom settled in remote areas of Malaya. There, they lived in poverty for the most part, supporting themselves by subsistence agriculture. The Malayan Communist Party (MCP) found ready support among these people.

Before World War II, the MCP had little support in Malaya, but invasion by the Japanese allowed the MCP to rise to a leadership role within the less political Malayan People's Anti-Japanese Army (MPAJA). The MPAJA was anti-Japanese rather than affiliated to any political group, but the MCP played a prominent role and gained credibility in the struggle against occupation.

Weapons

The MPAJA was partly armed by weapons air-dropped by the Allies during 1942–45, and was assisted by British officers assigned as advisors. Other weapons were scavenged from the battle sites of the 1942 invasion, in which British and Commonwealth troops unsuccessfully tried several times to halt the Japanese advance on their base at Singapore.

At the end of the war, British troops quickly arrived to retake control of Malaya and the MPAJA did not resist. In return for handing in weapons, the MCP received recognition as a legitimate political party. Support was still not strong, but the party had a following mainly among the Chinese segment of Malayan society.

MRLA forces began the conflict largely armed with weapons supplied during World War II for use against the Japanese occupiers. Although some of these had been handed in, large caches were hidden in the jungle for later use. These weapons were supplemented by arms brought in from China, many

◀ **Jungle patrol**
British special forces struggle through thick jungle somewhere in Malaya, 1957. The man in the foreground is armed with a Lee-Enfield No. 5 Mk 1 'Jungle Carbine', while his comrade behind carries an L1A1 SLR. In the background another soldier carries a Bren light machine gun.

of which were originally supplied to the Nationalist Chinese by the US.

Many British troops were armed with the Lee-Enfield No. 5 'Jungle Carbine', which had been developed for use in conditions much like those found in Malaya. A shortened and lightened version of the proven Lee-Enfield rifle, theoretically this was the ideal weapon for jungle fighting. In practice the Jungle Carbine underperformed sufficiently that production only lasted from 1944 to 1947, after which a replacement was sought. The main problems with the Jungle Carbine were excessive felt recoil, flash and noise. A rubber buttpad and large flash hider somewhat mitigated these faults but the weapon was soon phased out, with questions remaining about its accuracy.

After relying for a time on the rather better Lee-Enfield No. 4, British troops began receiving the L1A1 self-loading rifle. Whilst excellent for long-range marksmanship, the 'SLR' was less easy to handle in close jungle terrain. This limitation was offset by pairing it up with the Sterling submachine gun, which proved ideal for close-in fighting.

Emergency legislation

Tensions between the indigenous Malay population and the Chinese immigrants led to clashes in the 1945–48 period. The MCP championed the cause of the Chinese population, which gained it further support. Its power was sufficient that in 1948 the MCP launched an 'armed struggle' to take control of Malaya. At the same time, and not coincidentally,

Communist uprisings began in Burma, Indonesia and the Philippines.

Established by MCP personnel, former members of the MPAJA and disaffected segments of the population, the insurgents named themselves the Malayan People's Anti-British Army (MPABA) and began trying to take control of the country. The name was changed to Malayan Races' Liberation Army (MRLA) in 1949 even though only one in ten of its personnel were not of Chinese extraction.

With indigenous Malays as such a small minority, the MRLA did not gain significant support among the non-Chinese population. Nevertheless, the MPAJA was a formidable fighting force and had a network of supporters among the population who were willing to supply food and information.

The situation was not one that could be resolved by military force alone. There were no clear lines of battle and it was hard at times to tell innocent villagers from MRLA insurgents. Thus the measures adopted by the British were essentially political in nature, with the army deployed in force but as an aid to the civil power more than a warfighting force. Army units worked in conjunction with local police and civil authorities, and the intelligence services were effectively used to gather information on the insurgents' organization and operations.

The British response was to implement a set of emergency measures, starting in 1948. Suspects could be detained without trial, but cases were reviewed by non-government bodies to ensure fairness. Curfews and an identity card system were implemented, and

▲ **Lee-Enfield Rifle, No. 5 'Jungle Carbine'**

Royal West Kent Regiment, Kajang, 1952

The Rifle No. 5 was designed primarily for lightness. Unfortunately this low weight increased felt recoil considerably, but the weapon was still used successfully in Burma in World War II and later in Malaya during the Emergency.

Specifications

Country of Origin: United Kingdom	Barrel Length: 478mm (18.7in)
Date: 1944	Muzzle Velocity: 610m/sec (2000ft/sec)
Calibre: 7.7mm (.303in) British Service	Feed/Magazine: 10-round detachable box
Operation: Bolt action	magazine
Weight: 3.24kg (7.14lb)	Range: 1000m (3280ft)
Overall Length: 1000mm (39.37in)	

tied to an incentive scheme to encourage the population to look after their cards. Most importantly, perhaps, measures were taken to improve the loyal Malays' ability to defend themselves. While the Korean War was ongoing, British Army manpower in Malaya was limited. Great reliance was placed on local forces, which was a risky but ultimately rewarding strategy. The police force was expanded and rearmed, and Home Guards were created. These measures not only freed army units for operations against insurgent groups, but also demonstrated trust in the loyalist segment of the population. By giving the locals the strength to resist intimidation by the insurgents, the authorities denied the MRLA credibility and support.

The MRLA operated from bases in the jungle and with the support of the Chinese segment of the population, who mostly lived in remote areas. The major urban areas were secured by the authorities, but this did not prevent the MRLA from launching raids and ambushes in rural areas. European-owned property such as tin mines and rubber plantations were attacked, and in October 1951 the British High Commissioner was ambushed and killed.

Anti-guerrilla tactics

In 1950 the insurgents were able to operate in units of 100 or more, and were confident enough to attack police posts and other targets. A policy of aggressive response by mobile forces helped somewhat, but the situation was desperate for the authorities. Reacting to attacks was ineffective for the most part, and

operations against the guerrillas were problematic if their camps could not be found.

In a effort to deprive the guerrillas of support, the Chinese squatters, a prime recruiting ground for the MRLA, were relocated into 'new villages' and given land to farm. Most of these communities prospered; today the vast majority are thriving towns. In the shorter term, the new villages gave their inhabitants the chance of a better life. Most saw no point in fighting for what they were being given for free, and support for the MPLA dwindled.

Constant low-level patrolling and long-range missions by special forces units gathered information on the insurgents and inflicted a steady stream of casualties, driving down morale and providing prisoners who could be interrogated for information. A surprisingly large number were willing to lead the security forces to their former comrades in return for a pardon and a bounty.

The key to eventual victory was a combination of effective military operations and political measures. British, Gurkha and Malay units went into the jungle and fought the guerrillas in small-unit actions, keeping up constant pressure, while larger raids were launched when a camp was found. Meanwhile, the local population were given strong incentives not to support the insurgents.

Areas with significant guerrilla activity were subject to food rationing, curfews and other measures designed to make life hard for the guerrillas and their supporters. 'White' areas (those where there was little or no insurgent activity) had no such restrictions.

Specifications

Country of Origin: United Kingdom	Barrel Length: 535mm (21.1in)
Date: 1954	Muzzle Velocity: 853m/sec (2800ft/sec)
Calibre: 7.62mm (.3in) NATO	Feed/Magazine: 20-round detachable box
Operation: Gas, self-loading	magazine
Weight: 4.31kg (9.5lb)	Range: 800m (2625ft) +
Overall Length: 1055mm (41.5in)	

▲ **L1A1 Self-Loading Rifle (SLR)**

22 SAS, Ipoh, November 1954

From 1954 onwards the British Army began to be issued its first semi-automatic rifle, greatly increasing the firepower of the individual rifleman.

Protected by police and local Home Guard units, the people of these areas were strong enough to resist guerrilla attacks and had good reasons to want to keep them out of their territory.

Deprived of support and suffering constant casualties, the insurgents gradually lost heart, and many were willing to turn in their comrades. Some surrendered to avoid starvation, so successful were the measures to deprive them of support, and by the end of July 1960 the emergency was officially declared to be over. Although the military dimension was absolutely vital to victory in Malaya, the guerrillas were defeated in the hearts and minds of the local population. To this day the Malayan Emergency stands as a textbook example of how to conduct a counter-insurgency campaign.

▲ L4A1 Bren

3rd Battalion, Malay Regiment, Johore, 1960

The Malay Regiment was supplied with British-made weaponry such as the 7.62x51mm NATO conversion of the excellent Bren light machine gun.

Specifications

Country of Origin: United Kingdom
Date: 1958
Calibre: 7.62mm (.3in) NATO
Operation: Gas, air-cooled
Weight: 10.25kg (22.5lb)
Overall Length: 1150mm (45.25in)

Barrel Length: 625mm (25in)
Muzzle Velocity: 730m/sec (2400ft/sec)
Feed/Magazine: 30-round detachable box magazine
Range: 1000m (3280ft) +

Specifications

Country of Origin: United Kingdom
Date: 1951
Calibre: 9mm (.35in) Parabellum
Operation: Blowback
Weight: 2.7kg (5.9lb) empty
Overall Length: 686mm (27in) stock extended;
    481mm (18.9in) stock folded

Barrel Length: 196mm (7.7in)
Muzzle Velocity: 395m/sec (1295ft/sec)
Feed/Magazine: 34-round detachable box magazine
Range: 200m (656ft)

▲ Sterling L2A3

Royal Hampshire Regiment, Selangor, December 1955

Submachine guns proved their worth in vicious close-range firefights in the jungle, their high rate of fire increasing the chances of a hit on a fleetingly spotted human target.

Indochina
1946–54

After the end of World War II, a weakened France attempted to regain control of its South-East Asian territories.

FRANCE ACQUIRED SIGNIFICANT territories in South-East Asia in the latter half of the nineteenth century. Although nationalist movements did appear in the early years of the twentieth entury, French control was not seriously threatened until it was defeated by the Axis early in World War II. This left French colonial possessions vulnerable, and those in South-East Asia were overrun by Japanese forces.

The main force for national unity and independence in the region was the Indochina Communist Party, led by Ho Chi Minh. Under the title of Viet Nam Doc Lap Dong Minh Hoi (shortened to Viet Minh), the Communist Party organized resistance against the Japanese occupation. Its military chief was Vo Nguyen Giap.

Viet Minh control

Japanese defeat allowed the Viet Minh to take control of what is today northern Vietnam, with their capital at Hanoi in the region formerly known as Tongking. Communist support was strong in the north of the country but weaker in the south, where the United Party formed an administration.

The arrival of British troops soon after the end of the war resulted in the United Party losing control of the southern regions, with most towns and lines of

▲ **Squad machine gun**
French troops rest a Fusil Mitrailleur Mle 24/29 light machine gun on top of a US-made Garand M1 rifle, Indochina, 1952. The French Army in Indochina was armed with a lot of surplus American equipment.

FRENCH/VIET MINH BATTALION WEAPONS COMPARED, 1953*		
Armament	French forces	Viet Minh
Rifles	624	500
SMGs	133	200
LMGs	42	20
81mm (3.2in) mortars	4	8
60mm (2.4in) mortars	8	–
Recoilless rifles	3	–
Bazookas	–	3

*A comparison of the typical armament for French and VM battalions in 1953 was made by Capitaine Jacques Despuech (cited in Pierre Labrousse, *La Méthode Vietminh*).

communication soon firmly under British control. The Allies had decided at the Potsdam Conference in July 1945 that France would reclaim its former colonies, and in 1946 French troops began to take over from the British.

In the north, the French landed at Haiphong and pushed inland to Hanoi. However, the Viet Minh administration was left in place for the time being. Determined to fight for independence, the Viet Minh began to prepare for conflict. Their forces were marshalled in remote areas where the French had not yet penetrated, while guerrillas began attacking French outposts.

France
1946–54

France fielded a conventional army in Indochina, fighting a war that turned out to be anything but conventional.

FRANCE BEGAN THE POST-WAR PERIOD in considerable disarray. Recently liberated from German occupation, its armed forces had to be rebuilt from almost nothing. Reform required arming thousands of troops and providing artillery, vehicles and all other needs from whatever source presented itself. Quantities of French-made equipment were available from storage or new production, but this was not sufficient in the short term. Thus the French army was armed with large amounts of equipment donated by the other Allies, notably the USA.

Recent experience was of large-scale conventional conflict, and the army that France created was geared to fighting such a war. There really was no choice about this; France had been defeated and occupied by conventional means and its first priority was to prevent this defeat from happening again. However, a conventional army was not the ideal tool with which to tackle an insurrection in far-off colonies.

The force sent by France to her former colonies in Indochina was in many ways typical of the immediate post-World War II period. Primarily composed of infantry, who might be moved by truck or other vehicles but who fought in a traditional manner on foot, these forces were built around squads of riflemen supported by light machine guns.

The World War II-era rifle squad had proven effective in that conflict, but the jungle environment of Indochina was not ideal terrain for bolt-action rifles. Their long-range accuracy was wasted most of the time, and their slow rate of fire was a liability. Concentrated firepower was more effective when trying to repel an ambush or hit hostiles concealed by foliage. Rifle-calibre bullets did penetrate soft cover fairly well, whereas lighter rounds lost momentum fast when punching through the undergrowth.

Having been rebuilt almost from scratch after liberation during World War II, French forces were forced to use a mix of weaponry. Some came from pre-war stockpiles, while other weapons such as the M1 Garand were supplied by the United States. The new MAS-49 rifle became available during the conflict, and experience with it led to an updated MAS-49/56 model, which was introduced after the end of the war.

The French Army also made extensive use of submachine guns in Indochina. Although such weapons provided excellent close-range firepower,

▲ M1A1 Carbine

Far East Expeditionary Force / 1st Airborne Group, Mang Yang Pass, June 1954

The US-made M1A1 carbine was a popular weapon with airborne troops, combining lightness with a reasonable levels of power.

Specifications

Country of Origin: United States

Date: 1942

Calibre: 7.62mm (.3in) Carbine

Operation: Gas

Weight: 2.5kg (5.47lb)

Overall Length: 905mm (35.7in)

Barrel Length: 457mm (18in)

Muzzle Velocity: 595m/sec (1950ft/sec)

Feed/Magazine: 15- or 30-round detachable box magazine

Range: c.300m (984ft)

their pistol-calibre rounds were not always effective against hostiles behind even light cover. Something halfway between a full-bore battle rifle and a submachine gun was needed; a weapon firing high-velocity rounds rapidly using semi- or full-automatic fire. However, the French did not have access to the new generation of assault rifles then emerging, and largely had to make do with the bolt-action rifle/submachine-gun balance that had served many nations in World War II.

The most serious deficiencies were not in French equipment, however. What was most lacking was an understanding of the enemy and the nature of the war. In Europe, the recent conflict had been decided

by control of cities and, to a lesser extent, the communications routes between them.

Indochina was a very different matter. Despite some guerrilla activity, the French seemed to be well in control of the country until February 1950, when Viet Minh forces overran a small position at Lao Kai in the very north of the region. Further attacks on thinly spread French outposts were successful, although a robust response drove off a major attack on Dong Khe in May. A second assault in September resulted in a Communist victory. Viet Minh forces ambushed the French relief operation and forced a retreat from Lang Son. Having fought a successful guerrilla war thus far, the Viet Minh went over to

▲ MAS Modèle 36 rifle

Far East Expeditionary Force / Mobile Group 2, Cho Ben Pass, November 1951

Although replacement of the MAS 1936 with a semi-automatic weapon began in 1949, it continued to serve with some units until the mid-1960s.

Specifications

Country of Origin: France	Barrel Length: 575mm (22.6in)
Date: 1936	Muzzle Velocity: 853.6m/sec (2800ft/sec)
Calibre: 7.5mm (.295in)	Feed/Magazine: 5-round internal box magazine,
Operation: Bolt action	clip-fed
Weight: 3.7kg (4.1lb)	Range: 320–365m (1050–1198ft)
Overall Length: 1020mm (40in)	

▲ Pistolet Mitrailleur MAS Modèle 38

Far East Expeditionary Force / 1st Foreign Airborne Battalion, Dien Bien Phu, November 1953

Although a well-made weapon, the MAS 38 fired a weak cartridge that limited its effectiveness. The bolt recoiled into a space in the stock, reducing overall length.

Specifications

Country of Origin: France	Overall Length: 832mm (32.75in)
Date: 1938	Barrel Length: 247mm (9.75in)
Calibre: 7.65mm (.301in) Longue	Muzzle Velocity: 395m/sec (1300ft/sec)
Operation: Blowback	Feed/Magazine: 32-round box magazine
Weight: 4.1kg (9.1lb)	Range: 70m (230ft))

more conventional tactics, launching repeated attempts to gain control of the area around Hanoi in early 1951.

Here, French weaponry and doctrine were well suited to the situation at hand, and Giap's forces were heavily defeated. The French then set up a defensive perimeter around Hanoi, with a mobile reserve to counter-attack any new offensive that the Viet Minh might mount. More confident now, the French made the decision to begin offensive operations against the Viet Minh bases; a strategy that would lead ultimately to defeat.

▲ MAT 49

Far East Expeditionary Force / 3rd Colonial Parachute Battalion, Red River Delta, October 1953

The MAT 49 submachine gun used a 9x19mm round and was consequently more potent than the MAS 38. Examples captured by the Viet Minh were often converted to 7.65x25mm to use readily available Soviet ammunition.

Specifications

Country of Origin: France
Date: 1949
Calibre: 9mm (.35in) Parabellum
Operation: Blowback
Weight: 3.5kg (7.72lb)
Overall Length: 720mm (28.35in)

Barrel Length: 228mm (8.98in)
Muzzle Velocity: 390m/sec (1280ft/sec)
Feed/Magazine: 20- or 32-round detachable box
    magazine
Range: 70m (230ft)

▲ Fusil Mitrailleur Mle 24/29

Far East Expeditionary Force / French Foreign Legion, Dong Khe, September 1950

The standard light support weapon of the French Army and colonial forces, the FM 24/29 remained in service with some reserve forces long after its official replacement in the 1960s.

Specifications

Country of Origin: France
Date: 1924
Calibre: 7.5mm (.295in) M29
Operation: Gas, air-cooled
Weight: 9.25kg (20.25lb)
Overall Length: 1080mm (42.5in)

Barrel Length: 500mm (19.75in)
Muzzle Velocity: 825m/sec (2707ft/sec)
Cyclic Rate: 500rpm
Feed/Magazine: 25-round detachable box
    magazine
Range:1000m (3280ft) +

Viet Minh
1946–54

The Viet Minh used tactics developed in the recent Chinese Civil War to offset the greater firepower of the French Army.

HAVING SUFFERED A SEVERE SETBACK before Hanoi, morale among the Viet Minh forces dropped sharply. The French, on the other hand, were determined to push through to victory and in November 1951 Hoa Binh was seized by paratroops, with mobile ground and riverine forces pushing through to join up with them.

The operation was intended to drive the Viet Minh out of their base areas, but instead it played into Giap's hands. Rather than attack the garrison at Hoa Binh, Viet Minh forces ambushed patrols and supply convoys using similar techniques to those of the Communist forces in northern China during the civil war. Although the French had a strong position at Hoa Binh, their forces were being slowly choked by pressure on the supply lines and were withdrawn in February 1952. A similar French operation in October 1952 ended the same way. Powerful conventional forces successfully drove off the Viet Minh from their bases at

Phu Doan and Phu Tho, but were unable to remain in possession of the area and were withdrawn some months later. The French were increasingly forced onto the defensive in the area around Hanoi, with the Viet Minh in control of the countryside.

However, there seemed to be a chance to win. The Viet Minh controlled the countryside but France had significant air transport assets which could be used to supply forward bases. Viet Minh attacks on well-defended areas were beaten off with heavy casualties. So, if the Viet Minh could be induced to attack such a target then they could be drawn out and defeated in open battle.

In November 1953, French paratroops seized Dien Bien Phu for use as a forward base. The aim was to disrupt Viet Minh operations by attacking their supply lines. This action, it was hoped, would draw an attack. Dien Bien Phu was fortified and supplies flown in, and the hoped-for assault began. However,

▲ **Maxim heavy machine gun**

Viet Minh / 308th Division / 36th Regiment, Chan Muong gorge,
November 1952

The Viet Minh were supplied with weapons which had, in some cases, changed hands several times during their long career. Although dated, the Maxim gun was still effective, though not very mobile.

Specifications

Country of Origin: Soviet Union	Barrell Length: 721mm (28.38in)
Date: 1910	Muzzel Velocity: 740/m/sec (2427.2ft/sec)
Calibre: 7.62mm (.3in)	Feed/Magazine: 25-round belt
Operation: Short recoil, toggle locked	Cycle Rate: 500rpm
Weight: 64.3kg (139.6lb)	Range: 1000m (3280ft)
Overall Length: 1067mm (42in)	

the Viet Minh proved more capable than expected. Surrounding the base with large numbers of troops, the Viet Minh brought up artillery and anti-aircraft guns, making resupply and reinforcement by air increasingly difficult. Supported by artillery, the Viet Minh slowly ground their way into the base by overrunning successive defensive posts until, after a 55-day siege, the remaining defenders surrendered.

Viet Minh weapons came from a variety of sources. Arms were supplied by the Western Allies during World War II, for use by anti-Japanese resistance forces, and these were augmented by former Nationalist Chinese equipment passed on by the friendly Communist regime in China. Large quantities of Japanese equipment were captured at the end of World War II in both China and Vietnam, and this served to arm many of the early 'self defence groups' fielded by the Viet Minh.

French weapons also saw extensive use. Some were captured during the conflict, but most came from stockpiles held by the Japanese. These arms were taken originally following the Japanese occupation in 1941–42.

Weapons were also indigenously produced, in many cases in small workshops hidden in villages. Their products included copies of the British Sten gun as well as home-made versions of weapons supplied by China or taken from French forces.

Specifications

Country of Origin: USSR	Barrel Length: 254mm (10in)
Date: 1943	Muzzle Velocity: 500m/sec (1640ft/sec)
Calibre: 7.62mm (.3in) Soviet	Feed/Magazine: 35-round detachable box
Operation: Blowback	magazine
Weight: 3.36kg (7.4lb)	Cyclic Rate: 650rpm
Overall Length: 820mm (32.3in)	Range: 100m (328ft) +

▲ PPS-43

Viet Minh Guerrillas, North Vietnam, 1950

The cheap and simple PPS-43 was used to equip both regular troops and irregular militia of the Viet Minh. It was easy to maintain and highly effective in close assault operations.

Specifications

Country of Origin: USSR	Barrel Length: 605mm (23.8in)
Date: 1928	Muzzle Velocity: 840m/sec (2756ft/sec)
Calibre: 7.62mm (.3in) Soviet	Feed/Magazine: 47-round drum magazine
Operation: Gas, air-cooled	Cyclic Rate: 475rpm
Weight: 9.12kg (20.1lb)	Range: 1000m (3280ft)
Overall Length: 1290mm (50.8in)	

▲ Degtyarev DP

Viet Minh / 312th Division / 209th Regiment / Nghia Lo Valley, October 1951

Regular forces of the Viet Minh were organized in much the same way as Western armies, but with artillery, mortars and light support weapons supplied by Russia and China. Ammunition resupply came from the same sources.

The Vietnam War

The Geneva Accords of 1954 provided no long-term solution to political issues in Vietnam and soon a second, larger, conflict erupted.

THE GENEVA ACCORDS, which ended the Indochina War, were intended to pave the way for a permanent settlement, but this proved problematic. An initiative to recognize North and South Vietnam as separate nations foundered on the rocks of Cold War politics as the two halves of the region faced off over a Demilitarized Zone (DMZ) at the 17th Parallel. Refugees streamed south despite attempts by the North Vietnamese authorities to prevent the move; a rather smaller number went north to join the Communist state.

With US assistance, South Vietnam began to gain in economic and military strength, overcoming the problems caused by the influx of refugees and the difficulties of creating a state out of a former colonial territory. However, large numbers of former Viet Minh personnel still lived in South Vietnam and by 1959 they had begun waging a guerrilla war under

▲ **Squad capability**
A US Army squad prepares to move from cover somewhere in the Mekong Delta, 1967. The squad carries a Browning M1919 machine gun, while most of the riflemen are armed with either M1 carbines or M14 rifles – the standard infantry weapon until replaced by the M16 assault rifle from 1967.

the new banner of the Viet Cong, or Vietnamese Communists. The most effective response to the guerrilla threat came from small units of light infantry posted in villages, and the larger formations of the Civil Guard which responded to minor threats in their provinces. These forces did what they could, but were not equal to the task they faced. The Army of the Republic of Vietnam (ARVN) was not well suited to countering a guerrilla force. It had been built up along conventional lines to deal with an invasion across the Demilitarized Zone and was not trained for counter-insurgency warfare.

US intervention

With the situation deteriorating fast, American military aid was stepped up. Nevertheless, between 1959 and 1965 the Viet Cong gained in strength to the point where they could defeat ARVN units in conventional battle.

Meanwhile the South Vietnamese government was disintegrating. The US faced a choice between backing its anti-Communist stance with ground forces or pulling out entirely. The latter was not acceptable, so in February 1965 the first US combat units arrived to join the fighting.

US forces
1959–75

US forces began arriving in Vietnam in 1965. They faced an uphill struggle, entering a situation that was already almost beyond control.

WITH NORTH VIETNAMESE ARMY (NVA) units moving across the DMZ and the Viet Cong in the ascendant, the total collapse of South Vietnam seemed imminent as the first US troops arrived. Robust action was needed to remedy the situation, starting with the interdiction of North Vietnamese logistics routes. US combat aircraft attacked infrastructure, supply routes and supporting industry in North Vietnam, hoping to weaken the fighting power of the NVA.

However, the North Vietnamese were supplied by the Soviet Union and China, and the combat capability of the NVA was never seriously impaired. Attempts to prevent supplies from reaching the Viet Cong were similarly unsuccessful. Not only could they obtain support from local communities (not always willingly) but a major supply route, known as the Ho Chi Minh Trail, ran through Cambodia and Laos. This route was attacked from the air, which succeeded only in slowing the flow of supplies.

Conventional warfare

US forces were largely engaged in conventional operations against the NVA, which launched attacks across the DMZ and across the frontier from Cambodia and Laos. This strategy enabled NVA forces to retreat to a safe base if defeated; which they often were. US troops were better supported and had superior firepower, and could generally beat the NVA in the field without difficulty. Frequent victories led to false picture of success, with enemy withdrawals from the battle area and the infamous 'body count' coming out hugely in favour of the US forces. However, the strategic picture was quite different.

The conventional war was just a part of North Vietnamese strategy, which also relied upon gaining control of large areas of South Vietnam through insurgency warfare. Initially, it fell to South Vietnamese forces to counter the activities of the Viet Cong, a role to which they were poorly suited. Although political stability was somewhat rebuilt, the South Vietnamese government had little credibility in the rural areas.

US strategy was at first not overly concerned with building South Vietnam into a nation; it was more about the containment of Communism. It was originally hoped that by inflicting heavy casualties on the NVA and the Viet Cong, the US could force North Vietnam to pull out of the war. However, these measures were of little use to a high-population, totalitarian state that could keep putting men into the field to replace casualties.

Fireteam 1 Leader   **Automatic Rifleman**   **Assistant Automatic Rifleman**   **Scout**

Fireteam 2 Leader   **Automatic Rifleman**   **Assistant Automatic Rifleman**   **Scout**

Fireteam 3 Leader   **Automatic Rifleman**   **Assistant Automatic Rifleman**   **Scout**

US Marine Rifle Squad, 1968

Each marine squad was broken down into three fireteams of four men. Each fireteam had an NCO as leader (armed with an M3A1 SMG), an automatic rifleman (M14 modified with bipod) and two riflemen (assistant automatic rifleman and scout), also armed with the standard M14. The modified M14 was used as an squad support weapon. All personnel were equipped with the M14 prior to 1968, after which the USMC were issued with the M16, though it was not uncommon for units to retain the modified M14s for extra firepower when necessary.

ORGANIZATION

■ Rifle Company
   HQ

▷ 1 Rifle Platoon   ▷ 2 Rifle Platoon   ▷ 3 Rifle Platoon
   HQ   HQ   HQ
   1 2 3   1 2 3   1 2 3

▷ Weapons Platoon
   HQ

US MARINE CORPS RIFLE COMPANY: STRENGTH	
Personnel	Strength
Rifle platoons	3
Weapons platoon	1
Navy hospital corpsmen (one attached to each rifle platoon and the senior corpsman with the company headquarters)	4
Administrative clerk	1
Police sergeant (typically holding the rank of corporal or sergeant)	1
Training NCO	1
Company gunnery sergeant	1
First sergeant	1
Executive Officer (XO) typically a first lieutenant	1
Commanding officer (CO) typically a captain	1

US MARINE CORPS RIFLE PLATOON: STRENGTH	
Personnel	Strength
Platoon commander, usually a second lieutenant	1
Platoon sergeant (PSG), usually a staff sergeant	1
Platoon staff Radio-telephone operator (RTO) Forward observer (FO) FO's RTO Platoon medic	1 1 1 1
1 rifle squad	13
2 rifle squad	13
3 rifle squad	13
Total	45

▶ Browning High-Power pistol

Military Assistance Command, Vietnam – Studies and Observations Group

The 9mm (.35in) Browning was chosen as a sidearm by some members of US special forces acting as advisors to the South Vietnamese.

Specifications

Country of Origin: Belgium/United States	Barrel Length: 118mm (4.65in)
Date: 1935	Muzzle Velocity: 335m/sec (1100ft/sec)
Calibre: 9mm (.35in) Parabellum	Feed/Magazine: 13-round detachable box
Operation: Short recoil	magazine
Weight: .99kg (2.19lb)	Range: 30m (98ft)
Overall Length: 197mm (7.75in)	

◀ Smith & Wesson Model 10

1st Cavalry Division (Airmobile), Ia Drang Valley, November 1965

Revolvers were issued to helicopter pilots as emergency weapons only; pilots were not expected to have to engage hostiles under normal conditions.

Specifications

Country of Origin: United States	Overall Length: 190mm (7.5in)
Date: 1899	Barrel Length: 83mm (3.27in)
Calibre: 9.6mm (.38in)	Muzzle Velocity: 190m/sec (625ft/sec)
Operation: Double-action revolver	Feed/Magazine: 5-round cylinder
Weight: .51kg (1.1lb)	Range: 20m (66ft)

▲ Ithaca Model 37 M

1st Infantry Division / 28th Infantry Regiment, Bonh Duong Province, October 1967

Shotguns were extensively used by 'point men' leading patrols during search-and-destroy missions, enabling a fast response to any sudden threat or ambush.

Specifications

Country of Origin: United States	Barrel Length: 330–762mm (13–30in)
Date: 1970	Muzzle Velocity: Variable, depending on type of
Gauge/Calibre: 12-, 16-, 20- or 28-gauge	ammunition
Operation: Pump action	Feed/Magazine: 4-round integral tubular
Weight: Variable	magazine
Overall Length: Variable	Range: 100m (328ft)

Firebases

US tactics revolved around the application of heavy firepower. Heavily protected bases were used along the DMZ frontier, often in an interlocking pattern of 'firebases' from which artillery could support other fortified areas or fire on targets identified by ground or air reconnaissance.

These bases, and also supply bases located in what might otherwise have been considered rear areas, were the subject of constant harassment and occasional large-scale attack. To a great extent they suited US purposes; by drawing concentrated enemy forces onto their defences, the US forces could bring firepower to bear on their own terms while the enemy struggled through minefields and barbed wire.

The fire and support bases had to be resupplied, necessitating constant patrols along supply routes and the surrounding jungle. Response forces were dispatched from their base whenever an ambush or a patrol contact occurred, but were not always successful in bringing the enemy to battle. Sometimes the response force itself was ambushed en route or had to fight through a blocking force to assist the original victims.

Specifications

Country of Origin: United States	Barrel Length: 558mm (22in)
Date: 1957	Muzzle Velocity: 595m/sec (1950ft/sec)
Calibre: 7.62mm (.3in) NATO	Feed/Magazine: 20-round detachable box
Operation: Gas	magazine
Weight: 3.88kg (8.55lb)	Range: 800m (2625ft) +
Overall Length: 1117mm (44in)	

▲ M14 rifle

1st Infantry Division / 173rd Airborne Brigade, Operation Crimp, January 1966

The M14 was the standard US infantry rifle until replaced by the M16. It was effective in both small-scale patrol actions and divisional-level operations.

▲ M16A1 assault rifle

101st Airborne Division / 3rd Brigade, Firebase Ripcord, July 1970

The individual firepower offered by the fully automatic M16A1 was instrumental in the defence of Firebase Ripcord, the last major US ground engagement of the war.

Specifications

Country of Origin: United States	Barrel Length: 508mm (20in)
Date: 1963	Muzzle Velocity: 1000m/sec (3280ft/sec)
Calibre: 5.56mm (.219in) M193	Feed/Magazine: 30-round detachable box
Operation: Gas	magazine
Weight: 2.86kg (6.3lb)	Range: 500m (1640ft) +
Overall Length: 990mm (39in)	

Helicopter mobility was a key US asset in Vietnam, allowing troops to be deployed quickly, supported in the field and withdrawn. Helicopters were also extensively used for casualty evacuation and fire support. They gave rise to a new style of warfare, in which airmobile infantry were supported by relatively distant artillery at the firebases, and by helicopter gunships giving close support. Other aircraft, ranging from conventional fighter-bombers to converted cargo planes serving as gunships, also provided heavy fire support.

Air mobility allowed the US to put a lot of troops quickly into an area and to set up ambushes across the retreat routes of enemy forces. This tactic was at times highly effective, and the US won all the significant battles it fought. However, in order to gain control over the countryside it was necessary to send patrols into the jungle and fight the insurgents wherever they could be found.

Sniper war

Snipers played a significant part in this kind of operation, not only as shooters but also as observers. A two-man sniper team could disrupt a large enemy force by killing officers, pinning down the force as a whole, and calling in artillery or air support to inflict

▲ M21 sniper rifle

9th Infantry Division / 60th Infantry Regiment, Ben Tre, February 1969

Derived from the M14 rifle, the M21 sniper rifle could carry a telescopic sight, or a light-intensifying 'starlight scope' to assist in finding targets at night.

Specifications

Country of Origin: United States	Barrel Length: 559mm (22in)
Date: 1969	Muzzle Velocity: 853m/sec (2798ft/sec)
Calibre: 7.62mm (.3in) NATO	Feed/Magazine: 20-round detachable box
Operation: Gas	magazine
Weight: 5.55kg (12.24lb)	Range: 800m (2625ft) +
Overall Length: 1120mm (44.09in)	

Specifications

Country of Origin: United States	Barrel Length: 610mm (24in)
Date: 1966	Muzzle Velocity: 777m/sec (2550ft/sec)
Calibre: 7.62mm (.3in) NATO	Feed/Magazine: 5-round integral box magazine
Operation: Bolt action	Range: 800m (2625ft) +
Weight: 6.57kg (14.48lb)	
Overall Length: 1117mm (43.98in)	

▲ M40A1 sniper rifle

5th Marine Regiment, Sgt 'Chuck' Mawhinney, 1968–70

In the hands of a skilled sniper, a bolt-action rifle could inflict serious casualties on the enemy. Sergeant Mawhinney achieved more than 100 confirmed kills in his 16-month tour.

heavy casualties. Their skills in moving unseen through the jungle were critical to their effectiveness; a detected sniper team could be overwhelmed by enemy fire.

The sniper version of the M14 rifle, designated the M21, proved extremely effective. Its 20-round capacity and semi-automatic mechanism allowed a sniper to shoot repeatedly at targets who might take cover while he worked the action of a bolt-action weapon. The M21 also made a good battle rifle if the

sniper team became caught in a close-range firefight. Using a suppressor, the M21 made it hard for hostiles to locate the sniper, which improved survivability.

Infantry weapons and tactics

The standard US infantry platoon during the war was composed primarily of riflemen, with some specialists. 'Point men', who led patrols, were often armed with shotguns. While lacking range and penetration, the shotgun allowed a fast response to an

▲ M3A1 'Grease Gun'

9th Infantry Division / 47th Mechanized Infantry, Bin Phuoc, March 1970

The M3A1, an improved version of the original M3, was issued to vehicle crews and rear-echelon personnel as a self-defence weapon that could be stowed conveniently aboard a vehicle.

Specifications

Country of Origin: United States	Overall Length: 762mm (30in)
Date: 1944	Barrel Length: 203mm (8in)
Calibre: 9mm (.35in) Parabellum or	Muzzle Velocity: 275m/sec (900ft/sec)
11.4mm (.45in) .45 ACP	Feed/Magazine: 30-round detachable box
Operation: Blowback	magazine
Weight: 3.7kg (8.15lb)	Range: 50m (164ft)

▲ M60 general-purpose machine gun

9th Infantry Division / 31st Infantry Regiment, Ben Luc, April 1969

Despite a tendency to malfunction or become damaged, the M60 was valued for its sustained-fire capability. The Stellite-lined bore permitted firing even when the barrel was white-hot.

Specifications

Country of Origin: United States	Barrel Length: 560mm (22.05in)
Date: 1960	Muzzle Velocity: 855m/sec (2805ft/sec)
Calibre: 7.62mm (.3in) NATO	Feed/Magazine: Belt-fed
Operation: Gas, air-cooled	Cyclic Rate: 600rpm
Weight: 10.4kg (23lb)	Range: 1000m (3280ft) +
Overall Length: 1110mm (43.75in)	

▶ **Jungle firefight**

A US Marine recon squad aim an M60 machine gun into long grass during a patrol near Con Thien, 1969.

ambush or fleeting target and made a hit more likely.

Fire support was provided by a general-purpose machine gun, usually an M60. This weapon was effective when it worked properly but it was heavy and had so many problems that it was nicknamed 'the pig' by soldiers. Nevertheless the M60 could lay down effective suppressing fire and could be 'walked' onto a target. Its heavy 7.62x51mm rounds penetrated far into the jungle; the sound of bullets smashing into branches and through leaves could induce many hostiles to disengage or seek better cover.

Grenade launchers were also widely used. The M79 'thump gun' in skilled hands could put an explosive grenade into a target the size of a building window at 100–150m (328–492ft). Specialist ammunition such as 'multiple projectile' – essentially a giant 40mm shotgun shell – made the M79 more versatile, but the grenadier was issued a pistol for self-defence; alone the M79 was not an all-round weapon.

The standard US infantry rifle at the beginning of the war was the M14, a 7.62x51mm automatic rifle. It was potent but had significant drawbacks. Its 20-round magazine was quickly emptied when using automatic fire, which limited effectiveness compared with the 30-round capacity of the opposing AK-47. The M14 was hard to control under automatic fire, which further wasted ammunition. Most M14s were converted to semi-automatic fire, and an accurized version was produced to arm snipers.

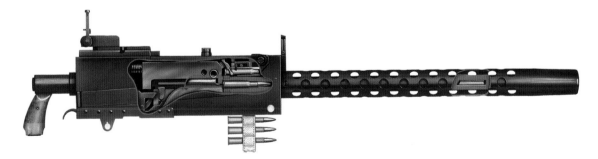

Specifications	
Country of Origin: United States	Barrel Length: 610mm (24in)
Date: 1936	Muzzle Velocity: 853m/sec (2800ft/sec)
Calibre: 7.62mm (.3in) Browning	Feed/Magazine: 250-round belt
Operation: Recoil, air cooled	Cyclic Rate: 400–600rpm
Weight: 15.05kg (31lb)	Range: 2000m (6560ft) +
Overall Length: 1041mm (41in)	

▲ **Browning M1919A4**

Mobile Riverine Force / River Assault Squadron 13, Mekong Delta, December 1968

Specialist forces patrolled the waterways of the Mekong Delta aboard heavily armed boats equipped with .30- and .50-calibre Browning machineguns, 20mm cannon and grenade launchers.

M16 arrives

From 1968 onwards, the M16 rifle began to become available. It first went to some special operations units before becoming standard issue. However, the original model had some serious flaws, notably a tendency to jam when exposed to the filthy conditions of the Vietnamese jungle. Some potential users viewed the M16 with suspicion, calling it a 'toy rifle', which referred to both its plastic components and its small calibre. Whatever faults weapons such as the M14 may have had, they fired a powerful 7.62mm (.3in) cartridge. The lighter 5.56mm (.21in) round had not proven its effectiveness in action, and there was an intuitive connection between a smaller bullet and lessened stopping power which concerned many users. It might be satisfactory for the needs of the first service to adopt it, the US Air Force, but combat troops had their doubts about the new weapon.

A chief concern was that the M16 might fail to fire at all. Despite being billed as a wonder rifle that never needed cleaning, it fouled quickly. This problem was compounded by a lack of cleaning kits. The fault did not, in truth, lie entirely with the weapon. The decision to dispense with cleaning kits was a cost-saving measure, compounded by a switch to cheaper ammunition whose propellant caused serious fouling.

These problems were gradually ironed out, creating the M16A1 model that included a cleaning kit carried in the stock and a forward assist to enable the bolt to be closed on even a badly fouled chamber. The M16A1 was altogether better, providing every US infantryman with the capability to lay down controllable suppressing fire. However, this firepower did lead to a tendency to 'spray and pray', resulting in enormous ammunition expenditure in return for relatively few hits.

Submachine guns and heavy weapons

Submachine guns were extensively issued in Vietnam, mainly to artillery and vehicle crews who needed a means of self-defence but were not intended to engage the enemy directly. The standard-issue US SMG was the M3 'Grease Gun', which had started out as a World War II expedient weapon but was produced in such numbers as to ensure longevity in military service.

Submachine guns had in the past been used for counter-ambush techniques, but automatic rifles took over this role. An assault rifle could lay down the same volume of fire as an SMG and in addition had longer range and better penetration. While some troops were issued shotguns for the point-man role, there was no need to deprive the squad of several riflemen to create a specialist close-range high-firepower capability.

Thus submachine guns played a relatively small part in combat initiated by the US forces. They were rarely deployed with troops going in search of the enemy, but when the Viet Cong or NVA ambushed a convoy or attacked a firebase, the firepower of multiple submachine guns was a welcome addition to the defensive effort. Repelling a convoy ambush or a base assault was often a close-quarters scramble,

Specifications

Country of Origin: United States	Overall Length: 783mm (29in)
Date: 1961	Barrel Length: 357mm (14in)
Calibre: 40mm (1.57in)	Muzzle Velocity: 75m/sec (245ft/sec)
Operation: Breech-loaded	Feed/Magazine: Single shot
Weight: 2.95kg (6.5lb) loaded	Range: 150m (492ft)

▲ **M79 grenade launcher**

199th Infantry Brigade / 7th Infantry Regiment, Long Binh, January 1968

The M79 'Thump Gun' provided infantry platoons with the capability to deliver indirect fire on enemy positions. Its break-open breech-loading action resulted in a low rate of fire, and the grenadier could not also carry a rifle.

sometimes in the dark, where long-range fire might be impossible. Here, the submachine gun was extremely potent.

Heavier weapons were generally used from fixed defensive positions or aboard vehicles, helicopters and river patrol boats. The venerable Browning M1919 and its water-cooled M1917 cousin served in the fire-support role with US and ARVN forces, where they proved themselves as effective as ever.

'Vietnamization'

A shift in US strategic perspective occurred in 1969, with the emphasis moving more towards 'Vietnamization'; taking control of the countryside back from the Viet Cong and developing the ability of South Vietnam to stand against the North as a

united nation. US forces were reduced to appease the anti-war movement, and negotiations with the North were opened in the hope of finding a settlement.

By 1972 the Viet Cong, already depleted by the 1968 Tet Offensive, had lost control over much of countryside. The NVA responded with a conventional offensive, which was exactly what the US forces were best at dealing with. However, despite a victory the USA had problems at home, and internal pressure eventually forced a decision to pull out. The USA took steps to enable South Vietnam to defend itself, but these eventually proved inadequate in the face of an overwhelming Northern invasion. By then, however, US involvement in Vietnam was over.

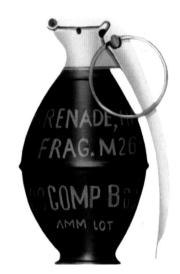

▶ M26 fragmentation grenade

1st Marine Regiment, Hue, February 1968

The city of Hue was the site of the only real Communist success in the NVA Tet Offensive, and even that didn't last. Bitter urban fighting went on for a month before the city was retaken by US and ARVN forces. Fragmentation grenades proved especially lethal in confined spaces.

Specifications

Country of Origin: United States	Diameter: 57mm (2.24in)
Date: 1950s	Detonation Mechanism: Timed friction fuse
Type: Fragmentation	Filling: Composition B
Weight: .454kg (1lb)	Lethal radius:15m (49ft)
Height: 99mm (3.89in)	

Specifications

Country of Origin: United States	Overall Length: 950mm (37.4in)
Date: 1963	Muzzle Velocity: 145m/sec (475ft/sec)
Calibre: 66mm (2.6in)	Feed/Magazine: Single-shot, muzzle-loaded
Operation: Rocket motor	Range: c.200m (650ft)
Weight: 2.5kg (5.5lb)	

▲ M72 LAW

196th Infantry Brigade / Operation Cedar Falls, January 1967

The M72 Light Anti-Tank Weapon was used in Vietnam primarily against bunkers and other fortified positions, as NVA tanks were rarely encountered.

US special forces
1967–75

A variety of special operations forces took part in the Vietnam conflict. They were given considerable latitude in choosing their weaponry.

THE US SENT MILITARY ADVISORS to South Vietnam long before its conventional forces became involved in the conflict. Increasing numbers of special forces personnel were deployed as the war went on, undertaking a wide variety of operations.

During World War II, special forces units had served mainly as covert raiding forces, but by 1960 they were heavily involved in training local personnel. The beneficiaries included the South Vietnamese regular army, as well as local defence units and irregulars recruited from indigenous peoples living in remote areas of Vietnam. Contacted and befriended by special operations groups, they were given training and weapons and fought against the Communists under US special forces leadership.

From 1960 to 1965 the US special forces learned their new role and developed their techniques to suit. The situation in Vietnam was novel, and beyond the existing experience of the US military, so a trial-and-error approach had to be used. Gradually, a body of knowledge was developed which could be applied to the unique demands of the situation. One key role of the special forces was reduction of Viet Cong

▲ **Advisory role**
A US special forces advisor accompanies two south Vietnamese irregulars. He is armed with a Colt Commando, a weapon issued primarily to US special forces.

influence by helping local communities defend themselves. Collectively known as the Civilian Irregular Defense Group (CIDG), this organization used special forces personnel to train local militias in weapons handling and small-unit tactics, and give

▲ **Heckler & Koch HK33**

5th Special Forces Group, Thong Binh, January 1968

The HK33 was used in very limited numbers by US special forces personnel, especially the US Navy SEALs, who prized its accuracy and reliability under difficult conditions.

Specifications

Country of Origin: West Germany	Barrel Length: 332mm (13.1in)
Date: 1968	Muzzle Velocity: 880m/sec (2887ft/sec)
Calibre: 7.62mm (.3in) NATO	Feed/Magazine: 20-round detachable box
Operation: Delayed blowback	magazine
Weight: 4.4kg (9.7lb)	Range: 500m (1640ft) +
Overall Length: 940mm (37in)	

them the confidence to defy the Viet Cong. CIDG was generally successful, and eventually CIDG personnel were able to go over from local defence duties to engaging the Viet Cong actively wherever they could be found.

Special forces personnel also engaged in more conventional operations, such as long-range reconnaissance and intelligence-gathering, ambushes, and rescues of personnel who had been captured or cut off. They had a range of weaponry at their disposal for these missions. The choice was usually high-firepower weapons that enabled the inevitably outnumbered special forces personnel to level the odds in an engagement.

Special forces units made extensive use of suppressed versions of standard firearms, which were highly useful in eliminating sentries or isolated personnel without alerting their comrades. Light, handy weapons such as submachine guns or the Colt Commando – a shortened version of the M16 rifle – were also popular. Weapons were selected to suit each mission; there was no standard issue.

Many weapons were 'sanitized', i.e. they had their serial numbers removed to prevent identification of the personnel involved in an incident. Some special forces troopers even favoured enemy equipment, making it easy to obtain ammunition during a long mission.

▲ **Ingram MAC 10**

CIA Operatives, Laos, 1971

The small size of the MAC 10 and its ability to use a suppressor made it an ideal weapon for covert operatives, whose mission might be compromised by even a victorious firefight.

Specifications

Country of Origin: United States	Overall Length: 548mm (21.57in)
Date: 1970	Barrel Length: 146mm (5.75in)
Calibre: 11.4mm (.45in)/45 ACP;	Muzzle Velocity: 366m/sec (1200ft/sec)
9mm (.35in) Parabellum	Feed/Magazine: 32-round detachable box
Operation: Blowback	magazine
Weight: 2.84kg (6.25lb)	Range: 70m (230ft)

▲ **Colt Commando**

US NAVY SEAL Teams / Mekong Delta, March 1970

The US Navy's Sea-Air-Land (SEAL) teams were active in Vietnam throughout the war, notably in operations to deny the enemy the use of waterways for logistics and troop movements.

Specifications

Country of Origin: United States	Overall Length: 780mm (30.7in)
Date: 1967	Barrel Length: 290mm (11.5in)
Calibre: 5.56mm (.219in) NATO	Muzzle Velocity: 796m/sec (2611ft/sec)
Operation: Gas	Feed/Magazine: 30-round box magazine
Weight: 2.44kg (5.38lb)	Range: 400m (1312ft)

Stoner Weapon System
1963–67

The Stoner Weapon System was built around a common receiver; it could be configured as a rifle, a carbine or a light machine gun.

EUGENE STONER designed the AR-15 rifle, which became the M16 in US military service, as well as several other weapons. His vision for the 'Stoner Weapon System' was to create a weapon that could be rapidly reconfigured to suit changing needs by fitting different barrels, feed mechanisms and stocks to a common receiver.

Evaluation

After experimenting with 7.62x51mm calibre, Stoner settled on 5.56x45mm and developed a prototype for military evaluation. Examples were deployed to Vietnam with special forces and some US Marine Corps units. There, the weapon system was found to be overcomplex and difficult to maintain in the field, though small numbers remained in use with the US Navy's SEAL teams for some years.

The Stoner receiver could be fed from a 20- or 30-round box magazine, a 100-round drum or a 100- or 150-round belt. The belt could be carried in a box or drum, allowing the weapon to be used as an assault rifle with huge ammunition capacity. The drum configuration proved to be the most popular of the possible options with US special forces, largely for this reason.

Barrels were designed for quick interchangeability, which also allowed a hot machine gun barrel to be rapidly swapped under sustained-fire use. A

Specifications

Country of Origin: United States
Date: 1963
Calibre: 5.56mm (.219in)
Operation: Gas, air-cooled
Weight: 5.3kg (11.68lb)
Overall Length: 1022mm (40.25in) standard barrel

Barrel Length: 508mm (20in) standard; 399mm (15.7in) short
Muzzle Velocity: 1000m/sec (3280ft/sec)
Feed/Magazine: 150-round disintegrating-link boxed belt or a detachable box magazine
Cyclic Rate: 700–1000rpm
Range: 1000m (3280ft)

▲ **M63 tripod-mounted machine gun**
US Navy SEALS (location unknown)

Mounted on a tripod, the Stoner M63 could fulfil a sustained-fire role for defence of a base or installation. It was still closer to a light machine gun than a general-purpose machine gun, however.

detachable bipod was often used in the light machine gun role, but could be removed or replaced with a tripod mount.

Different configurations

The weapon could be configured with a standard or folding stock and different barrels, and set up to fire from a closed or open bolt depending on its intended role. The carbine version, with a short barrel and folding stock, did not prove popular for various reasons. Notably, it was heavy for a weapon of its type. The assault rifle version fared little better, for much the same reasons.

As a light machine gun, the Stoner weapon system was a modest success. US special forces liked it, especially in 'Commando' configuration. This was a drum-fed variant of the LMG, which was light enough to be used as a rifle.

▲ M63 assault rifle

1st Marine Division / 1st Marine Regiment (location unknown), 1967

USMC units trialled the Stoner Weapon System in rifle configuration during 1967, but did not recommend it for adoption as a service weapon.

Specifications

Country of Origin: United States
Date: 1963
Calibre: 5.56mm (.219in)
Operation: Gas, rotating bolt
Weight: 5.3kg (11.68lb)
Overall Length: 1022mm (40.25in)

Barrel Length: 508mm (20in)
Muzzle Velocity: 3250ft/sec (991m/sec)
Feed/Magazine: 30-round detachable box
  magazine
Range: 200–1000m (656–3280ft)

Specifications

Country of Origin: United States
Date: 1963
Calibre: 5.56mm (.219in)
Operation: Gas, air-cooled
Weight: 5.3kg (11.68lb)
Overall Length: 1022mm (40.25in) standard
barrel

Barrel Length: 508mm (20in) standard; 399mm
  (15.7in) short
Muzzle Velocity: 1000m/sec (3280ft/sec)
Feed/Magazine: 150-round disintegrating-link
  boxed belt or a detachable box magazine
Range: 1000m (3280ft)

▲ M63 light machinegun

US Navy SEALs (location unknown)

The light machine gun version was used by some Navy SEAL teams. Its chief advantage was a huge ammunition capacity in a weapon not much heavier than a standard assault rifle.

AVRN forces
1959–75

The Army of the Republic of Vietnam (ARVN) was created with US assistance, and was armed and equipped along American lines.

AFTER THE INDOCHINA WAR ENDED, it was necessary to help South Vietnam create a military capable of defending against the Communist threat from the north. The recent Korean conflict shaped the thinking of US advisors sent to train the new force, and the strategists who decided what form it would take.

In Korea, the threat was a massive conventional attack by hordes of infantry and possibly tanks. The conventional force fielded by the USA and other nations, based on World War II experience, had proved effective against this threat, and so it was logical to build the ARVN along those lines.

This policy turned out to be a mistake. The ARVN lacked the training and confidence to deal with a mass insurgent campaign of the sort waged by the Viet Cong. It might possibly have handled a conventional invasion, but as post-US

▲ **'Tommy Gun'**

US Army special advisors instruct South Vietnamese militia in the use of the Thompson submachine gun. 'Tommy Guns' were widely used by South Vietnamese army troops and security forces.

▲ **M14A1 squad support weapon**

25th ARVN Division / 50th ARVN Infantry Regiment, An Loc, April 1972

The M14 was not a huge success as an automatic rifle, and many examples were converted to squad-level support weapons, with a modified handgrip and stock. Ammunition supply and the lack of a quick-change barrel limited sustained-fire capability.

Specifications

Country of Origin: United States
Date: 1963
Calibre: 7.62mm (.3in) NATO
Operation: Gas
Weight: 3.88kg (8.55lb)
Overall Length: 1117mm (44in)

Barrel Length: 558mm (22in)
Muzzle Velocity: 595m/sec (1950ft/sec)
Feed/Magazine: 20-round detachable box
magazine
Range: 800m (2625ft) +

withdrawal events showed, it could well have been as overmatched by the conventional forces of the NVA in 1959 as it was in 1975.

Imported weaponry

There was nothing wrong with the weaponry of the ARVN units. Much of it was perhaps obsolescent, such as the Thompson submachine gun, but it was still effective. Indeed, Thompsons were still being issued to some US troops due to insufficient numbers of the 'official' submachine gun, the M3 'Grease Gun'.

Significant amounts of ARVN equipment was bought overseas with US dollars, such as the Danish Madsen submachine gun. Other weapons were handed over as they became obsolete in US service. As the M14 rifle was replaced by the M16, quantities became available for other purposes. Some (in semi-automatic and full-automatic configurations) went to ARVN units, while others were converted to squad support weapons as the M14A1. Whilst not ideal for the role, the M14A1 did provide reasonable squad-level automatic fire support.

▲ Thompson Model 1928

25th ARVN Division / 25th Recon Battalion, An Loc, April 1972

Although its range was limited, the Thompson's reliability and good stopping power made it popular with reconnaissance and 'point' troops who might have to respond to a sudden contact or an ambush.

Specifications

Country of Origin: United States	Barrel Length: 266mm (10.5in)
Date: 1928	Muzzle Velocity: 280m/sec (920ft/sec)
Calibre: 11.4mm (.45in) M1911	Feed/Magazine: 18-, 20- or 30-round detachable
Operation: Delayed blowback	box magazine
Weight: 4.88kg (10.75lb)	Range: 120m (394ft)
Overall Length: 857mm (33.75in)	

Specifications

Country of Origin: Denmark	530mm (20.85in) stock folded
Date: 1950	Barrel Length: 197mm (7.75in)
Calibre: 9mm (.35in) Parabellum	Muzzle Velocity: 380m/sec (1274ft/sec)
Operation: Blowback	Feed/Magazine: 32-round detachable box
Weight: 3.17kg (6.99lb)	magazine
Overall Length: 800mm (31.5in) stock extended;	Range: 150m (492ft) +

▲ Madsen M50

1st ARVN Airborne Task Force, Hue, February 1968

The Madsen M50 had the unusual feature of a safety lever located just behind the magazine well, which functioned as a foregrip. If the weapon was not securely held in both hands, it could not fire.

Overall, the equipment of ARVN units was generally somewhat inferior to that of US forces, but not by such a great margin that they were massively outgunned by the NVA and Viet Cong. Indeed, the Communist forces were often using their own versions of the same weapons.

The main factors limiting the effectiveness of ARVN units were strategic, based on misconceptions about the nature of the war they were to fight, plus a lack of training and skilled leadership. Nevertheless, ARVN formations could and did fight well in the right circumstances.

▶ Weapons training

A US Army advisor trains ARVN irregulars in the use of a mortar. Most of the ARVN soldiers are armed with M1 carbines, although one can be seen holding a Thompson submachine gun.

Specifications

Country of Origin: United States	Barrel Length: 610mm (24in)
Date: 1918	Muzzle Velocity: 850m/sec (2800ft/sec)
Calibre: 7.62mm (.3in)	Feed/Magazine: Belt-fed
Operation: Recoil, water-cooled	Cyclic Rate: 600rpm
Weight: 15kg (32.75lb)	Range: 2000m (6560ft) +
Overall Length: 980mm (38.5in)	

▼ Browning M1917

7th Infantry Division / 11th Infantry Regiment, Ap Bac, January 1963

The water-cooled M1917, predecessor to the highly successful M1919, was primarily useful for defensive operations. Heavy and bulky, it required a steady supply of water for the cooling jacket.

Australian/NZ forces
1962–73

Both Australia and New Zealand deployed significant numbers of troops to Vietnam, and both suffered anti-war protests as a result.

CONCERNED ABOUT THE RISE OF COMMUNISM in nearby South-East Asia, Australia began sending military advisors to South Vietnam from 1962 onwards. New Zealand also sent military personnel, but these assisted in civilian construction and medical projects. From 1965, the New Zealand contribution included combat troops in the form of artillery and infantry, which were integrated into a joint Australian/New Zealander (ANZAC) battalion.

The Australian contribution was rather larger, creating an all-arms force which at first assisted US troops and then began to undertake operations within its own area of responsibility. The Australian units included special forces personnel and tanks as well as tactical air support elements.

The ANZAC forces proved to be extremely good jungle fighters, drawing on expertise gained in World War II, the Malayan Emergency and in Indonesia. They were capable in both small-scale patrol actions and larger battles, inflicting heavy casualties in defence of their bases. In 1968 the ANZAC force took part in resisting the Tet Offensive, with many troops established in blocking or ambush positions to prevent NVA infiltration.

Cordon-and-search operations
Most commonly, ANZAC forces were involved in typical cordon-and-search operations of a sort used by the British in dealing with many insurgencies. An area would be cordoned off and then systematically combed for hostiles and weapons caches. Those who tried to escape the encirclement were dealt with by the cordoning troops. Although slow and manpower-intensive, these operations were successful in reducing the enemy's ability to operate in the countryside.

Cordon-and-search operations, and patrols in the jungle, required good leadership at junior levels, skill and patience. ANZAC operations were often very methodical, reducing the chances of being ambushed but inviting criticism from US commanders who favoured a firepower-and-aggression approach to driving the enemy from his hiding places.

Although the ANZAC contingent did have armoured, air and artillery support, it was rifle squads that fought the bulk of actions. Whereas the US policy was to call in air and artillery support to inflict casualties on the enemy wherever possible, the ANZAC force preferred to use small-unit tactics and to stay in contact with a withdrawing enemy. Small units would be used to locate and track the enemy, with larger forces then brought up for an attack.

Artillery or air bombardment would have forced friendly ground troops to halt out of the danger zone and allowed enemy survivors a chance to disengage, but by relying only on their squad weapons the ANZAC infantry could maintain a close pursuit and deny the guerrillas their primary advantage – the ability to break contact and disappear.

▲ **Anti-guerrilla operations**
Armed with trusty L1A1 SLR rifles, Australian troops exchange fire with Communist forces somewhere in Vietnam.

The primary infantry weapon of Australian and New Zealander forces was the FN FAL/L1A1 rifle, chambered for 7.62x51mm ammunition. In the hands of troops whose training emphasized individual marksmanship over suppressive fire, this was an effective weapon, although its long-range accuracy was somewhat wasted in jungle engagements. For high firepower at close range, Australian troops favoured the indigenous F1 submachine gun. Although a curious top-loading design it proved reliable and easy to handle, and less prone to stoppages than many other contemporary submachine gun designs.

Overall, the ANZAC forces fought their part of the war on a small scale, using similar tactics to the guerrillas they hunted, and they were feared by their opponents. However, increasing opposition to the war and a lack of confidence in the US commitment to it after 1968 led to a gradual reduction in commitment and a complete withdrawal in 1973.

Specifications

Country of Origin: Belgium	Barrel Length: 533mm (21in)
Date: 1954	Muzzle Velocity: 853m/sec (2800ft/sec)
Calibre: 7.62mm (.3in) NATO	Feed/Magazine: 20-round detachable box
Operation: Gas, self-loading	magazine
Weight: 4.31kg (9.5lb)	Range: 800m (2625ft) +
Overall Length: 1053mm (41.46in)	

▲ FN FAL/L1A1

1st Australian Task Force / 6th Battalion, Royal Australian Regiment, Long Tan, August 1966

The 7.62x51mm L1A1 (the British and Australian version of the Belgian FN FAL) was best suited to actions in the open at medium to long range, where its user's marksmanship was a big advantage. At closer range it was arguably outgunned by assault rifles like the AK-47.

Specifications

Country of Origin: Australia	Overall Length: 715mm (28.1in)
Date: 1963	Barrel Length: 203mm (8in)
Calibre: 9mm (.35in)	Muzzle Velocity: 365m/sec (1200ft/sec)
Operation: Blowback	Feed/Magazine: 34-round magazine
Weight: 3.26kg (7.1lb)	Range: 100–200m (328–656ft)

▲ F1 submachine gun

173rd Airborne Brigade (US) / 1st Royal Australian Regiment, Gang Toi, November 1965

The F1 submachine gun favoured by Australian forces used a two-stage trigger for fire selection; halfway for single shots and a full trigger pull for automatic fire.

Specifications

Country of Origin: United Kingdom	660mm (26in) stock folded
Date: 1967	Barrel Length: 198mm (7.8in)
Calibre: 9mm (.35in) Parabellum	Muzzle Velocity: 300m/sec (984ft/sec)
Operation: Blowback	Feed/Magazine: 34-round detachable box
Weight: 3.6kg (7.94lb)	magazine
Overall Length: 864mm (34in) stock extended;	Range: 120m (394ft)

▲ **L34A1 Sterling**

1st Australian Task Force / Special Air Service Regiment, Suoi Pha Chau, August 1967

The Australian SAS made extensive use of the suppressed Sterling L34A1 during reconnaissance patrols and covert operations.

NVA/Vietcong Forces
1959–75

The North Vietnamese Army (NVA) and Viet Cong were separate forces operating in different ways towards a common political goal.

THE NORTH VIETNAMESE ARMY was a conventionally equipped force capable of undertaking large-scale operations in the field. Although it was also entirely able of carrying out small-scale guerrilla actions, its main role was that of any regular army – the defeat of the enemy's major forces and the capture of their bases.

The Viet Cong, on the other hand, was a guerrilla force unsuited to major conventional actions. Its personnel were equipped with a variety of armament and, usually, little in the way of support weapons. The Viet Cong was well suited to contesting control of the countryside. Its units needed little in the way of resupply; food, clothing and ammunition were all that was required and much of this could be extorted from villages or scavenged from enemy casualties.

Weapons

NVA and Viet Cong forces inherited a large quantity of arms left over from the previous war against France. This was augmented by locally produced weapons based on Soviet designs or near-identical copies of them, and examples of the original weapons themselves supplied by the Soviet Union and China. Viet Cong units often had to make do with whatever weapons were left over after equipping NVA infantry units, and so were issued a wide range of equipment. This included obsolete but effective weapons such as unlicensed Chinese copies of the Mauser C/96 pistol and other European weapons. Other, near-identical, weapons were originals supplied for use in earlier conflicts.

Regular NVA units were equipped as uniformly as possible and with the best weapons available. These included the Soviet AK-47 and the Chinese Type 56, which was a direct copy. Although lacking the long-range accuracy of Western rifles, the AK-47 was robust, easy to maintain and reliable even in jungle conditions. Its 30-round magazine and powerful round gave greater and more controllable firepower than US M14 rifle, while the M16 was (at least at first) far less reliable than its less advanced opponent.

Viet Cong capabilities

The Viet Cong did have considerable popular support in many areas, though this tended to vary according to how effectively the government's counter-insurgency measures were working. Genuine supporters were greatly outnumbered by those who could be swayed by a show of strength, and as the Viet Cong's power in the south waned, so did the degree of support it received.

However, the Viet Cong also received support via the Ho Chi Minh Trail through Laos and Cambodia, despite US efforts to interdict the flow of supplies. Thus many of its units were armed with Chinese, Soviet or North Korean weapons, while others had to make do with whatever could be scavenged.

Some personnel were armed with extremely outdated equipment, though this did not equate to

ineffectiveness in combat. Like all successful guerrillas, the Viet Cong were skilled at striking and then disappearing into the countryside or hiding among the general populace. Here again, the relative power of the Viet Cong in a region would often determine how willing the local population would be to hide guerrillas from the authorities.

In the early years of the conflict, the Viet Cong were the main instrument used by the Communists, and up until 1965 they were successful enough that political collapse in South Vietnam seemed likely. Lightly-equipped NVA units were slipped into South

▶ Mauser C96

Viet Cong / 514th Battalion, Ap Bac, January 1963

Chinese copies of the venerable Mauser C96 were supplied to Viet Cong fighters along with thousands of other weapons made available by the end of the Chinese Civil War.

Specifications

Country of Origin: Germany	Barrel Length: 140mm (5.51in)
Date: 1896	Muzzle Velocity: 305m/sec (1000ft/sec)
Calibre: 7.63mm (.3in)	Feed/Magazine: 6- or 10-round integral or
Operation: Short recoil	detachable box magazine
Weight: 1.045kg (2.3lb)	Range: 100m (328ft)
Overall Length: 295mm (11.6in)	

Specifications

Country of Origin: USSR	Barrel Length: 415mm (16.34in)
Date: 1959	Muzzle Velocity: 600m/sec (2350ft/sec)
Calibre: 7.62mm (.3in) Soviet M1943	Feed/Magazine: 30-round detachable box
Operation: Gas	magazine
Weight: 4.3kg (9.48lb)	Range: 400m (1312ft)
Overall Length: 880mm (34.65in)	

▲ AKM assault rifle

North Vietnamese Army / 325th Division, A Shau, March 1966

The NVA equipped many of its units with an updated version of the AK-47 designated AKM, supplied in large numbers by the Soviet Union. The AKM was introduced into Soviet Army service in 1959, and became the most ubiquitous variant of the entire AK series.

Vietnam in 1964 in anticipation; once in place they would be quickly able to restore order and install the Communist regime in a unified country.

However, instead of accepting victory, the NVA formations found themselves deep in enemy territory as the US intervention began. Unable to take on the Americans directly, many units dispersed to add to the strength of the Viet Cong. Although casualties were high in the clashes that followed, they never exceeded half the birth rate and were acceptable to the leaders and population of North Vietnam.

The NVA faced major US formations across the DMZ, exchanging artillery fire and engaging in near-constant skirmishing. Its forces also operated out of Laos and Cambodia, launching attacks into South Vietnam and then withdrawing to safety. Meanwhile, other elements were engaged in defensive operations in North Vietnam itself. The possibility of a US invasion was never ruled out, and the NVA had to be ready to respond at any time.

The Viet Cong, meanwhile, launched ambushes and attacked outposts throughout South Vietnam. One tactic was to attack an isolated post and then ambush the relief force, which of course had to proceed along a predictable route. The main role of the Viet Cong, however, was political rather than military. The casualties it inflicted on the US forces would have been acceptable in a major conflict like World War II or even Korea, but by the mid 1960s the mood 'back home' had changed and even

relatively low casualties provoked a negative response. The Viet Cong not only inflicted a steady stream of casualties but also drained US and South Vietnamese resources. Bridges, roads and towns had to be guarded; movement in many areas was only possible in heavily escorted convoys. Artillery firebases and supply bases were constantly harassed, tying down yet more resources. The Viet Cong also exerted strong influence over the population of the countryside, who lost faith in a government that seemed unable to protect them.

By 1968, the conflict had settled into a fairly steady pattern. The NVA tied up large-scale US formations and the Viet Cong wore down the political will of, and support for, the US and South Vietnamese governments. Nowhere in South Vietnam was entirely safe from guerrilla attacks and larger NVA offensives were capable of reaching areas a considerable distance from the Laotian or Cambodian border. The US forces had reason to believe that they were winning the war, however. Body counts were massively in favour of the USA and every major battle against the NVA had been won.

Tet Offensive

In January 1968, the North launched an operation that became known as the Tet Offensive, named after the period of the Vietnamese calendar in which it occurred. Attacks were coordinated between the NVA and the Viet Cong, which committed its entire

Specifications

Country of Origin: China	Barrel Length: 415mm (16.34in)
Date: 1956	Muzzle Velocity: 600mps (1969ft/sec)
Calibre: 7.62mm (.3in) Soviet M1943	Feed/Magazine: 30-round detachable box
Operation: Gas	magazine
Weight: 4.3kg (9.48lb)	Range: 400m (1312ft)
Overall Length: 880mm (34.65in)	

▲ **Chinese Type 56 assault rifle**

NVA 2nd Corps / 304th Division, Hue, March 1975

The Type 56 rifle supplied by China to many NVA units was distinguishable from the AK-47, of which it was a copy, mainly by the folding bayonet, though not all Type 56 rifles had this feature.

strength. More than 50 provincial capitals were attacked as well as outposts, bases and towns all over the country.

Tet was a failure for the North Vietnamese. It took a month to clear NVA forces from the ancient city of Hue, but most other objectives were either successfully defended or were cleared within a few days. The Viet Cong suffered such a mauling that it ceased to be much of a factor after Tet.

Connected with the Tet offensive was the siege of Khe Sanh, a major US base close to the border. Although there were fears that the North Vietnamese might succeed in turning Khe Sanh into another Dien Bien Phu, the base was never seriously threatened and the siege was called off after heavy fighting once the failure of Tet made it irrelevant.

The attacks on Khe Sanh were conventional infantry assaults with artillery support, carried out by regular troops. Although some assaults were successful, the US forces within the base were able to hold their perimeter and were eventually relieved by a ground and airmobile advance. After the Tet Offensive, the power of the Viet Cong was broken and the NVA carried on the war. It attempted to wage a guerrilla campaign in the south but was not very successful, and gradually the military balance tipped towards the US and South Vietnam. However, Tet had shaken the confidence of the USA to win the war, and prompted ever more intense anti-war sentiment. Despite being a military failure, Tet was a war-winning political success for the North.

Re-equipped

As the US tried to strengthen South Vietnam so that it could extricate itself from the conflict, the North attempted another major offensive in 1972. Re-

◀ **Tula-Tokarev TT-33**

Viet Cong / 186th Battalion, Mekong Delta, January 1965

The Soviet-supplied Tokarev handgun fired a weak cartridge but was reliable in combat. It was used more for intimidation purposes or covert attacks than as a serious combat weapon.

Specifications

Country of Origin: USSR	Barrel Length: 116mm (4.57in)
Date: 1933	Muzzle Velocity: 415m/sec (1362ft/sec)
Calibre: 7.62mm (.3in) Soviet	Feed/Magazine: 8-round detachable box
Operation: Short recoil	magazine
Weight: .83kg (1.83lb)	Range: 30m (98ft)
Overall Length: 194mm (7.6in)	

▲ **Simonov SKS**

Viet Cong / 275th Regiment, Long Tan, August 1966

Fed by an internal 10-round magazine, the SKS belonged to an earlier generation of rifles but remained effective in the hands of concealed guerrilla marksmen.

Specifications

Country of Origin: China/USSR	Overall Length: 1021mm (40.2in)
Date: 1945	Barrel Length: 521mm (20.5in)
Calibre: 7.62mm (.3in)	Muzzle Velocity: 735m/sec (2411ft/sec)
Operation: Gas short-stroke piston	Feed/Magazine: 10-round integral box magazine
Weight: 3.85kg (8.49lb)	Range: 400m (1312ft)

equipped with armament supplied by the Soviet Union, the NVA could field 130mm (5.1in) artillery and T54 tanks. Small arms included AK-47s from the Soviet Union and Type 56 rifles from China, which was more or less a direct copy. Some units still had to make do with what weapons they could get but on the whole the NVA was well equipped as a modern fighting force, and was quite capable of taking on ARVN formations equipped in the US style.

Advances were made into the north of the country from Laos and across the DMZ, while other NVA forces attacked towards Saigon from bases in Cambodia. The offensive was initially successful, defeating many ARVN formations in conventional battle, but gradually stalled in the face of stiffening resistance and US air support. Logistical difficulties plagued the NVA forces, along with a lack of experience at coordinating all arms in large-scale mobile operations. After years of relatively subtle guerrilla warfare, the NVA commanders resorted to frontal assaults against prepared positions, and their forces suffered accordingly.

The 1972 spring offensive collapsed so decisively that the NVA desperately needed time to reorganize and bring its depleted units up to strength. Negotiations were opened to stall for time, preventing a counter-offensive by ARVN forces, and over the next months the NVA rebuilt its strength.

Specifications

Country of Origin: Germany	Barrel Length: 418mm (16.5in)
Date: 1944	Muzzle Velocity: 700m/sec (2300ft/sec)
Calibre: 7.92mm (.312in) Kurz	Feed/Magazine: 30-round detachable box
Operation: Gas	magazine
Weight: 5.1kg (11.24lb)	Range: c.400m (1312ft)
Overall Length: 940mm (37in)	

▲ **Sturmgewehr 44**

Viet Cong Irregulars, Mekong Delta, April 1962

The StG44 was the world's first true assault rifle. Examples generally found their way into Viet Cong hands by way of the Soviet Union, which had captured large numbers during the invasion of Germany at the end of World War II.

Specifications

Country of Origin: USSR	Barrel Length: 520mm (20.5in)
Date: 1962	Muzzle Velocity: 735m/sec (2410ft/sec)
Calibre: 7.62mm (.3in) M1943	Feed/Magazine: 100-round belt contained in
Operation: Gas, air-cooled	drum
Weight: 7kg (15.43lb)	Cyclic Rate: 700rpm
Overall Length: 1041mm (41in)	Range: 900m (2953ft)

▲ **RPD light machine gun**

North Vietnamese Army / 304th Division / 66th Regiment, Khe Sanh, January 1968

The Soviet-supplied RPD was essentially an overgrown Kalashnikov rifle fed by a 100-round belt carried in a drum. It offered heavy squad-level firepower using the same ammunition as the surrounding riflemen.

US departure

US forces in South Vietnam were gradually reduced, with the last ground formations leaving in 1973. They left behind a situation that seemed generally positive despite continued NVA attacks. The ARVN had a numerical superiority over its opponents and was well equipped with artillery and armoured vehicles. However, the NVA had learned from its disastrous offensive in 1972 and had been extensively rearmed. By early 1974 it once again outnumbered its opponent, not least due to force reductions in South Vietnam after the withdrawal of US military aid. No longer needing to worry about the possibility of a US invasion, the NVA could commit its whole strength to a new offensive, and could concentrate at a point of its choosing. The whole eastern frontier of South Vietnam was open to attack, along with the obvious route across the DMZ from the north.

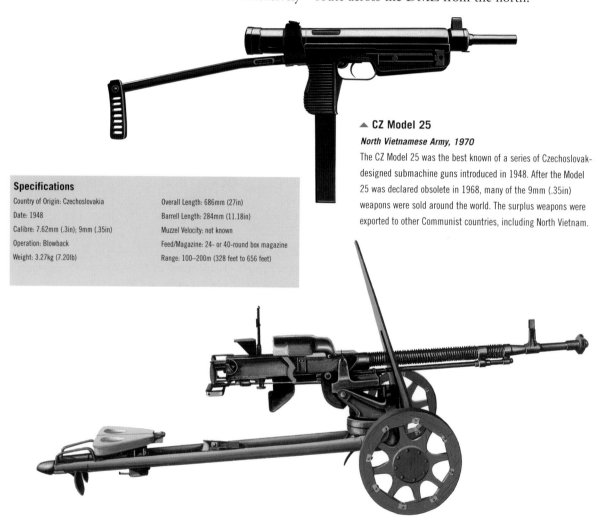

▲ **CZ Model 25**

North Vietnamese Army, 1970

The CZ Model 25 was the best known of a series of Czechoslovak-designed submachine guns introduced in 1948. After the Model 25 was declared obsolete in 1968, many of the 9mm (.35in) weapons were sold around the world. The surplus weapons were exported to other Communist countries, including North Vietnam.

Specifications

Country of Origin: Czechoslovakia	Overall Length: 686mm (27in)
Date: 1948	Barrell Length: 284mm (11.18in)
Calibre: 7.62mm (.3in); 9mm (.35in)	Muzzel Velocity: not known
Operation: Blowback	Feed/Magazine: 24- or 40-round box magazine
Weight: 3.27kg (7.20lb)	Range: 100–200m (328 feet to 656 feet)

▲ **DShK heavy machine gun**

North Vietnamese Army / 304th Division / 24th Regiment, Lang Vei, January 1968

The DShK machine gun was used in an infantry support role and also as an anti-aircraft weapon. Some examples in NVA service came from the Soviet Union; others were near-identical Chinese copies.

Specifications

Country of Origin: USSR	Barrel Length: 1066mm (42in)
Date: 1938	Muzzle Velocity: 850m/sec (2788ft/sec)
Calibre: 12.7mm (.5in) Soviet	Feed/Magazine: 50-round belt
Operation: Gas, air-cooled	Cyclic Rate: 550rpm
Weight: 35.5kg (78.5lb)	Range: 2000m (6560ft) +
Overall Length: 1586mm (62.5in)	

Afghanistan
1979–89

Intervention by the Soviet Union in Afghanistan led to a drawn-out counter-insurgent war that has been called 'The Soviet Vietnam'.

RUSSIA, AND LATER THE SOVIET UNION, had a long-standing interest in Afghanistan, dating from the middle of the nineteenth century. In the 1950s, Afghanistan requested financial aid from both the USA and the Soviet Union, which was granted for political reasons. For some years the country benefited from the superpowers competing for influence, but US aid was curtailed in the 1960s. Although still officially independent, Afghanistan was now firmly in the Soviet sphere of influence and reliant on financial aid from Moscow.

Turbulent Afghan politics produced a revolution in 1973 and a counter-revolution in 1978. The new government, with Soviet assistance, pushed through a number of reforms which alarmed traditionalists within Afghan society. Rebellion followed, spreading out from the Kunar Valley into most of Afghanistan's provinces.

The Soviet Union was concerned at this threat to its influence in Afghanistan and supplied modern weaponry to the Afghan Army, along with advisors to improve training standards. It also advised the Afghan government to slow down the pace of reforms and also to negotiate with the rebels, actions that caused a split in the Afghan government and an attempted coup.

With matters getting out of hand, the Soviet Union reluctantly decided upon a full-scale intervention. The incursion was presented as assistance to the Afghan government rather than an invasion, but all the same it provoked international sanctions and fierce resistance from Afghan rebels.

With advisors in place, gathering intelligence was not a problem for the Soviet forces, but the units that carried out the invasion were on the whole inexperienced. Many formations were composed of reservists who had been activated for the operation. There were some high-quality units involved, however, such as the Guards Airborne Division, which secured Bagram airbase in order to permit reinforcements to be flown in directly.

The Afghan response was derailed partly by deception. Many units were told by their advisors that their vehicles were to be upgraded or replaced; they were actually taken out of service by their own maintenance crews. At Bagram, Soviet troops were expected. They were supposedly coming to help with the security situation, which was at least partially true. Much of the Afghan army was disarmed and disbanded after the Soviets secured themselves in the country. A significant proportion of these troops joined the rebels – the real struggle was beginning.

▶ **Makarov PM pistol**

Soviet advisors to the Afghan Army, December 1979

The standard Soviet military handgun, the Pistolet Makarova (PM), fired a 9x18mm round that was incompatible with 9mm weapons used in the rest of the world.

Specifications

Country of Origin: USSR	Barrel Length: 91mm (3.5in)
Date: 1951	Muzzle Velocity: 315m/sec (1033ft/sec)
Calibre: 9mm (.35in) Makarov	Feed/Magazine: 8-round detachable box
Operation: Blowback	magazine
Weight: .66kg (1.46lb)	Range: 40m (131ft)
Overall Length: 160mm (6.3in)	

Soviet forces
1979–89

Soviet forces brought decent weapon systems to the war in Afghanistan, although as events demonstrated these could not compensate for poor training.

THE SOVIET ARMY that entered Afghanistan was shaped by the needs of the Cold War and the unique circumstances of the Soviet Union and its Warsaw Pact allies. With enormous manpower available, the Soviet Union relied on a short-service conscript army backed up by reserve units that could be filled out to full strength as needed. As a result, training levels were not high and most tactics were simple. The vast number of men fielded by the Soviet Union meant that the cost of equipment was critical. It also had to be simple and rugged; as 'soldier-proof' as possible to survive in the hands of relatively unskilled conscripts. This did not make Soviet equipment ineffective; large amounts of adequate weaponry may in some circumstances be more useful than smaller quantities of more advanced equipment.

The standard rifle used by the Soviet forces, the AK-74, was first and foremost easy to use and maintain, and extremely tolerant of abuse. It was developed from the AK-47 through the improved AKM and used the same basic mechanism. However,

it fired a lighter 5.45x39mm round and thus produced less recoil.

Range limits

Like all assault rifles, the AK-74 was primarily designed for combat at 200–300m (656–984ft) ranges or closer, and was less accurate at longer ranges than the M16. Its capabilities could be a limiting factor in Afghanistan, where combat ranges might be several hundred metres, but in any case the average conscript lacked the marksmanship skills to shoot effectively at such ranges. Where the AK-74 excelled was in delivering mass suppressive fire at moderate range, which suited the Soviet way of fighting.

The limited effective range of the AK-74 was somewhat offset by the inclusion in each platoon of a designated marksman armed with a Dragunov SVD rifle. These men were not snipers as such; their role was essentially that of a long-range marksman within the 'ordinary' infantry formations. While others delivered suppressive fire, the marksman was to pick off high-

▲ **Kalashnikov AK-74**

Soviet 40th Army / 5th Guards Division, Kandahar, January 1979

The AK-74 used a lighter round than the AK-47. The round reduced the gun's felt recoil and made the weapon more controllable to fire in both automatic and semi-automatic modes.

Specifications

Country of Origin: USSR	Barrel Length: 400mm (15.8in)
Date: 1974	Muzzle Velocity: 900m/sec (2952ft/sec)
Calibre: 5.45mm (.215in) M74	Feed/Magazine: 30-round detachable box
Operation: Gas	magazine
Weight: 3.6kg (7.94lb)	Range: 300m (984ft)
Overall Length: 943mm (37.1in)	

value targets such as officers and radio men. In Afghanistan this role was usually modified to one of engaging long-range or difficult targets, such as enemy riflemen hidden in high rocks during an ambush.

Fire support

Fire support was provided by RPK-74 and PKM machine guns, which had slightly different roles. The RPK-74 was essentially an AK-74 with a larger magazine capacity and a heavy barrel to dissipate heat. For squad-level light support it was effective, but it was not capable of sustained fire in the manner of a 'true' machine gun, due to ammunition capacity and overheating. It was lighter and more mobile however, which made it a useful weapon when operating in the difficult terrain of Afghanistan's mountains.

The PKM was a true machine gun, capable of sustained fire. Versions were used for infantry support and mounted on armoured vehicles. The BMP armoured personnel carrier used by the Soviet Army generally carried a pintle-mounted PKM, which could be used to support the infantry when dismounted.

Some Soviet units were issued the AKS-74, a version of the standard AK-74 with a folding stock. This was useful for troops who moved in and out of vehicles a lot, but was otherwise similar to the standard infantry rifle. The AKS-74U was a shortened carbine version of the AK-74 with a folding stock. It was largely used by airborne troops and special forces, as well as being issued to vehicle and artillery crews.

Uncoventional enemy

The Soviet forces that entered Afghanistan were well suited to conventional action against a clear enemy, and at first this is what they encountered. Some elements of the Afghan Army tried to oppose the intervention. In open battle they were no match for the Soviets, who had good air and artillery support. Popular uprisings in some urban centres were also relatively easy to put down.

The Soviet Army thus found it relatively straightforward to occupy and secure the cities of Afghanistan, but provincial areas were more of a problem. Most of the country was outside government control, and Soviet forces initially concentrated on securing the main communications

RED ARMY MOTORIZED RIFLE COMPANY, HQ EQUIPMENT	
Personnel	Equipment
Company HQ	BMP
Company Commander	PM (Makarov pistol)
Deputy Commander/Political Officer	PM
Senior Technician	PM
First Sergeant	AK-74
BMP Commander/Gunner	PM
BMP Driver/Mechanic	PM

RED ARMY MOTORIZED RIFLE COMPANY, PLATOON EQUIPMENT	
Personnel	Equipment
Platoon HQ	3 x BMPs
Platoon Leader	PM
Assistant Platoon Leader	AK-74

RED ARMY MOTORIZED RIFLE COMPANY, SQUAD EQUIPMENT	
Personnel	Equipment
Squad	BMP
Squad Leader/BMP Commander	AK-74
Assistant Squad Leader/BMP Gunner	AK-74
BMP Driver/Mechanic	PM
Machine Gunner	RPK-74
Machine Gunner	RPK-74
Grenadier	RPG-16/PM
Senior Rifleman	AK-74
Rifleman/Assistant Grenadier	AK-74
Rifleman	AK-74

One squad in each platoon was equipped with an SVD sniper rifle, in addition to the weapons listed above.

routes. Once established, and with a pro-Soviet Afghan government in place, the army began to launch operations against the rebels, or Mujahadeen.

Government installations in many of the provinces were in a state of virtual siege, and a major goal of operations against the insurgents was to break up or at least drive off nearby rebel groups, allowing the government apparatus to function as it was supposed to. This strategy was successful for a time after each operation, but control of most regions was lost soon after the troops returned to base.

Initially, the Soviets hoped to take a supporting role, assisting the Afghan Army in clearing the insurgents. Low morale, massive desertion and inadequate training made the Afghan Army ineffective in this role, and it was not greatly helped by a Soviet strategy that was interpreted as hiding behind the Afghan troops. Soviet personnel took on specialist roles such as artillery, armoured and air support while the bulk of the infantry work, and therefore casualties, fell on the Afghans. This situations caused resentment and drove down morale.

Unable to rely on the personnel they were ostensibly helping, the Soviets were forced to undertake operations on their own. Search-and-destroy operations were common, not unlike those used by the Americans in Vietnam. Ground troops were used to locate insurgent groups, which were then attacked by helicopter gunships and infantry with armoured vehicles in support.

Other measures included air attacks on villages suspected of offering support to the Mujahadeen, in the hope of depriving the insurgents of some of their bases of operations. Covert operations by Soviet special forces and infiltration by Afghan agents were also somewhat successful in reducing the effectiveness of the Mujahadeen in some areas.

However, the Mujahadeen were still able to attack installations, from public buildings to pipelines and power stations. They assassinated government figures, contested control over the countryside, and ambushed Soviet patrols or military convoys wherever they could.

There are few routes suitable for military convoys in the entire country, and these often run through mountainous areas full of excellent ambush spots. The Afghan tribes have a long tradition of resisting foreign invaders, and at times attacked Soviet convoys at points that had been used to ambush British troops a century before. Attacks ranged from harassment by the occasional sniper high up in the rocks beside the road to full-scale assaults with the intent of overrunning a convoy or part of it. Afterward, the insurgents withdrew into the mountainous terrain and broke contact.

One solution to the problem of ambushes along the mountain roads was to use airmobile forces to occupy high ground ahead of the convoy, picking up troops after the convoy had passed and moving them forward to the next overwatch point. This method was an extremely expensive and resource-intensive way to provide security, but it did prove effective. Helicopter gunships were also used against insurgent groups and were often successful in dispersing their attacks.

▲ **AKS-74**

Soviet 40th Army / 201st Motor Rifle Division, Kunduz, April 1979

The AKS-74 had a folding stock, which made it convenient for troops using motorized transport. It could be fired with reasonable short-range accuracy with the stock folded.

Specifications

Country of Origin: USSR	Barrel Length: 400mm (15.8in)
Date: 1974	Muzzle Velocity: 900m/sec (2952ft/sec)
Calibre: 5.45mm (.215in) M74	Feed/Magazine: 30-round detachable box
Operation: Gas	magazine
Weight: 3.6kg (7.94lb)	Range: 300m (984ft)
Overall Length: 943mm (37.1in) stock extended;	
690mm (27.2in) stock folded	

Up until 1985, the Soviets tried to defeat the insurgency by bringing the Mujahadeen to action and defeating them in the field. If enough bases could be destroyed, the insurgents could be driven from a region and the government could take control. Also, if enough casualties could be inflicted, the rebels might lose heart. However, despite successes in action, the Soviet Army was primarily engaged in holding onto its position in Afghanistan rather than making any real headway against the Mujahadeen.

The Soviet Army was generally effective in direct combat against the Mujahadeen forces, and could bring much greater numbers to bear at any given point than most insurgent bands. Yet it could only

exert control over a region by direct action. Once the Soviet troops moved on, the insurgents came out of hiding or returned from other regions. Only by strengthening the control of the Afghan government could the insurgency be defeated.

To this end, attempts were made to build up the Afghan Army along Soviet lines. Provided with good, modern weapons and properly trained, the Afghan Army might be able to take over the fight against the Mujahadeen. After 1985, this effort was more about ending the Soviet involvement in Afghanistan than winning the fight. The cost of remaining in Afghanistan was becoming too high, in terms of casualties, money and also international politics.

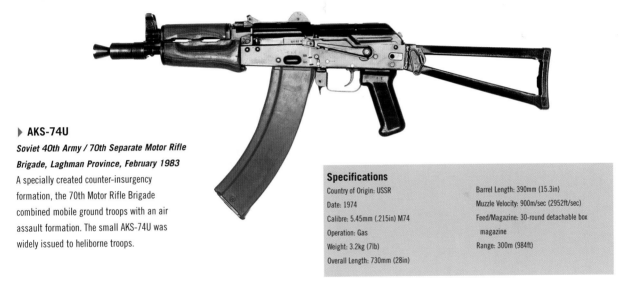

▶ **AKS-74U**

Soviet 40th Army / 70th Separate Motor Rifle Brigade, Laghman Province, February 1983

A specially created counter-insurgency formation, the 70th Motor Rifle Brigade combined mobile ground troops with an air assault formation. The small AKS-74U was widely issued to heliborne troops.

Specifications

Country of Origin: USSR	Barrel Length: 390mm (15.3in)
Date: 1974	Muzzle Velocity: 900m/sec (2952ft/sec)
Calibre: 5.45mm (.215in) M74	Feed/Magazine: 30-round detachable box
Operation: Gas	magazine
Weight: 3.2kg (7lb)	Range: 300m (984ft)
Overall Length: 730mm (28in)	

Specifications

Country of Origin: USSR	Barrel Length: 610mm (24in)
Date: 1963	Muzzle Velocity: 828m/sec (2720ft/sec)
Calibre: 7.62mm (.3in) Soviet	Feed/Magazine: 10-round detachable box
Operation: Gas	magazine
Weight: 4.31kg (9.5lb)	Range: 1000m (3280ft)
Overall Length: 1225mm (48.2in)	

▲ **Dragunov SVD**

Soviet 40th Army / 108th Motor Rifle Brigade, Jalalabad, March 1989

The Dragunov SVD provided infantry platoons with long-range firepower, extending the effective engagement range out to about 600m (1970ft). Its users were not snipers in the conventional sense, but infantry marksmen who were integrated with the rest of the unit.

▲ **PKM general-purpose machine gun**

Soviet 40th Army / 5th Guards Motor Rifle Division / 68th Guards Separate
Engineer Battalion, Adraskan, July 1984

The PKM machine gun was a workhorse that could be used for infantry support or
to create defended positions in a secured base area. It was fed by 25-round belts,
several of which could be linked together to create a longer belt.

Specifications

Country of Origin: USSR	Barrel Length: 658mm (25.9in)
Date: 1969	Muzzle Velocity: 800m/sec (2600ft/sec)
Calibre: 7.62mm (.3in) M1943	Feed/Magazine: Belt-fed (belts contained in
Operation: Gas, air-cooled	boxes)
Weight: 9kg (19.84lb)	Cyclic Rate: 710rpm
Overall Length: 1160mm (45.67in)	Range: 2000m (6560ft) +

This investment in the Afghan Army was partially successful, but the Afghan force was still prone to high levels of desertion. In some cases this was deliberate; insurgents would join in the hope of obtaining training, weaponry and information about government operations, then return to their comrades in arms. Sometimes they were able to take Soviet-supplied weapons with them.

The Soviets returned to a policy of using Afghan troops for the majority of infantry operations, with Soviet personnel in support. By this time the Mujahadeen were sufficiently powerful that they would sometimes contest a region rather than dispersing when large government forces moved in, and though the Afghan Army achieved some successes they came at the cost of serious casualties.

Despite the fact that the Afghan Army was not confident enough, nor capable enough, to take on the insurgents alone, the Soviets began a withdrawal from Afghanistan in 1987. This was in part to extricate itself from an impossible and costly situation, and partly driven by politics. Under new leadership, the Soviet Union was seeking better relations with the rest of the world, and ending the contentious involvement in Afghanistan removed a significant bone of contention.

Towards the end of their involvement in Afghanistan, Soviet forces were limited to self-defence and limited local operations to ensure the security of their supply lines. In 1989, Soviet forces made their withdrawal from Afghanistan. Negotiations with the Mujahadeen were generally successful in permitting a bloodless pullout in most areas, but a major clash occurred in the Panjshir valley. Soviet forces declined to close with the enemy but instead used air power and artillery to inflict casualties from a distance.

After the Soviet withdrawal, the Afghan Army abandoned some regions where the Mujahadeen were considered too strong to take on, but had victories in other engagements. The situation in Afghanistan did not greatly change in the immediate aftermath of the Soviet withdrawal. However, the government was still reliant on Soviet financial support. Economic troubles in the Soviet Union reduced the funds available for assistance, and the Afghan government could not maintain its forces in the field.

The defection of previously pro-government militias to the Mujahadeen sealed the fate of the government, which collapsed into factional infighting. Mujahadeen forces entered Kabul in 1992 and, after fighting among themselves for control of the capital, succeeded in creating the Islamic State of Afghanistan. This was toppled in 1996 by the

▲ **Basic army**
Armed with a variety of Soviet-made small arms, Afghan Army soldiers pose during the Soviet withdrawal from Kabul. 1989.

forces of the Taliban, which set up the Islamic Emirate of Afghanistan.

The Taliban government received little international recognition and was frequently condemned for its disregard of human rights. In 2001 it was removed from power by another invasion, this time by Western forces. By then, however, the Soviet Union had ceased to exist and its successor states showed little interest in further involvement with Afghanistan.

Specifications

Country of Origin: USSR	Barrel Length: 658mm (25.9in)
Date: 1974	Muzzle Velocity: 800m/sec (2600ft/sec)
Calibre: 5.45mm (.215in) M74	Feed/Magazine: 30- or 45-round detachable
Operation: Gas, air-cooled	box magazine
Weight: 9kg (19.84lb)	Range: 2000m (6560ft) +
Overall Length: 1160mm (45.67in)	

▲ **RPK-74 light support weapon**
Soviet 40th Army / 201st Motor Rifle Division / 149th Motor Rifle Regiment, Takhar Province, January 1984
The RPK light support weapon was issued with 45-round magazines, though it could also take 30-round AK-74 magazines if needed. It was operated almost exactly the same way as an AK-74, allowing any squad member to take over the gun in an emergency.

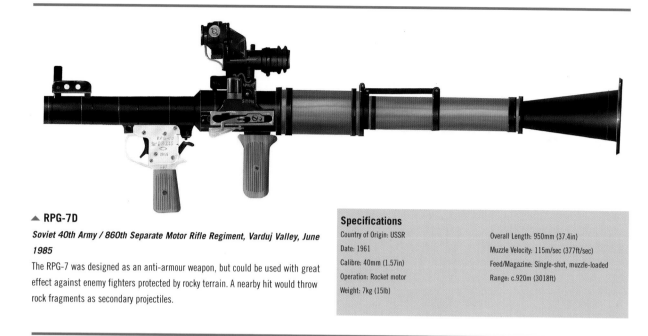

▲ RPG-7D

Soviet 40th Army / 860th Separate Motor Rifle Regiment, Varduj Valley, June 1985

The RPG-7 was designed as an anti-armour weapon, but could be used with great effect against enemy fighters protected by rocky terrain. A nearby hit would throw rock fragments as secondary projectiles.

Specifications

Country of Origin: USSR	Overall Length: 950mm (37.4in)
Date: 1961	Muzzle Velocity: 115m/sec (377ft/sec)
Calibre: 40mm (1.57in)	Feed/Magazine: Single-shot, muzzle-loaded
Operation: Rocket motor	Range: c.920m (3018ft)
Weight: 7kg (15lb)	

Mujahadeen
1979–89

The Mujahadeen was an alliance of several factions, all opposed to the pro-Soviet Afghan government. Its forces became more organized as the conflict went on.

RESISTANCE TO THE SOVIET OCCUPATION came primarily from tribal groups loosely aligned with regional warlords. These groups were effective guerrilla fighters from the start, drawing upon the experience of previous generations who had opposed other foreigners. The Mujahadeen were not strong enough to take on the Soviets directly, and were too disjointed to put together a sufficiently large force, but each group did what it could in isolation or, sometimes, in loose cooperation with others.

The result was to turn the areas controlled by the Afghan government and the Soviet armed forces into islands in a hostile sea, and even the islands were not safe. Mujahadeen personnel ambushed lone Soviet soldiers or small groups and carried out a campaign of sabotage and defiance in the cities.

Initially, the Mujahadeen were equipped with whatever weapons they had possessed before the conflict. These added up to a significant amount of small arms, as weapons ownership was a strong

tradition in many tribes. Additional weaponry was captured from Afghan or Soviet army units, or stolen from armouries. The weapons were generally Soviet types, notably AK-47s, or identical Chinese copies that used the same ammunition. Heavier weapons such as Stinger anti-aircraft missiles were also supplied via the CIA. Foreign aid also provided large quantities of arms. The US provided significant numbers of Stinger missiles to permit the insurgents to fight back against Soviet helicopter gunships, and to attack transport aircraft. These were delivered to the Mujahadeen via neighbouring Pakistan.

This external support provided the Mujahadeen with equivalent firepower to their opponents in some cases. However, their fighting methods were based around individuals and small groups, with few commanders able to field more than 200–300 men. Tactics generally revolved around ambushes or hit-and-run raids, avoiding stand-up fights which the Soviet Army was almost certain to win.

The most prized personal weapons among the Mujahadeen were assault rifles of the AK series. AK-47s and more modern AK-74s were popular for their reliability and ease of use. The effectiveness of these weapons depended very much on the user; most Mujahadeen fighters were individually courageous but lacked skills in fighting as a unit.

Older weapons such as bolt-action rifles were widely used, and could be deadly in the hands of a marksman concealed in the rocks above a road or outpost. One common Mujahadeen tactic was to harass an outpost with sniper fire at night, denying the troops posted there proper rest. There was no way to know whether the sniper was alone or an ambush force was waiting to attack a patrol sent out to deal with the sniper. The Mujahadeen also possessed quantities of captured heavy weapons and machine guns, but ammunition supply was always a limiting factor in their use. Even when the Mujahadeen groups became more organized and were able to field larger forces they remained essentially militias rather than trained and organized military forces, and lacked the logistical 'tail' required to keep the fighting 'teeth' supplied with much more than food and small-arms ammunition. Thus even the capture of the Afghan government's tanks and aircraft at Kabul did not change the essential character of the Mujahadeen as a guerrilla force.

▲ **Short Magazine Lee-Enfield (SMLE) Rifle No. 1 Mk III**

Mujahadeen Insurgents, Kunar Province, May 1979

The Mujahadeen possessed many weapons left over from previous conflicts. The British Lee-Enfield rifle was accurate and reliable, making it deadly in the hands of a gunman concealed in the rocks above a road.

Specifications

Country of Origin: United Kingdom	Barrel Length: 640mm (25.2in)
Date: 1906	Muzzle Velocity: 751m/sec (2465ft/sec)
Calibre: 7.7mm (.303in)	Feed/Magazine: 10-round box, loaded with 5-
Operation: Bolt action	round charger clips
Weight: 4.14kg (9.125lb)	Range: 500m (1640ft)
Overall Length: 1129mm (44.4in)	

Specifications

Country of Origin: USSR	Barrel Length: 415mm (16.34in)
Date: 1947	Muzzle Velocity: 600m/sec (1969ft/sec)
Calibre: 7.62mm (.3in) Soviet M1943	Feed/Magazine: 30-round detachable box
Operation: Gas-operated	magazine
Weight: 4.3kg (9.48lb)	Range: 400m (1312ft)
Overall Length: 880mm (34.65in)	

▲ **AK-47 assault rifle**

Mujahadeen Insurgents, Helmand Province, September 1986

AK rifles, and Type 56 Chinese copies, were supplied to the Mujahadeen in large quantities by other nations. Several Islamic nations, and also the United States, supported the Mujahadeen with funds and arms.

Chapter 9

Middle East and Africa, 1950–2000

The collapse of European colonial empires
in Africa created a volatile situation, as new states and
factions arose to seek a national identity. Some conflicts in
the region have roots going back centuries; others are
relatively new. Many African conflicts in the latter half of the
twentieth century pitted ill-armed militias against one
another or against European-equipped forces.
In the Middle East, a series of wars were fought between
Israel and its Arab neighbours. These conflicts were more
conventional in nature than the majority of African wars, and
were characterized by armoured warfare supported by air
power. However, in the final analysis it was infantry
equipped with small arms who took and held ground.

◀ **Congo force**
May 1978: Zairean Army troops strike an aggressive pose for photographers at Kolwezi Airport after they
recaptured it from the Katangan rebels after fierce fighting. Most are armed with FN FAL rifles.

Introduction

World War II itself had relatively little effect on the Middle East and sub-Saharan Africa, though the consequences of the war were far-reaching.

THE COASTAL STRIP along the Mediterranean coast was the scene of heavy fighting, but elsewhere, World War II did not much affect the people of the region. Similarly, the Middle East was the scene of relatively limited action; the main contest for ownership of the Middle Eastern oil fields was played out along the north coast of Africa.

After the war, its political consequences were felt throughout the region. Perhaps the greatest upheaval was the creation of a Jewish state. Jews and Arabs had lived, peaceably for the most part, in the region that is now Israel for centuries. The creation of a Jewish homeland and the arrival of thousands of European Jews, whose culture was radically different from that of those they came to join, caused massive upheaval and a violent backlash. The early history of Israel was troubled, and in 1956 Egypt implemented a blockade that resulted in an Israeli invasion of the Sinai Peninsula, timed to coincide with an Anglo-French attempt to capture the Suez Canal. Although the Suez affair was something of a fiasco for the British and French, it did establish Israel's reputation for military effectiveness, and secured Israel a strong bargaining position in the subsequent ceasefire negotiations.

With the blockade lifted, Israel once again had access to overseas trade. However, enmity between the new Jewish state and its neighbours continued to grow. Many Arab nations had expelled their Jewish population, or discriminated against them, and many of these dispossessed Jews settled in Israel. Meanwhile, many non-Jewish residents of the new Israel were opposed to the Jewish state. Many hundreds of thousands had left or been driven out, and later returned. There was no clear-cut solution

▲ **Freedom fighters**

Guerrilla fighters from the Liberation Front of Mozambique (FRELIMO) listen as their leader Samora Machel addresses them in a jungle camp in Mozambique, 1975. They are armed with a mixture of Portuguese and other European-made rifles and submachine guns.

▲ **Overwatch duties**

A US Marine mans an M60 general purpose machine gun during peacekeeping operations in the Lebanese capital Beirut, 1982.

and internal troubles were common. External influences exacerbated this situation, with neighbouring Arab countries backing insurgents against the Israeli government. In 1964 the Palestine Liberation Organization (PLO) was formed with the express intent of destroying Israel. Surrounding nations made no secret that this was also their goal. The result was that Israel became an armed camp, surrounded on all sides by enemies. A large proportion of the population were reservists in a military system designed to be rapidly activated. Rapid response was a stark necessity; Israel's borders are in some places just hours from the capital as the tank drives.

Decolonization

Meanwhile, European nations were losing their colonial possessions in Africa. Some tried to hold onto them. Others, like Britain, made a conscious choice to divest themselves of colonies that had become a burden. The 'retreat from Empire' that ensued was characterized by what became known as 'brushfire wars'. These were often complex affairs, with numerous factions fighting one another as well as the former colonial powers.

The small wars became, in many cases, proxy conflicts for the Cold War. The Soviet Union was willing to provide arms, funding and advisors to pro-Communist forces. Western powers felt compelled to counter with assistance to anti-Communist factions,

leading to Western support for highly dubious factions. A similar situation occurred in the 1980s, after the overthrow of the Shah of Iran by fundamentalist Muslim forces. The main enemy of the newly Theocratic Iran was Iraq, ruled by the brutal but at least not anti-Western regime of Saddam Hussein.

Fearing a fundamentalist takeover of the critical oil-producing Persian Gulf region, Western nations supported Saddam Hussein and turned a blind eye to his internal repression and use of chemical weapons against the Iranians. This necessary evil led to the Gulf War, after the end of the Iran–Iraq War in 1988.

Faced with crippling debt to neighbours such as Kuwait, who had supported the war against Iran, Iraq found a twofold solution to the problem. An invasion and annexation of Kuwait would not only remove the necessity to repay the debt, but would also give access to Kuwait's massive oil reserves, which could be used to rebuild the Iraqi economy.

The invasion was easy enough to accomplish, as Kuwait's armed forces were massively overmatched. The result, however, was an international coalition to remove Iraqi forces from Kuwait, which brought the world's most advanced military forces into conflict with the huge Iraqi Army.

Revolt in Algeria
1954–62

Military success against the Algerian insurgency was ultimately nullified by a changed political stance that was unacceptable to many within the French Army.

ALTHOUGH ALGERIA was recognized as part of metropolitan France, the political situation was typical of a colonial possession; a small minority of white settlers held political and economic power while a much larger Muslim population got by as best it could. The desire for independence and self-rule had always existed, but by 1954 it was being expressed in violence against the white settlers and French government possessions. The organization responsible was the FLN, or Front de Liberation Nationale. The FLN was a Muslim group which represented a large segment of the population through a number of popular leaders. Its opponents, the French government and the white settlers, were often at odds with one another, which complicated the situation significantly.

The French Army was effective in countering the early attacks, despite its recent humiliation in Indochina, and by early 1955 several key FLN leaders were either dead or imprisoned. The FLN was reduced to ineffectiveness, but even as the French government tried to win over the Muslim population with measures that were viewed with mistrust by the white settlers, the FLN was rebuilding its strength.

Violence erupted again, with massacres and revenge attacks launched by both the FLN and the settler militias. Operating from bases in newly-independent Tunisia and Morocco, the FLN launched attacks and terrorist operations, targeting in particular the capital, Algiers.

Army intervention

With the situation in Algiers out of control, the French Army was given a free hand to restore the situation, ordered only to do whatever was necessary to deal with the FLN. The city was subdivided by checkpoints and searches were conducted, but these measures were only partially successful. Without good intelligence about the FLN it was hard to find them, unless they revealed themselves in an attack.

Much of the army's work was routine: patrolling and standing guard or carrying out cordon-and-search operations. However, firefights with the FLN were not uncommon, as were sniper attacks on army personnel. Arrest operations were also carried out against targets suspected by the police of being FLN sympathizers or members. These people were interrogated, sometimes under torture, and yielded

▶ **MAS Mle 1950**

10th Parachute Division, Algiers, January 1957

The MAS 1950 was a robust weapon popular with its users. French paratroops searching houses for FLN personnel and weaponry found handguns more easily manoeuvrable than their rifles, especially when detaining suspects at gunpoint.

Specifications

Country of Origin: France	Overall Length: 195mm (7.7in)
Date: 1950	Barrel Length: 111mm (4.4in)
Calibre: 9mm (.35in) Parabellum	Muzzle Velocity: 315m/sec (1033ft/sec)
Operation: Short recoil, locked-breech	Feed/Magazine: 9-round detachable box
Weight: .86kg (1.8lb)	magazine

enough information to eventually cripple the FLN in Algiers.

Meanwhile, support for the FLN from outside the country was impeded by the 'Morice Line', an electrified fence and minefield along the Tunisian border. The line was patrolled constantly and breaches in the fence set off alarms that would trigger a response ranging from artillery bombardment to the deployment of tank, helicopter and mobile infantry forces to oppose any large-scale incursion.

French Army forces also took the offensive against FLN 'safe areas' in the countryside, and were generally very effective. Yet with the insurgents all but defeated, the French government changed its stance towards Algerian independence. Despite the revolt of elements within the French Army who found Algerian independence unacceptable after the sacrifices they had made fighting the insurgents, France pulled out and Algerian independence was declared in 1962.

▲ Fusil Mitrailleur Modele 49 (MAS 49)

25th Parachute Division, Algiers, January 1960

Re-arming after World War II, France sought to replace the assortment of older weapons then in service with a new semi-automatic rifle. The resulting MAS 49 was highly reliable and chambered a 7.5mm (.295in) round instead of the NATO standard 7.62mm (.3in) ammunition. .

Specifications
Country of Origin: France	Overall Length: 1010mm (39.7in)
Date: 1949	Barrel Length: 521mm (20.51in)
Calibre: 7.5mm (.295in)	Muzzle Velocity: 817m/sec (2680ft/sec)
Operation: Gas	Feed/Magazine: 10-round fixed box magazine
Weight: 3.9kg (8.6lb)	Range: 500m (1640ft)

Specifications
Country of Origin: France	Barrel Length: 600mm (23.62in)
Date: 1952	Muzzle Velocity: 840m/sec (2756ft/sec)
Calibre: 7.5mm (.295in)	Cyclic Rate: 700rpm
Operation: Lever-delayed blowback	Feed/Magazine: 50-round metal-link belt
Weight: 10.6kg (23.37lb)	Range: 1200m (3937ft)
Overall Length: 1080mm (42.5in)	

▲ MAS AAT-52

10th Parachute Division, Algiers, April 1955

Designed for mass production, the MAS AAT-52 used simple stamped and welded components. Static checkpoints allowed the French Army to restrict the movements of FLN personnel. Protected by sandbagged machine guns, these positions were usually strong enough to deter attack.

Arab–Israeli wars

1948–2000

Surrounded by nations intent on its destruction, Israel has fought several wars for survival; sometimes on the defensive and at times as the aggressor.

THE MODERN NATION OF ISRAEL was founded in 1948, in a region that has historical significance for both Arabs and Jews. Conflict was perhaps inevitable, and even before the United Nations had agreed on the creation of a new state, Jewish and Arab militias were fighting for control of the territories they claimed. It is not always possible to separate Israel's internal and external conflicts; both were aspects of the complex political situation in the troubled region.

On the day that Israel declared its independence, 14 May 1948, it was in control of strategic territories within its claimed borders, but was immediately invaded by forces from the surrounding Arab nations. A successful defence and counter-attack led to Israel's borders actually expanding as a result of this first war of survival.

The first major test for the Israel Defense Forces (IDF) was the 1956 invasion of Sinai, in response to the Egyptian blockade and closing of the Suez Canal. Skirmishing on the border and externally sponsored insurgency within Israel had been near-constant, but in October 1956 the nations of Egypt, Jordan and Syria openly declared their intent to launch a joint destruction of Israel under Egyptian command. The 1956 Israeli campaign into Sinai was to a great extent the only option available; a pre-emptive strike whose success bought Israel 11 years of relative security. Then, in 1967, Egypt re-implemented the blockade of Israel and openly made preparations for invasion. Another pre-emptive strike derailed this plan, but the Arab leaders continued to express their intent to destroy Israel. In 1973, it was the Arabs that struck first, inflicting severe losses on the unprepared Israeli forces before being driven back by a desperate counter-attack.

Tensions subsided somewhat after 1973, with peace treaties signed between Israel and some Arab countries, notably Egypt. The PLO continued to attack Israel, sometimes with Syrian assistance. This prolonged campaign led to an Israeli invasion of Lebanon in 1978 to drive out the PLO and eliminate Syrian missiles based there. Political initiatives have attempted to reduce the level of conflict between the PLO and Israel itself, with some success. However, terrorist attacks from the likes of Hamas and Hezbollah and aggressive Israeli responses still continue.

▶ **Militia fighters**
Armed with a variety of weapons, including FN FAL rifles, AK-47s, RPGs and M16 assault rifles, members of the Army of South Lebanon (ASL), a Christian militia, pose for the camera, Lebanon 1985.

Israel Defense Forces
1956–2000

The Israel Defense Forces (IDF) were initially armed with World War II-era equipment, but experience in action resulted in the development of weaponry and systems better tailored to the Israeli needs.

ONE EXAMPLE IS THE MERKAVA TANK, a uniquely Israeli design with the engine at the front. This gives the crew additional protection and leaves room for a compartment at the rear that can be used to transport infantry or supplies. Other success stories to come out of the Israeli arms industry are the Galil rifle series and the Uzi submachine gun. Early models of the Uzi were fitted with a fixed wooden stock, but soon a folding stock became available. This made the Uzi an ideal weapon for issue to vehicle crews and other personnel who might need a high-firepower self-defence capability, but could not carry a full-sized rifle. The Uzi was also issued to special forces and paratroop units, who prized its lightness, small size and deadly firepower.

Development of the Galil

Israel's Arab opponents were chiefly armed with Soviet weapons, including the ubiquitous AK-47 assault rifle. This weapon sufficiently impressed the Israelis that they decided to create an assault rifle of their own – the Galil – based on the Kalashnikov's mechanism. As other militaries discovered, the combination of a semi-automatic battle rifle and a submachine gun (the FN FAL and Uzi in the case of the Israeli Defence Force) was effective in some ways but limited in others. At long ranges, only rifle-armed troops could engage, while in close combat the FAL was less effective than Arab assault rifles. The adoption of the Galil enabled every Israeli soldier to engage at all ranges, increasing the overall effectiveness of the force. The Galil was every bit as rugged as the AK-47, and was overall a better rifle, giving the Israelis a man-for-man advantage in later conflicts which was beneficial to a nation whose forces were always outnumbered.

The Galil rifle made use of the extremely robust Kalashnikov rifle mechanism, but was constructed to a much higher standard than most AK rifles. The result was a highly effective assault rifle that has been gradually updated over the years. The 7.62mm (.3in) and 5.56mm (.219in) versions, configured as carbines, assault rifles and light support weapons, were an export as well as domestic success.

The Galil Sniper variant demonstrates the Israeli attitude to weaponry. It is essentially a very accurate semi-automatic version of the Galil. As such, it is not as accurate as a dedicated sniper weapon and has a shorter effective range. However, it is very tough and tolerant of arduous desert conditions. The Israeli

▶ **Beretta M1951**

IDF / 27th Armoured Brigade, Rafah, November 1956

The 9mm Beretta M1951 was used by both Arab and Israeli forces as a sidearm for officers and vehicle crews. It proved reliable and popular with its users.

Specifications

Country of Origin: Italy	Barrel Length: 114mm (4.5in)
Date: 1951	Muzzle Velocity: 350m/sec (1148ft/sec)
Calibre: 9mm (.35in) Parabellum	Feed/Magazine: 8-round detachable box
Operation: Short recoil, locked-breech	magazine
Weight: .87kg (1.92lb) empty	Range: 50m (164ft)
Overall Length: 203mm (8in)	

military believes that it is better to deploy a robust weapon that will continue to function under almost all circumstances than a sophisticated one that may not be available due to failure in field service.

Campaigns

In 1956, the Israeli units that took part in the offensive into the Sinai were largely composed of reservists called up for the conflict. The plan emphasized speed and aggression as there was little room for subtlety in the Sinai desert. Paratroops dropped in front of a rapid advance across the peninsula and southwards towards the Egyptian base at Sharm el Sheikh. The first Uzis saw combat during the Suez campaign, and proved useful for mechanized infantry needing a compact weapon, and for infantry units clearing bunkers and other confined spaces.

The Egyptian Army had significant forces deployed close to the Israeli border, but few reserves on the eastern side of the Suez Canal, and once the outer positions were cracked the Egyptians were unable to recover enough to mount an effective defence in most areas. This problem was compounded by the Anglo-French invasion of Suez, which forced the Egyptians to pull back from the Sinai in order to defend more critical territory.

◣ Uzi

IDF / 7th Armoured Brigade, Valley of Tears, October 1973

The Uzi saw action in 1956 in its original form with a fixed wooden stock. It was later issued with a folding metal stock and featured in virtually every Israeli conflict of the twentieth century. Handy, reliable and accurate, it was popular with vehicle crews and security forces.

Specifications

Country of Origin: Israel	Barrel Length: 260mm (10.23in)
Date: 1953	Muzzle Velocity: 400m/sec (1312ft/sec)
Calibre: 9mm (.35in) Parabellum	Feed/Magazine: 25- or 32-round detachable
Operation: Blowback	box magazine
Weight: 3.7kg (8.15lb)	Range: 120m (394ft)
Overall Length: 650mm (25.6in)	

▶ Mini Uzi

Israeli Special Forces, Lebanon, June 1982

The Mini-Uzi is well suited to use by special forces personnel operating in the close urban terrain of a city such as Beirut.

Specifications

Country of Origin: Israel	Barrel Length: 197mm (7.76in)
Date: 1980	Muzzle Velocity: 352m/sec (1155ft/sec)
Calibre: 9mm (.35in) Parabellum	Feed/Magazine: 20-, 25- or 32-round detachable
Operation: Blowback	box magazine
Weight: 2.7kg (5.95lb)	Range: 50m (164ft)
Overall Length: 600mm (23.62in)	

Israel Defense Forces Platoon, 1956

The Israel Defense Forces were initially equipped with weapons left over from World War II. Some of these came from stocks captured or confiscated from Germany by the Allies at the end of the war. This equipment was gradually replaced by home-produced weaponry.

Platoon HQ (6 x Uzis, 2 x Mauser Kar 98 rifles, 1 x Bazooka)

Rifle Squad 1 (1 x Uzi, 1 x Bren LMG, 8 x Mauser Kar 98 rifles)

Rifle Squad 2 (1 x Uzi, 1 x Bren LMG, 8 x Mauser Kar 98 rifles)

Rifle Squad 3 (1 x Uzi, 1 x Bren LMG, 8 x Mauser Kar 98 rifles)

Specifications

Country of Origin: Israel

Date: 1972

Calibre: 5.56mm (.219in) NATO

Operation: Gas

Weight: 4.35kg (9.59lb)

Overall Length: 979mm (38.54in)

Barrel Length: 460mm (18.11in)

Muzzle Velocity: 990m/sec (3250ft/sec)

Feed/Magazine: 35- or 50-round detachable box magazine

Range: 800m (2625ft) +

▲ **Galil**

IDF / 91st Division, Southern Lebanon, August 1982

Based on the ever-popular AK-47, the Galil was introduced to replace the FN FAL in Israeli service. The Galil is unusual in that it uses a 35-round magazine instead of the more typical 30 rounds. The long magazine can make firing from a prone position awkward.

The conflict ended with a UN-supervised Israeli withdrawal and the capture of large amounts of Egyptian vehicles and equipment. Some of this was pressed into service in other wars. Meanwhile, other Israeli forces pushed into Gaza, where there was fighting against Palestinian forces.

The 1956 campaign demonstrated the effectiveness of the tank to the IDF. Thus far the main arm had been infantry, with tanks and weapons mounted on light vehicles used for support. After 1956 the emphasis was placed on armoured forces, to the point where other arms received perhaps too little attention. Other lessons were learned but perhaps too well. Initiative and aggression rather than careful cooperation and mutual support had permitted a rapid advance and a successful campaign. The victory led to the belief that a headlong armoured charge would carry all before it, which created the potential for disaster as well as excellent success.

By 1967, Israel once again faced an imminent threat and responded with a pre-emptive strike. The conflict that became known as the Six-Day War opened with an all-out attack by the Israeli Air Force (IAF) against the air forces of its enemies. The first strikes were against Egyptian targets, but by the end of the first day the air forces of Jordan, Iraq and Syria had also been shattered.

The offensive against Egypt took the form of armoured thrusts along much the same routes as the 1956 attacks had followed. Surprise and sheer aggression allowed the leading armoured units to punch holes in the defence and overrun unprepared units. However, the Egyptian forces put up a stubborn resistance and held up the advance at several points. Total Israeli air superiority allowed heavy air attacks that broke numerous positions and allowed the advance to continue, and air power allowed a daring raid by helicopter-borne troops on a major Egyptian artillery concentration. As the Egyptian army disintegrated, both sides raced for the Suez Canal. The Israelis were able to trap large Egyptian forces on the western size, eliminating most of the Egyptians' armoured strength.

Meanwhile, other elements of the IDF attacked Syria and Jordan. Jordanian forces fought bravely but were no match for the better-equipped IDF. In Syria, the Israeli goal was to capture the Golan Heights, which would serve as a defensive barrier against future threats. By the end of the war Israel had expanded its borders out to natural barriers: the Golan Heights, the River Jordan and the Suez Canal. However, the IDF had acquired a dangerous level of overconfidence which would cost it dear in action six years later.

Specifications

Country of Origin: Israel

Date: 1972

Calibre: 7.62mm (.3in) NATO

Operation: Gas, self-loading

Weight: 6.4kg (14.11lb)

Overall Length: 1115mm (43.89in)

Barrel Length: 508mm (20in)

Muzzle Velocity: 815m/sec (2675ft/sec)

Feed/Magazine: 20-round detachable box magazine

Range: 800m (2625ft) +

▲ **Galil AR sniper**

IDF / Golani Brigade, Siege of Beirut, August 1982

The Galil Sniper is more accurately described as a 'designated marksman rifle' than a sniper weapon. It gives infantry formations additional long-range firepower.

In 1973, the Arab nations struck first, attacking on the Israeli holy day of Yom Kippur. Syrian armoured forces pushed into the Golan Heights while the Egyptians used Soviet river-crossing techniques to make an assault across the Suez Canal.

The IDF responded aggressively but in an uncoordinated fashion. This played into the Egyptians' hands; tank forces attacked without support and ran into new anti-armour weapons supplied by the Soviet Union. Despite heavy losses the IDF was able to seize the initiative and bring about the sort of mobile battle it was best suited for, driving back the Egyptians to the Suez Canal. Meanwhile the Syrian armoured thrusts had been narrowly defeated and a successful counter-attack was in progress. Diplomatic pressure secured a ceasefire, leading to more permanent treaties. For the IDF, the lesson learned was that all-arms cooperation was necessary, returning infantry and artillery to a more prominent role.

▲ **IMI Negev**

IDF / Givati Brigade, Gaza Strip, 2000

Designed as a multi-purpose weapon, the Negev machine gun can be fed using a 150-round belt or Galil rifle magazines. With the assistance of an adapter it can take standard M16 magazines.

Specifications

Country of Origin: Israel	Barrell Length: 460mm (18.1in)
Date: 1997	Muzzle Velocity: 915m/sec (3,002ft/sec)
Calibre: 5.56mm (0.21in)	Feed/Magazine: 150 round amunition belt or
Operation: Gas, rotating bolt	35-round box magaizine
Weight: 7.40kg (16.31lb)	Range: 300–1000m (984–3280ft)
Overall Length: 1020mm (40in)	

▲ **IMI Tavor TAR 21**

IDF / Golani Brigade, Operation Defensive Shield, Jenin, 2002

The TAR 21 is the IDF's latest servce weapon. It follows a general trend towards 'bullpup' configuration weapons (the action set behind the pistol grip), which are easy to handle in the confined spaces of urban combat.

Specifications

Country of Origin: Israel	Overall Length: 720mm (28.3in)
Date: 2001	Barrel Length: 460mm (18.1in)
Calibre: 5.56mm (.219in) NATO	Muzzle Velocity: 910m/sec (2986ft/sec)
Operation: Gas, rotating bolt	Feed/Magazine: Various STANAG magazines
Weight: 3.27kg (7.21lb)	Range: 550m (1804ft)

Arab forces
1956–82

While there has always been conflict among the people of the Middle East, clashes between Arabs and Jews became much more prevalent in the 1920s.

JEWS BEGAN TO SETTLE in what is now Israel in order to escape Nazi persecution, and there is strong evidence that some anti-Jewish activity in the Middle East was funded by the Nazi Party. Whatever the root cause, conflict gradually intensified. Even when Israel was not engaged in hostilities with her neighbouring countries, insurgent forces were at work within the state. Conflict over disputed territories such as the Gaza Strip created an endless cycle of attack and retribution, with Jewish irregular forces carrying on their own local wars even when the IDF was not involved.

The creation of the PLO in 1964 represented a serious threat to Israel's internal and international security. The PLO received support from neighbouring Arab countries and could field well-armed fighters who had, in some cases, received formal training from overseas advisors.

The main threat to Israel's existence, however, was from Egypt and her allies. Largely equipped with Soviet-supplied weaponry or locally made derivatives, Egypt's military was, on the whole, willing and able to fight but poorly led. In particular, officers and enlisted men tended to come from entirely different social classes and lacked confidence in one another. Thus Egyptian formations proved brittle in some actions. Egyptian forces were relatively poor in fluid combat, largely because their armoured forces were inadequately trained for the complex nature of mobile warfare. The infantry and artillery, whose operations were not so complex, tended to perform better. Thus the Egyptians were at their best in static defensive operations. At times, Egyptian defensive positions were breached by Israeli armour, which then raced on to new objectives leaving its supporting arms unable to push through the battered but stubborn defence.

However, extensively equipped with the AK-47 assault rifle, Arab forces enjoyed a significant firepower advantage over their Israeli opponents at all ranges. Each soldier could deliver suppressing fire, making fire-and-manoeuvre tactics more effective. When aimed fire was more appropriate, the AK-47 was accurate out to a reasonable distance; at least as far as the typical soldier can shoot effectively. Although the AK-47's performance dropped off after around 300-400 metres (950–1300 feet), this was not a significant disadvantage, especially during fighting on the relatively cluttered terrain of the Golan Heights.

▶ **Tokagypt 58**

Palestinian Irregulars, Gaza Strip, June 1967

An export version of the Tokarev semi-automatic pistol, the 'Tokagypt' was intended for army use but was adopted by the Egyptian police instead. Some examples of the weapon found their way into the hands of Egyptian-supported Palestinian militias.

Specifications

Country of Origin: Egypt/Hungary

Date: 1958

Calibre: 9mm (.35in) Parabellum

Operation: Short recoil

Weight: .91kg (2.01lb)

Overall Length: 194mm (7.65in)

Barrel Length: 114mm (4.5in)

Muzzle Velocity: 350m/sec (1150ft/sec)

Feed/Magazine: 7-round detachable box
  magazine

Range: 30m (98ft)

▶ **Helwan pistol**

Egyptian Army / 3rd Armoured Battalion, El Arish, October 1956

The 'Helwan' pistol was an Egyptian copy of the Beretta M1951, which was used under its own name by the Israeli forces.

Specifications

Country of Origin: Egypt	Barrel Length: 114mm (4.5in)
Date: 1955	Muzzle Velocity: 350m/sec (1148ft/sec)
Calibre: 9mm (.35in) Parabellum	Feed/Magazine: 8-round detachable box
Operation: Short recoil	magazine
Weight: .89kg (1.96lb)	Range: 50m (164ft)
Overall Length: 203mm (8in)	

Specifications

Country of Origin: Egypt	Barrell Length: 638mm (25.1in)
Date: Early 1950s	Muzzel Velocity: 853.44m/sec (2800ft/sec)
Calibre: 7.62mm (.3in)	Feed/Magazine: 10-round box magazine
Operation: Gas, tilting bolt	Range: 457m (1500ft)
Weight: 4.4kg (9.7lb)	
Overall Length: 1216mm (25.1in)	

▲ **Hakim rifle**

Egyptian Army / 5th Brigade, Rafah, October 1956

The Hakim rifle was derived from a Swedish weapon and fired a full-power battle rifle cartridge. It was replaced in service by the AK series, but many examples remained in reserve.

Improved training

With assistance from Soviet advisors, the standard of Egyptian training and combat doctrine improved considerably. After the crushing defeat of 1967, the IDF became complacent, while the Egyptian Army was rebuilt and retrained with the lessons of the Six-Day War in mind. In 1973, the Egyptian Army proved that it could not only conduct a river crossing in the Soviet style, but could adapt and innovate to meet the unique challenges of crossing the Suez Canal.

While greatly improved, the Egyptian armoured forces were still not a match for the Israelis, at least not tank for tank. This disadvantage was offset by the use of new Soviet-supplied guided anti-tank weapons and better tactics. Where possible the Egyptians halted and allowed the Israelis to launch their customary headlong armoured counter-attack. This allowed the (often unsupported) tanks to be engaged by both the tank guns of Egyptian armoured forces but also by infantry firing large numbers of guided missiles.

The Israelis learned to support their tanks properly, and to counter the Egyptians' wire-guided missiles by hosing the crews' suspected location with machine-gun fire. If the operator was forced to take cover, the missile could not be successfully guided. Nevertheless, the Egyptian Army inflicted heavy losses on the Israelis before being driven back across the canal by a counter-attack.

Syria, too, increased in capability. In 1967, the Israeli advance into the Golan Heights was contested by only part of the Syrian Army, and without great determination. In 1973, the Syrian Army made a massive effort in the Golan Heights and almost succeeded in breaking the Israeli resistance. The assault was made on a broad front by infantry divisions, each of which had some tanks, while the two Syrian armoured divisions were held in reserve to make a breakthrough or exploit an opportunity that might arise.

In the first two days of fighting the Israeli forces holding the heights suffered massive casualties, but managed to cling to their positions long enough for

reinforcements to arrive. That scratch Israeli forces, thrown together from whatever tanks and troops could be assembled, were able to delay the Syrian advance owes much to Israeli superiority of equipment.

However, the Israelis had been planning to fight a defensive action on the heights since 1967, and wrung the absolute maximum value out of each scrap of defensive terrain. Against such a strong defence any army would have been sorely tested.

▲ Rasheed carbine

Egyptian Army / 9th Reserve Brigade, Umm Ketef – Abu Aelia Defensive Perimeter, October 1956

The Rasheed carbine was derived from the Hakim rifle, but was issued only in small numbers before being phased out in favour of the AK series assault rifle.

Specifications

Country of Origin: Egypt
Date: 1960
Calibre: 7.62mm (.3in)
Operation: Gas
Weight: 4.19kg (9.25lb)
Overall Length: 1035mm (40.75in)

Barrel Length: 520mm (20.5in)
Muzzle Velocity: Not known
Feed/Magazine: 10-round detachable box
 magazine
Range: 300m (984ft)

Specifications

Country of Origin: USSR
Date: 1947
Calibre: 7.62mm (.3in) Soviet M1943
Operation: Gas
Weight: 4.3kg (9.48lb)
Overall Length: 880mm (34.65in)

Barrel Length: 415mm (16.34in)
Muzzle Velocity: 600m/sec (1969ft/sec)
Feed/Magazine: 30-round detachable box
 magazine
Range: 400m (1312ft)

▲ AK-47

Egyptian Army / 2nd Infantry Division, Sinai, October 1973

Having obtained advisors and weaponry from several sources at times, the Egyptian Army was re-equipped in the Soviet style after 1967. In 1973 it proved to be a much more effective fighting force than previously.

Civil wars and revolutions

1960–PRESENT

In a continent the size of Africa, it is inevitable that there will be conflict ongoing somewhere at any given time. Some of these conflicts have origins going back to colonial intervention by European powers or the power vacuum left by their withdrawal.

IN 1960, THE CONGO became independent from Belgium and immediately descended into civil war. As is common in civil strife, there were no 'frontlines' as such, though some areas were recognized as the territory of one faction or another. Operations were launched by organized forces, but for the most part the conflict was one of low-level skirmishes between bands of 50–100 gunmen or soldiers. Massacres were common, and foreign troops were not exempt from being the victims of atrocities.

The Congo conflict was characterized by the use of European mercenaries. They trained local forces, protected white citizens who were being victimized by various factions, and took part in combat operations. Later in the conflict, mercenaries were involved in revolts and coup attempts. In 1971 the country was renamed Zaire, by which time the conflict was over.

The Portuguese withdrawal from their holdings in Africa (Angola, Guinea and Mozambique) was also very troubled. In each of these territories, the small Portuguese garrisons were caught unprepared by revolts and forced to fight increasingly large guerrilla forces. The conflicts were influenced by the insurgents' use of bases in other countries; many of the guerrillas fighting in Angola were based out of Zaire, while those operating in Mozambique could take refuge in Tanzania or Zambia where the Portuguese could not pursue them.

The Portuguese forces used a combination of concessions, improvements in conditions for the local population, and military force to combat the insurgents. Extensive use was made of trainer aircraft converted to the light strike role and acting in conjunction with ground units. Horsed cavalry was deployed in areas impassable to motor vehicles, and much of the infantry was from high-quality units such as marines and paratroops. However, lack of support for the war eventually caused the Portuguese to withdraw,

The insurgents' arsenal was augmented by foreign powers, enabling the guerrillas in Angola to make extensive use of mines. Among the insurgents, mine injuries were more common than wounds sustained from direct combat. Most insurgent groups were small, but as the conflict progressed the average

▶ **Vigneron M2**

Belgian Parachute Commando Regiment, Stanleyville, November 1964

Belgian paratroops were deployed to the Congo to rescue civilians trapped by the fighting. Their light, high-firepower weapons were well suited to rapid operations but limited in protracted fighting

Specifications

Country of Origin: Belgium	705mm (27.75in) stock folded
Date: 1952	Barrel Length: 305mm (12in)
Calibre: 9mm (.35in) Parabellum	Muzzle Velocity: 365m/sec (1200ft/sec)
Operation: Blowback	Feed/Magazine: 32-round detachable box
Weight: 3.29kg (7.25lb)	magazine
Overall Length: 890mm (35in) stock extended;	Range: 200m (656ft) +

formation went from about 20 men armed with an assortment of weapons to 100–150 equipped with AK-series assault rifles. Mortars, rocket launchers and artillery were deployed by the rebels at times, with ground-to-air missiles appearing from about 1973.

International intervention was also a critical factor in the Nigerian Civil War. At the beginning of the conflict in 1967, the Nigerian military was equipped with World War II armaments, mostly of British origin, as were the forces of newly independent Biafra. As the conflict continued, various nations sent aid to one side or the other, ranging from small arms

to jet fighters. The Biafran revolt was crushed, largely by the small Nigerian armoured force, and Biafra was reintegrated into Nigeria.

Ethiopia is one of the poorest regions in the world, and has been troubled for much of its history. In 1974, conflict in the breakaway region of Eritrea was compounded by a revolution in Ethiopia. The revolution was followed by further coup attempts and widespread use of terror tactics. Support came from the Soviet Union, whose relations with neighbouring Somalia were cooling rapidly. Meanwhile Somalia, which had been trying to wrest the province of

Specifications

Country of Origin: USSR	Barrel Length: 520mm (20.5in)
Date: 1962	Muzzle Velocity: 735m/sec (2410ft/sec)
Calibre: 7.62mm (.3in) M1943	Feed/Magazine: 100-round belt contained in
Operation: Gas, air-cooled	a drum
Weight: 7kg (15.43lb)	Cyclic Rate: 700rpm
Overall Length: 1041mm (41in)	Range: 900m (2953ft)

▲ **RPD**

Guerrilla Forces, Angola, September 1969

Although dated, the RPD was an effective weapon that combined mobility with firepower. Using the same cartridge as Soviet-supplied rifles simplified the supply situation for the rebel groups.

Specifications

Country of Origin: Spain	Barrel Length: 450mm (17.72in)
Date: 1958	Muzzle Velocity: 800m/sec (2625ft/sec)
Calibre: 7.62mm (.3in) NATO	Feed/Magazine: 20- or 30-round detachable box
Operation: Delayed blowback	magazine
Weight: 4.4kg (9.7lb)	Range: 500m (1640ft) +
Overall Length: 1015mm (40in)	

▲ **CETME assault rifle**

Portuguese Paratroop Battalion No 31, Mozambique, 1972

Developed in Spain by a German team continuing their wartime work on the StG45 project, the CETME was a simple and easy-to-use assault rifle. The CETME assault rifle was the basis for the H&K G3, and was developed into a family of assault rifles in 5.56 and 7.62mm calibres.

Ogaden from Ethiopia using small-scale guerrilla forces, took advantage of the situation and invaded. Both sides largely used Soviet-supplied equipment, but the decisive factor was direct Soviet intervention on the Ethiopian side.

Ethiopian forces, which included tanks and aircraft, were able to inflict heavy losses on Eritrean insurgents and weakened their control of many areas, but this success was illusory. Heavy-handedness on the part of the Ethiopians caused recruits to flock to the cause of Eritrean independence, and along with a reduction in Soviet assistance this situation denied

Ethiopia the clear victory to which it aspired. Eritrea was granted independence in 1993, but this did not end either internal conflict or clashes with Ethiopia. Disputes over territory led to a renewed war in 1998–2000, along with intermittent clashes between militias in the border areas.

Meanwhile, Somalia also descended into civil war, beginning in 1991. This conflict started as a factional dispute, but gradually changed in character. Today, there is a great deal of militant Islamic involvement in the war which, despite United Nations' efforts, remains ongoing.

Specifications

Country of Origin: USSR	Barrel Length: 266mm (10.5in)
Date: 1941	Muzzle Velocity: 490m/sec (1600ft/sec)
Calibre: 7.62mm (.3in) Soviet	Feed/Magazine: 35-round box magazine or 71-
Operation: Blowback	round drum magazine
Weight: 3.64kg (8lb)	Range: 120m (394ft)
Overall Length: 838mm (33in)	

▲ **PPSh-41**

Ethiopian People's Militia, Addis Ababa, 1977

The Soviet Union supplied large quantities of arms to various factional and government forces in Africa. Some weapons, like the PPSh-41, were of World War II vintage but were still highly effective.

Specifications

Country of Origin: Sweden	Barrel Length: 213mm (8.38in)
Date: 1945	Muzzle Velocity: 410m/sec (1345ft/sec)
Calibre: 9mm (.35in) Parabellum	Feed/Magazine: 36-round detachable box
Operation: Blowback	magazine
Weight: 3.9kg (8.6lb)	Range: 120m (394ft)
Overall Length: 808mm (31.81in)	

▲ **Carl Gustav 45**

Somalian Pirates, Horn of Africa, October 2009

An assortment of weapons from the Somalian and Ethiopian conflicts found their way into the hands of gunmen and pirates operating along the Somali coast. The seas off the Horn of Africa are among the worst of the world's piracy hotspots.

▲ SKS carbine

Guerrilla Forces, Guinea, August 1971

The SKS rifle, supplied by the Soviet Union, was a typical personal weapon among
the guerrilla forces. Some fighters managed to obtain AK-47s instead.

Specifications

Country of Origin: USSR	Overall Length: 1021mm (40.2in)
Date: 1945	Barrel Length: 521mm (20.5in)
Calibre: 7.62mm (.3in)	Muzzle Velocity: 735m/sec (2411ft/sec)
Operation: Gas short-stroke piston	Feed/Magazine: 10-round integral box magazine
Weight: 3.85kg (8.49lb)	Range: 400m (1312ft)

▲ FN FAL

Nigerian Federal Forces, March 1970

Britain contributed quantities of small arms to the Nigerian government, largely
as a counter to Soviet influence. Poor training levels reduced the effectiveness of
these weapons in federal hands.

Specifications

Country of Origin: Belgium/UK	Barrel Length: 533mm (21in)
Date: 1954	Muzzle Velocity: 853m/sec (2800ft/sec)
Calibre: 7.62mm (.3in) NATO	Feed/Magazine: 20-round detachable box
Operation: Gas, self-loading	magazine
Weight: 4.31kg (9.5lb)	Range: 800m (2625ft) +
Overall Length: 1053mm (41.46in)	

▲ FBP submachine gun

Portuguese Paratrooper Battalion No. 21, Angola, 1961

The FBP was primarily issued to officers and NCOs, giving them greater firepower
than a sidearm without the weight of a rifle. It was phased out in favour of the
Uzi submachine gun.

Specifications

Country of Origin: Portugal	Barrell Length: Not known
Date: 1948	Muzzle Velocity: 390m/sec (1280ft/sec)
Calibre: 9mm (0.35in)	Feed/Magazine: 21- or 32-round detachable
Operation: Blowback	box magazine
Weight: 3.77kg (8.31lb)	Range: Not known
Overall Length: 807mm (31.8in)	

South African security forces
1970–90

The legacy of European colonialism resulted in conflict in southern Africa as new national identities were forged.

IN 1970, BOTH SOUTH AFRICA and Rhodesia were ruled by a white minority, with the much larger black population as second-class citizens. Naturally, there was resentment against this system and this anger bubbled over into conflict. In addition, other clashes occurred along tribal lines or arose out of factional differences. The security forces of South Africa and Rhodesia attempted to maintain the status quo, which meant operating both in urban areas and over vast distances in the bush.

After a series of political organizations were banned in the 1960s in Rhodesia, guerrilla forces began to appear. These cooperated with South African insurgents, leading to joint operations between South African and Rhodesian security formations. The early guerrilla groups were poorly armed and disorganized, and were easily broken up.

From 1976 onwards, a new wave of insurgent activity began, inspired in part by the Portuguese withdrawal from neighbouring Mozambique. Attempts to find a peaceful solution failed, while guerrilla activity increased in both effectiveness and intensity. By the late 1970s large areas of Rhodesia were effectively under guerrilla control.

To counter the guerrillas, the government of Rhodesia could field a conventional infantry-based force backed up by an armoured car regiment, plus special security forces. These included the Rhodesian Special Air Service (which was essentially an elite counter-insurgency force at this point), the Selous Scouts and a mounted unit named Grey's Scouts, which operated over long distances in the bush.

The counter-insurgency forces specialized in tracking and ambushing guerrilla units, using hunting skills. They operated without the usual helicopter and ground vehicle support that might tip off guerrillas that security forces were in the area. Some operations were carried out by the elite units themselves; at other times they passed information to the regular forces, which could then launch a conventional operation. Despite the successes of these units, the guerrillas were able to force the ruling elite to the negotiating table and in 1980 Rhodesia became Zimbabwe under a new government.

The South African apartheid system, under which the black and white populations were segregated, had long been the subject of internal and external opposition. South Africa was the subject of an arms embargo and so developed its own armament industry. A number of small arms and heavier weapons systems were created, which were uniquely suited to the needs of the South African forces.

◀ **BXP submachine gun**
South African Security Forces, 1980–present
The BXP was designed for both military and security applications. It can be fired one-handed with reasonable effectiveness, and can launch rifle grenades from a muzzle adapter.

Specifications

Country of Origin: South Africa	Barrel Length: 208mm (8.2in)
Date: 1980	Muzzle Velocity: 370m/sec (1214ft/sec)
Calibre: 9mm (.35in) Parabellum	Feed/Magazine: 22- or 32-round detachable
Operation: Blowback	box magazine
Weight: 2.5kg (5.5lb)	Range: 100m (328ft) +
Overall Length: 607mm (23.9in)	

Security forces were at times involved in wider conflicts but also struggled to keep order within South Africa's borders. Attempts to train guerrillas to fight against the government were made prior to 1970, but the guerrilla groups were largely broken up and their parent organizations destroyed or driven underground. Nevertheless, a low-level resistance continued in the countryside, with occasional riots in the cities. These were dealt with using very heavy-handed methods, often sparking further violence.

Insurgent groups attempted to disrupt the national infrastructure with attacks on power stations and other services, The security forces also had to deal with serious levels of violent crime and gang wars within the cities, as well as terrorist attacks. In addition, it was necessary to conduct operations over large areas of the countryside

Externally, South African forces made forays into neighbouring states. After the departure of the Portuguese, South African forces moved into Angola and Mozambique to oppose the South-West African People's Organization (SWAPO), which was already fighting against South African troops in Namibia. Other forces assisted the Rhodesian government in resisting internal insurgency, until the 1980 elections changed the political landscape completely. Eventually, political change in South Africa created an entirely new situation, with the scrapping of apartheid and the creation of a state that was acceptable to the wider world.

Specifications

Country of Origin: South Africa	Barrel Length: 460mm (18.11in)
Date: 1982	Muzzle Velocity: 980m/sec (3215ft/sec)
Calibre: 5.56mm (.219in) M193	Feed/Magazine: 35- or 50-round detachable
Operation: Gas	box magazine
Weight: 4.3kg (9.48lb)	Range: 500m (1640ft)
Overall Length: 1005mm (35.97in)	

▲ Vektor R4

South African Security Forces, Angola, 1986

The Vektor assault rifle was derived from the Israeli Galil. A very robust and reliable rifle, it was issued to infantry while vehicle crews received a shortened carbine variant designated R5.

▲ Striker shotgun

South African Security Forces, 1990

The Striker solved the problem of limited ammunition capacity in a shotgun by using a revolving drum. However, reloading is slow, as each round must be separately loaded through a gate.

Specifications

Country of Origin: South Africa	Barrel Length: 304mm (12in) or 457mm (18in)
Date: 1985	Muzzle Velocity: Variable
Gauge/Calibre: 12-gauge	Feed/Magazine: 12- or 20-round revolving
Operation: Rotary cylinder	magazine
Weight: 4.2kg (9.25lb)	Range: 100m (328ft)
Overall Length: 792mm (31.18in)	

▲ **Milcor MGL**

South African Army, 1995

The MGL (Multiple Grenade Launcher) is a lightweight 40mm (1.57in) semi-automatic grenade launcher. The MGL allows six grenades to be fired in rapid succession. It can be used as a battlefield support weapon or for security applications, firing less-lethal ammunition directly at a target.

Specifications

Country of Origin: South Africa	Barrel Length: 300mm (11.8in)
Date: 1983	Muzzle Velocity: 76m/sec (249ft/sec)
Calibre: 40mm (1.57in)	Feed/Magazine: 6-round rotating swing-out-type
Operation: Double-action	cylinder
Weight: 5.3kg (11.68lb)	Range: 400m (1312ft)
Overall Length: 778mm (30.6in)	

Gulf War: Coalition forces
1991

The 1991 Gulf War pitted a coalition of nations against the large but obsolescent army of Iraq, which was defeated after 100 hours of high-tempo ground operations.

TENSIONS HAD ALWAYS BEEN HIGH between Iran and Iraq, and after the revolution which deposed the Shah and did away with Iranian monarchy, Iraq invaded the country. Iran possessed significant quantities of modern military equipment, but the revolutionary state lacked the skilled personnel to make good use of it. The war gradually became one between the modern, Soviet-equipped forces of Iraq and the massed infantry mobs of Iran. Despite an enormous casualty rate, stalemate resulted and by 1988 a ceasefire brought the Iran–Iraq War to an end.

At the end of the Iran–Iraq War, Iraq's economy was badly damaged and vast sums were owed to Kuwait and Saudi Arabia to repay war loans. Demands by Iraq to write off the debt were declined, so Iraqi President Saddam Hussein decided to solve the problem by military force. Invading Kuwait would not only eliminate the debt but also increase Iraq's oil reserves and further strengthen the country.

The invasion began on 2 August 1990. At this time the Iraqi Army was one of the largest in the world, and had little difficulty in overrunning Kuwait. It seemed entirely possible that Iraq might move on Saudi Arabia next. The United Nations issued a resolution demanding withdrawal, and economic sanctions were imposed. Iraq refused to withdraw unless various concessions, unacceptable to other nations, were made. The UN response was to set a deadline for withdrawal – 15 January 1991 – after which military action would be taken to remove the Iraqi presence from Kuwait.

Desert Shield/Storm

Thus began Operation *Desert Shield*, a massive build-up of forces from many nations. The main contributions were from the United States and Britain, but they were part of a huge international coalition, including many Arab nations. The build-

US INFANTRY PLATOON, 1991	
Unit	Strength
Platoon HQ	
Platoon leader	1
Platoon sergeant	1
Platoon RATELO	1
Machine gunners	2
Assistant machine gunners	2
Rifle Squad 1	
Squad leader	1
Fireteam (x 2)	
Team leader	1
Rifleman	1
Automatic rifleman	1
Grenadier	1
Rifle Squad 2	
Squad leader	1
Fireteam (x 2)	
Team leader	1
Rifleman	1
Automatic rifleman	1
Grenadier	1
Rifle Squad 3	
Squad leader	1
Fireteam (x 2)	
Team leader	1
Rifleman	1
Automatic rifleman	1
Grenadier	1

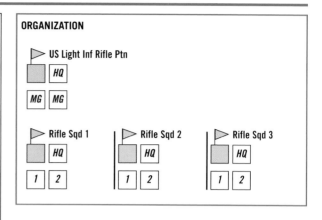

ORGANIZATION

▲ **Training exercise**

Marines from the 22nd Marine Expeditionary Unit train during preparations for Operation *Desert Storm*. The Marine in the foreground is armed with an M16A2/M203 grenade launcher.

up would take time, and during this period preparations for eventual ground operations began with air attacks. The intent was to weaken Iraq's ability to fight by crippling its infrastructure as well as launching direct strikes on command posts and troop concentrations. The codename for active operations against Iraqi forces was Operation *Desert Storm*.

The Coalition forces were limited by their UN remit, which was to expel the Iraqis from Kuwait. An advance into Iraq to depose Saddam Hussein's regime seemed desirable to many, but it was not UN-sanctioned and could not be considered. This did not rule out incursions into Iraq of course.

Special forces patrols were inserted to gain intelligence and to locate the launchers for Iraq's mobile SCUD missiles. Special forces patrols were lightly equipped, as they often had to move on foot, but still carried considerable firepower. Light machine guns and assault rifles, sometimes with an under-barrel grenade launchers, were typical weapons. Although the patrols had relatively similar weaponry to the Iraqi forces they encountered, their high levels of skill, aggression and confidence multiplied their weapons' effectiveness. The special forces troops were also able to call on air support from helicopters and fast jets, often using laser-designated bombs to eliminate targets found by the ground troops.

Sniper weapons

Snipers played an important part in the ground campaign as well. Not only could they shoot high-value personnel such as officers and radio operators, but snipers armed with heavy anti-materiel rifles such as the M82A1 could destroy equipment. Primary targets included communications and radar

▲ M16A2

US 101st Airborne Division, Forward Operations Base Cobra, February 1991

The M16A2 was developed from earlier versions of the weapon. Rather than being capable of full-automatic fire it featured a burst limiter, allowing the choice of single shots or three-round bursts.

Specifications

Country of Origin: United States
Date: 1984
Calibre: 5.56mm (.219in) M193
Operation: Gas
Weight: 2.86kg (6.3lb)
Overall Length: 990mm (39in)

Barrel Length: 508mm (20in)
Muzzle Velocity: 1000m/sec (3280ft/sec)
Feed/Magazine: 30-round detachable box
    magazine
Range: 500m (1640ft) +

▲ M21 sniper rifle

US 24th Infantry Division, Jalibah Airfield, February 1991

The M21 sniper rifle proved highly effective in eliminating well-dug-in support weapon positions that were resistant to less precise small-arms fire.

Specifications

Country of Origin: United States
Date: 1969
Calibre: 7.62mm (.3in) NATO
Operation: Gas, self-loading
Weight: 5.55kg (12.24lb)
Overall Length: 1120mm (44.09in)

Barrel Length: 559mm (22in)
Muzzle Velocity: 853m/sec (2798ft/sec)
Feed/Magazine: 20-round detachable box
    magazine
Range: 800m (2625ft) +

Specifications

Country of Origin: United States
Date: 1983
Calibre: 12.7mm (.5in) / 50 BMG
Operation: Short recoil, semi-automatic
Weight: 14.7kg (32.41lb)
Overall Length: 1549mm (60.98in)

Barrel Length: 838mm (33in)
Muzzle Velocity: 843m/sec (2800ft/sec)
Feed/Magazine: 11-round detachable box
    magazine
Range: 1000m (3280ft) +

▲ Barrett M82A1 anti-materiel rifle

US Special Forces, Southern Iraq, February 1991

Anti-materiel sniper rifles were used to eliminate enemy command and control facilities and light vehicles, adding to the confusion and command paralysis when the ground offensive began.

equipment, but vehicle engines and even heavy weapons could be rendered useless by a well-aimed shot. If a machine-gunner were killed by a sniper, another man could take his place. An armour-piercing round through the receiver of the weapon would render it useless in anyone's hands.

Conventional ground combat took place mainly at the end of the campaign, during the Coalition attack

Specifications

Country of Origin: Belgium	Barrel Length: 466mm (18.34in)
Date: 1982	Muzzle Velocity: 915m/sec (3000ft/sec)
Calibre: 5.56mm (.219in) NATO	Feed/Magazine: 30-round STANAG magazine or
Operation: Gas, air-cooled	100-round belt
Weight: 6.83kg (15.05lb)	Cyclic Rate: 750–1100rpm
Overall Length: 1040mm (40.56lb)	Range: 2000m (6560ft) +

▲ FN Minimi

US 1st Marine Division, Kuwait City, February 1991

Designated M249 in US military service, the FN Minimi saw action as a squad support weapon, mounted aboard vehicles, and also in defensive positions, undertaking the general-purpose machine gun role.

▲ L85A1 (SA80)

British 1st Armoured Division / 4th Mechanized Brigade, Southern Iraq, February 1991

Significantly improved over the original L85, the L85A1's short length was an advantage for mechanized troops who might have to dismount and remount their vehicles rapidly during fluid mobile operations. The optical sight attached to most L85 rifles is extremely useful as a surveillance tool, effectively giving every soldier a telescope to monitor the situation at a safe distance.

Specifications

Country of Origin: United Kingdom	Barrel Length: 442mm (17.4in)
Date: 1985	Muzzle Velocity: 940m/sec (3084ft/sec)
Calibre: 5.56mm (.219in) NATO	Feed/Magazine: 30-round detachable box
Operation: Gas	magazine
Weight: 3.71kg (8.1lb)	Range: 500m (1640ft)
Overall Length: 709mm (27.9in)	

on Iraqi forces. There were clashes before this, however. The city of Khafji in Saudi Arabia was attacked in late January. The attack was initially successful against light resistance, but a counter-attack by mainly Saudi and US Marine Corps forces drove the Iraqis out of the city.

Ground campaign

The ground campaign to liberate Kuwait began on 23 February 1991 and was characterized by a short but tremendously intense period of mobile armoured warfare. The Coalition advance was spearheaded by US and British armoured units, whose tanks were a generation more advanced than the T-72s of the Iraqi army. More importantly, the Coalition armoured forces were better trained and had the advantage of total air superiority.

The result was a classic armoured breakthrough, followed by a 'rolling up' of the Iraqi defensive line by the armoured forces. Mechanized infantry, supported by armoured vehicles, was able to advance rapidly and attack unprepared enemy units. Artillery, command and logistics formations, thinking themselves safe in the rear, were quickly overrun, while even dug-in infantry and armoured units were flanked or punched out of their positions.

The rapid collapse of the Iraqi Army was followed by a precipitate flight northwards, pursued by Coalition ground forces and attacked from the air. Huge numbers of armoured vehicles were lost and it is not likely that the Iraqis could have stopped an advance on Baghdad. However, this was beyond the scope of the operation at hand, and the Saddam Hussein regime survived.

Alongside the main armoured thrusts were other operations. US and Arab troops, including a large US Marine contingent, pushed into Kuwait City while airborne forces seized air bases. In some cases these attacks were supported by a mechanized advance; in others they were an airborne infantry affair.

The ground offensive was halted after 100 hours of extremely intense combat, with the Iraqi Army in full flight and Kuwait liberated. The ceasefire that followed became permanent, allowing Saddam Hussein to deal brutally with uprisings that followed his defeat in Kuwait. At the time, there were those who predicted that they 'were going to have to do it again', i.e. fight Iraq once more at some point in the future. In 2003, that prediction came true.

BRITISH INFANTRY PLATOON (MECHANIZED), 1991		
Unit	Equipment	Strength
Platoon	Warrior	1
Commander	SA80	1
Sergeant	SA80	1
Radio operator	SA80	1
Mortar operator	51mm mortar	1
Section 1	432 AIFV	1
Fireteam 1		
Comd Cpl	SA80	1
Rifleman	SA80	1
Rifleman	SA80	1
LMG gunner	LMG	1
Fireteam 2		
2 i/c Comd LCpl	SA80	1
Rifleman	SA80	1
Rifleman	SA80	1
LMG gunner	LMG	1
Section 2	432 AIFV	1
Fireteam 1		
Comd	SA80	1
Rifleman	SA80	1
Rifleman	SA80	1
LMG gunner	LMG	1
Fireteam 2		
2 i/c Comd	SA80	1
Rifleman	SA80	1
Rifleman	SA80	1
LMG gunner	LMG	1
Section 3	432 AIFV	1
Fireteam 1		
Comd	SA80	1
Rifleman	SA80	1
Rifleman	SA80	1
LMG gunner	LMG	1
Fireteam 2		
2 i/c Comd	SA80	1
Rifleman	SA80	1
Rifleman	SA80	1
LMG gunner	LMG	1

L85 in combat

The Gulf War was the first major conflict fought by the British using their new L85 assault rifle. Various problems with early models of this weapon were exacerbated by the harsh desert conditions, with weapon malfunctions being unacceptably common. The L85 was difficult to maintain properly in an environment where sand and dust were prevalent. Experience in action prompted a set of revisions and upgrades to the weapon, eventually resulting in the A2 version, which was available in time for the Iraq War in 2003.

British Army Infantry Platoon (Mechanized), 1991

The organization of a platoon into three sections, each with its own support weapons, allows for a great deal of tactical flexibility. The classic 'two up, one back' arrangement keeps a section in reserve while the others alternate fire and manoeuvre, and is the basis of infantry tactics used by many nations.

Platoon HQ (3 x L85A1, 1 x 50mm mortar)

Section 1 (6 x L85A1, 2 x L86A1 LSW)

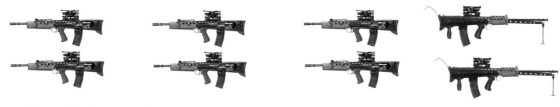

Section 2 (6 x L85A1, 2 x L86A1 LSW)

Section 3 (6 x L85A1, 2 x L86A1 LSW)

Specifications

Country of Origin: United Kingdom	Barrel Length: 654mm (26in)
Date: 1985	Muzzle Velocity: 840m/sec (2830ft/sec)
Calibre: 7.62mm (.3in) NATO and others	Feed/Magazine: 10-round detachable box
Operation: Bolt action	magazine
Weight: 6.2kg (13.68lb)	Range: 1000m (3280ft)
Overall Length: 1163mm (45in)	

▲ **L96A1 sniper rifle**

British 22 SAS, Iraq, February 1991

The L96A1 was adopted for British Army service in 1982. Its long-range accuracy proved to be an asset in open desert terrain. The sniper rifle has seen service in every conflict involving British forces since the mid 1980s.

Believing that there was no such thing as too much firepower, the US Army had made a more or less off-the-shelf purchase of the FN Minimi light support weapon, introducing it as the M249 Squad Automatic Weapon (SAW). Unlike the rifle-based light support weapons deployed by some nations, the M249 was a true light machinegun with a quick-change barrel and large ammunition capacity provided by belt feed. Like most other weapons, the M249 suffered from occasional malfunctions in the desert, but most troops developed a positive impression of its firepower, lightness and reliability.

▲ L86A1 LSW

British Royal Regiment of Fusiliers, Wadi Al Batin, February 1991

The L86 is a heavy-barrel version of the L85 assault rifle. It is accurate and can be used by any infantryman, but lacks the sustained firepower of a true general-purpose machine gun.

Specifications

Country of Origin: United Kingdom	Barrel Length: 646mm (25.43in)
Date: 1985	Muzzle Velocity: 970m/sec (3182ft/sec)
Calibre: 5.56mm (.219in) NATO	Feed/Magazine: 30-round detachable box
Operation: Gas, air-cooled	magazine
Weight: 5.4kg (11.9lb)	Range: 1000m (3280ft)
Overall Length: 900mm (35.43in)	

▲ L7A1/A2 (FN MAG)

British King's Own Scottish Borderers, Southern Iraq, February 1991

Although officially replaced by the L86A1 LSW as the standard light support weapon of the British Army, a large number of FN MAG machine guns (designated L7 in British service) reappeared in time to deploy to the Gulf.

Specifications

Country of Origin: Belgium	Barrel Length: 546mm (21.5in)
Date: 1955	Muzzle Velocity: 853m/sec (2800ft/sec)
Calibre: 7.62mm (.3in) NATO	Feed/Magazine: Belt-fed
Operation: Gas, air-cooled	Cyclic Rate: 600–1000rpm
Weight: 10.15kg (22.25lb)	Range: 3000m (9842ft)
Overall Length: 1250mm (49.2in)	

Gulf War: Iraqi forces
1991

The Iraqi Army of 1991 was one of the largest in the world, with huge numbers of tanks. Its strength, however, was somewhat illusory.

T HE IRAQI ARMY WAS CRIPPLED by a lack of initiative among its commanders and a habit of interference by political figures in Baghdad. These factors slowed reaction speeds at the best of times, and in an environment where command, control and communications had been severely disrupted by Coalition airstrikes it was a recipe for disaster. The communications issue ran both ways; the political leaders could not obtain a clear picture of the situation, and their orders were often out of date or lost in transmission.

The army was also beset by internal problems. The best units belonged to the Republican Guard, whose function was as much political as military. The Republican Guard received higher pay, greater benefits and much better equipment than the regular army, and was intended, among other things, to ensure the political reliability of the army.

The army itself was a conscript organization, poorly led and trained, and equipped with older weaponry. Its units were unenthusiastic at best, and prone to desertion. Doctrine, like equipment, was Soviet in origin, with some Chinese-supplied

weaponry as well. The Iraqi Army was thus at a disadvantage when facing the cutting-edge military technology of US and British armoured forces.

The invasion of Kuwait was led by the Republican Guard, whose armoured forces were able to overrun the unprepared Kuwaitis. Commando formations launched an airmobile assault on Kuwait City as well as key military installations. Within two days resistance ended and the occupation began. A strangely hesitant foray into Saudi Arabia was defeated, after which the Iraqis showed no real inclination to go on the offensive.

As the Coalition build-up continued, Iraqi forces adopted a highly defensive deployment, digging in tanks as bunkers and establishing strong static positions. This tactic had worked well in the previous war, against ill-armed but fanatical Iranian infantry hordes, but against the Coalition they invited attack on the enemy's terms and therefore defeat.

With no effective counter to the Coalition air campaign, Iraqi forces were steadily worn down. Many units were badly shaken by air attack, especially carpet bombing by US B-52 bombers, and

▲ AK-74

Republican Guard / Medina Division, Medina Ridge, February 1991

The AK-74, which armed Republican Guard units, can be distinguished from AK-47 and AKM rifles (which use different ammunition) by the long groove in the gun's stock.

Specifications

Country of Origin: USSR

Date: 1974

Calibre: 5.45mm (.215in) M74

Operation: Gas

Weight: 3.6kg (7.94lb)

Overall Length: 943mm (37.1in)

Barrel Length: 400mm (15.8in)

Muzzle Velocity: 900m/sec (2952ft/sec)

Feed/Magazine: 30-round detachable box
magazine

Range: 300m (984ft)

mass desertions were at times triggered by airdropped leaflets warning of an imminent bombing attack. Nevertheless, the Iraqi forces held their positions.

The Coalition ground offensive directed massive force at a few key points, and once breakthroughs were made the entire defensive line was compromised. The only real chance was an armoured counter-attack, but although some local offensives were made, in a piecemeal and disorganized manner, no serious counterthrust developed. This was in part due to successful Coalition deception about the location of the main attacks, and lack of initiative on the Iraqi side. Nevertheless, several stiff actions were fought. The Republican Guard demonstrated a greater tendency to hold its ground than the rest of the Iraqi Army, but was eventually broken by the relentless Coaltion pressure and driven northwards under heavy air attack.

In Kuwait City, most Iraqi forces put up a token resistance and then surrendered or tried to withdraw. The heaviest fighting took place for the airport, which was stubbornly defended against US Marines and Kuwaiti troops. Once this action ended, the Iraqi presence in Kuwait had been dislodged.

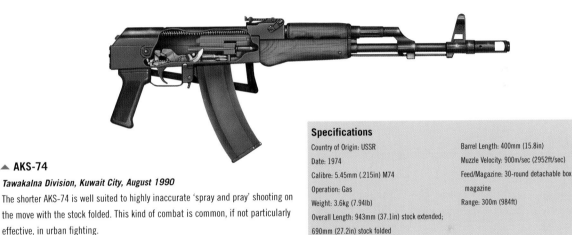

▲ AKS-74

Tawakalna Division, Kuwait City, August 1990

The shorter AKS-74 is well suited to highly inaccurate 'spray and pray' shooting on the move with the stock folded. This kind of combat is common, if not particularly effective, in urban fighting.

Specifications

Country of Origin: USSR	Barrel Length: 400mm (15.8in)
Date: 1974	Muzzle Velocity: 900m/sec (2952ft/sec)
Calibre: 5.45mm (.215in) M74	Feed/Magazine: 30-round detachable box
Operation: Gas	magazine
Weight: 3.6kg (7.94lb)	Range: 300m (984ft)
Overall Length: 943mm (37.1in) stock extended;	
690mm (27.2in) stock folded	

Specifications

Country of Origin: USSR	Barrel Length: 658mm (25.9in)
Date: 1974	Muzzle Velocity: 800m/sec (2600ft/sec)
Calibre: 5.45mm (.215in) M74	Feed/Magazine: 30- or 45-round detachable box
Operation: Gas, air-cooled	magazine
Weight: 9kg (19.84lb)	Range: 2000m (6560ft) +
Overall Length: 1160mm (45.67in)	

▲ RPK-74

Hammurabi Armoured Division, Jal Atraf, Kuwait, August 1990

The RPK-74 is as easy to use and maintain as an AK-74. For an ill-trained army of conscripts this serviceability is a critical issue, as more sophisticated weapons may quickly become unworkable.

Peacekeeping forces, Africa
1990–2000s

Peacekeeping is one of the hardest tasks a military force can undertake. It requires patience and fortitude in a tense and hazardous environment.

THE ARMED FORCES of most nations are organized and trained for warfighting, i.e. engaging a major opposing force in conditions of open conflict. However, this state of conflict is relatively rare. In recent years it has been more common for armed forces to become involved in 'war-like situations' with no declared enemy, or in attempting to keep the peace in a troubled region. Such is a rather different challenge than warfighting, and cannot effectively be carried out by tanks and air power. Instead, the burden is carried by infantry and light vehicles equipped with small arms and support weapons.

Peacekeeping can be a matter of 'being seen to be there', with troops on the ground acting as a deterrent to conflict. In other cases, it is necessary to protect victims or refugees actively. Aid workers or the supplies they use are common targets for robbery and extortion, and also have to be guarded.

Peacekeeping is somewhat different to counter-insurgency warfare, though there is considerable overlap at times. Where the counter-insurgency force is primarily concerned with dealing with guerrillas or terrorists, peacekeepers are often constrained to fight only in self-defence. This situation can be intensely frustrating, with peacekeepers often attacked yet unable to retaliate or pre-empt the attack.

During the 1990s, peacekeeping forces under UN jurisdiction were deployed to Somalia in order to protect humanitarian aid workers there. Civil war and factional conflicts in an already desperately poor nation led to mass starvation, but assistance proved difficult to provide. Aid intended for needy refugees was stolen for sale on the black market, with the proceeds used to buy arms, or was taken to supply the militia of one faction or another. In this environment peacekeepers were tasked with protecting aid workers and non-combatants, as well as the supply lines to the civilian population.

After many years of effort, matters have improved in Somalia, and the suffering of innocents has been alleviated by international efforts. This would not have been possible without armed peacekeepers to

▲ **FR-F1**

United Nations Organization Stabilization Mission in the Democratic Republic of the Congo, Katanga Province, May 2005

The FR-F1 rifle is highly precise, which is of critical importance when non-combatant casualties must be avoided. Peacekeepers are often unable to shoot at obvious hostiles due to rules of engagement or the risk of collateral casualties.

Specifications

Country of Origin: France	Overall Length: 1138mm (44.8in)
Date: 1966	Barrel Length: 552mm (21.37in)
Calibre: 7.5mm (.295in)	Muzzle Velocity: 852m/sec (2795ft/sec)
Operation: Bolt action	Feed/Magazine: 10-round integral box magazine
Weight: 5.2kg (11.46lb)	Range: 800m (2625ft)

deter at least some of the violence and to ensure that aid reached those for whom it was intended.

Somalia is just one example of a situation that is all too common. Five years of war (1998–2003) in the Democratic Republic of the Congo caused thousands of deaths from secondary causes such as disease and starvation as well as directly in the violence. The United Nations deployed an international peacekeeping force in 2000 in order to support attempts to create a lasting ceasefire and, in 2003, the conflict was declared ended. As in many such regions, peace remains a fragile thing and is often maintained only if it is supported, ironically perhaps, by overt military force.

Specifications

Country of Origin: United Kingdom	Overall Length: 780mm (30in)
Date: 1985	Barrell Length: 518mm (20in)
Calibre: 5.56mm (0.219in) NATO	Muzzel Velocity: 940m/sec (3083ft/sec)
Operation: Gas, rotating bolt	Feed/Magazine: 30-round box magazine
Weight: 4.13kg (9.10lb)	Range: 500m (1640ft)

▲ **L85A2**

British Royal Marines, Somali Coast, November 2008

Magazines issued with the L85A1 were aluminium and not very robust. The L85A2 has three types of magazine, including the plastic Magpul EMAG. From 2007 an upgrade included Picatinny rails with optional hand grip.

▲ **L110A1**

Royal Irish Regiment, Sierra Leone, September 2000

A version of the FN Minimi used by the British Army, the L110 Para has a shortened barrel and sliding stock. It is deployed as a squad support weapon, giving greater firepower than the L86 LSW.

Specifications

Country of Origin: Belgium	Barrel Length: 466mm (18.34in)
Date: 1982	Muzzle Velocity: 915m/sec (3000ft/sec)
Calibre: 5.56mm (.219in) NATO	Feed/Magazine: 30-round STANAG magazine or
Operation: Gas, air-cooled	100-round belt
Weight: 6.83kg (15.05lb)	Cyclic Rate: 750–1100rpm
Overall Length: 1040mm (40.56in)	Range: 2000m (6560ft) +

Chapter 10

Latin America, 1950–Present

Many of the nations of Latin America were
originally European colonies, and began their nationhood in
revolution and civil war. Some achieved lasting stability, but
many areas of Latin America have a long history of internal
troubles or disputes with neighbours that have sometimes
boiled over into open warfare.

In the second half of the twentieth century,
Latin America was wracked by a series of revolutions that
threatened to replace the existing regimes with ones
sympathetic to or supported by the Communist bloc nations.
This situation was of grave concern to the United States,
which did not want a Communist foothold
in its 'backyard'.

◀ **Armed struggle**
Cuban revolutionary leader Fidel Castro (left, in spectacles) gives firing instructions to guerrilla fighters
who have come to join his armed forces in the Sierra Maestra, a mountainous region in the heart of Cuba,
January 1958.

Introduction

A successful revolution requires leaders, popular support and some source of equipment or funding. Where all three were available to rebels, governments are seriously threatened.

LATIN AMERICA'S PEOPLE are no more or less prone to revolution than anyone else. People everywhere tend to want, first and foremost, to be able to live their lives without undue disruption. An armed insurrection and the government measures required to oppose it will greatly affect the lives of ordinary people, and so for ordinary people to want a revolution, certain factors have to be present.

A revolution can be 'sold' to the people by popular leaders, at least to some extent. However, for the average person to be willing to risk the danger and disruption associated with a rebellion, the status quo must be unacceptable to them. The turning point can happen for many reasons; outrage at some event such as political arrests or blatant government corruption, desperation caused by starvation or impossible living conditions, or perhaps indoctrination into supporting a radical political or religious system.

With sufficient popular support, a revolutionary group can overcome government countermeasures and take power. Without it, all that is possible is to prolong the struggle long enough to obtain concessions at the negotiating table. Likewise, it is possible for a government to crush a rebellion simply through repression, but the hatred so caused can create another rebellion at a later date. Overall, in order to prevent revolution it is not necessary to please all of the people all of the time, nor in fact to please any of the people at any given moment. What

▼ **Sterling service**

British Royal Marine officers and men pose for the camera during the Falklands campaign, 1982. Many are armed with L2A3 Sterling submachine guns, issued to serving officers during the campaign. The Sterling was used by British armed forces from the Korean War until the Gulf War in 1991, with a total of 400,000 being manufactured over a 40-year period.

▲ **Loyal members**
Guatemalan government troops salute in the Quiche province of Guatemala, November 1982. They are armed with a mixture of small arms, including the Israeli-made Galil ARM assault rifle with its folding stock.

is necessary is to ensure that not too many of the people are angry at the same time. When this happens, governments fall.

The wave of Communist revolutions that swept through Latin America from 1959 onwards prompted US worries that each revolution would trigger others. This 'Domino Theory' suggested that a chain of successful revolutions might ripple through Latin America and create Communist-friendly regimes across the region. This did not occur. Only the Cuban revolution was a notable success.

Other revolts were put down or came to a negotiated settlement. Some continued at a level that permitted the country to continue functioning as such, but which caused severe economic damage and suffering to the population. The USA has intervened in several of these conflicts, for various reasons. The most obvious is the containment of Communism, but there have also been strong economic reasons for wishing to support a US-friendly government or rebel group.

Some US involvement has been overt, some less so. The global community does not, as a rule, approve of nations supporting rebel groups against the legitimate government of their country, no matter how corrupt and repressive that government may be. Covert or at least low-key support is usually the order of the day when working alongside rebels and revolutionaries – and there is always the chance that they will turn on their overseas supporters in the event of victory.

International struggles

Internal troubles were often a factor in external conflicts within Latin America. The 1982 invasion of the Falkland Islands by Argentina was part of an old dispute with Britain about ownership of the islands, but it also served to distract the Argentine public from internal problems and reduce opposition to the unpopular regime.

This is a common political gambit – attempting to create a popular cause such as an external war in order to rally support for an unpopular government. A real or claimed victory can pay dividends, but a lost war usually means even greater unpopularity and can lead to the fall of a government.

Cuban revolution
1956–59

Fidel Castro's revolution in Cuba was a startling success despite a near-fatal early setback. The key ingredient was lack of support for the government among the population.

GENERAL FULGENICO BATISTA was a dictator who came to power through a coup in 1952. His actions forestalled elections which, it had been hoped, would produce a government less corrupt than its predecessors. In the event Batista ran the country as little more than a money-making scheme for himself and his associates.

Batista's coup and subsequent government was opposed – at first through entirely legal channels – by, among others, a young politician named Fidel Castro. Unable to prevent Batista from taking power, Castro fled overseas and rallied support for what he viewed as a last resort – armed revolution.

Castro and his band of less than 100 followers landed in Cuba in December 1956, in a move designed to coincide with uprisings in various parts of the island. The revolts were put down by the security forces, and Castro's band was engaged by Cuban troops within days of landing. Scarcely more than a dozen survived the encounter. Fortunately for Castro, Batista's forces were not trained for counter-insurgency warfare and lacked any real loyalty to the government. Some elements within the army were opposed to Batista, and large segments of the population also disliked the regime. From these came new recruits for Castro's forces.

The revolutionaries had no real international backing, so were required to buy weapons on the black market. They armed themselves with whatever weapons they could obtain, many of which were of World War II vintage and came from Eastern Europe. Other equipment was captured from government forces, with the result that the revolutionaries became gradually better armed as the conflict went on.

Castro trod carefully, attacking 'soft' targets such as sugar mills owned by the rich elite. When the government forces responded, usually clumsily, Castro's men disengaged after inflicting a few casualties, deterring pursuit by using snipers to eliminate those who seemed too enthusiastic about chasing the rebels. By picking fights that he could win, Castro showed the people that his revolution

▲ **Thompson M1928**

Cuban Government Forces, Sierra Maestra, May 1956

The Thompson submachine gun was ideal for close-range ambushes in urban or overgrown terrain. A revolutionary could deliver withering firepower then make a quick escape while the survivors were still emerging from whatever cover they had found.

Specifications

Country of Origin: United States	Barrel Length: 266mm (10.5in)
Date: 1928	Muzzle Velocity: 280m/sec (920ft/sec)
Calibre: 11.4mm (.45in) M1911	Feed/Magazine: 18-, 20- or 30-round detachable
Operation: Delayed blowback	box magazine
Weight: 4.88kg (10.75lb)	Range: 120m (394ft)
Overall Length: 857mm (33.75in)	

▶ **People power**

Cuban revolutionaries attack a Nationalist army post at Camajuani during the battle for Santa Clara, Cuba, December 1958. The fighter in the centre appears to be resting a World War I-era Lewis Gun on a temporary barricade.

was worth backing. Meanwhile, Batista's troops responded with a campaign of more or less indiscriminate intimidation and repression. Opposition politicians who were against Batista, but nothing to do with the revolution, were murdered by the security forces.

Batista's brutal response alienated large segments of the population. Some were driven to join the rebels, though most just tried to stay out of the way and hoped that things would calm down. Even this passive opposition to the government worked against Batista, as it deprived him of sources of information among the general populace.

Government forces were largely armed with weapons of US origin, including Thompson submachine guns and M1 Garand rifles. Some of the latter had arrived by way of a convoluted deal that involved US arms dealers buying World War II lend-lease guns back from Britain, then supplying them to the Cuban armed forces.

By 1958, Castro was beginning to develop a large support base among the rural and urban populations. His forces achieved parity of numbers with the army, though the security forces were better equipped. In May, an attempt was made by the army to bring the rebels to action in Oriente province and defeat them.

The operation was a fiasco, with government forces ambushed or driven off with losses despite air support. This victory prompted Castro to launch a

more general offensive all over the island, seizing his moment of opportunity. The Cuban Army was severely demoralized by its recent defeat, and fought poorly in the clashes that followed. These were small-scale affairs and were quite within the capabilities of Batista's army to cope with, but the troops were prone to panic and were repeatedly defeated. The result was a further drop in morale, which was not helped by Batista's orders to have an aircraft loaded with gold and money ready for him to escape.

As his control over the country collapsed, Batista made use of his plane and left the country, enabling Castro to take power with the overwhelming support of the population. He was, by his own assertion, not a Communist at this point. However, since the only nations willing to recognize the Castro regime were the Communist bloc, Cuba was forced into a new political allegiance.

▶ **Makarov pistol**

Revolutionary Forces, Sierra Maestra, May 1956

Easily concealed handguns like the Makarov were ideal weapons for urban insurgents, who were willing to exchange fire with the police on the streets of the national capital.

Specifications

Country of Origin: USSR	Barrel Length: 91mm (3.5in)
Date: 1951	Muzzle Velocity: 315m/sec (1033ft/sec)
Calibre: 9mm (.35in) Makarov	Feed/Magazine: 8-round detachable box
Operation: Blowback	magazine
Weight: .66kg (1.46lb)	Range: 40m (131ft)
Overall Length: 160mm (6.3in)	

Specifications

Country of Origin: United States	Overall Length: 1103mm (43.5in)
Date: 1936	Barrel Length: 610mm (24in)
Calibre: 7.62mm (.3in) US .30-06	Muzzle Velocity: 853m/sec (2800ft/sec)
Operation: Gas	Feed/Magazine: 8-round internal box magazine
Weight: 4.37kg (9.5lb)	Range: 500m (1640ft) +

Guatemala and Nicaragua
1960s–1990s

Central America was the scene for several revolutions and counter-revolutions, some of which became proxy wars between East and West.

MANY OF THE WEAPONS used in both Guatemala and Nicaragua were of Western European or Eastern European origin, in many cases purchased in large numbers by the government and then captured or stolen by insurgents. Other weapons were supplied to various factions by the United States and the Soviet Union.

As elsewhere in the world, the Soviet Union was willing to support a revolution that might bring about a friendly government. Conversely, US opposition to the spread of Communism prompted the supply of arms, often accompanied by CIA advisors to train personnel in their use.

Central American revolutions

In the wake of the successful Cuban revolution, it seemed that suitably determined insurgent forces could be successful in many other countries. One adherent of this idea was Ernesto 'Che' Guevara, one of Castro's lieutenants. Guevara attempted to foster a rural insurgency in Bolivia but was killed by the security forces in 1967

Guevara's failure in Bolivia was largely due to lack of popular support. He had hoped to create the conditions necessary for a successful revolution by undertaking attacks on government and military targets. The general population were not motivated to join the insurgency or even support it to any great degree. What Guevara had failed to appreciate was that a successful revolution requires an opportunity – it cannot simply be imposed.

A suitable opportunity did exist in Guatemala as the result of blatant corruption within the government. Coups and sham elections created a succession of military governments that damaged the economy and undid generally popular social reforms. A large segment of the population was disaffected and some, such as indigenous Mayan peoples, were actively persecuted. In 1960, therefore the Guatemalan civil war began in earnest. A group of military officers launched a coup against the existing government while guerrilla activity began in the cities. These were separate events, and both were easily put down. The military rebels moved to remote areas of the country and began a long civil war under the banner of MR-13 (*Movimiento Revolucionario 13 Novembre*), a name derived from the date of the abortive coup.

The Guatemalan government, corrupt as it was, received support from the CIA. This fact was largely due to its anti-Left leanings; a corrupt Guatemala was a more desirable neighbour for the United States than a Communist one. US advisors were sent to assist the Guatemalan government in dealing with the insurgency. A separate insurgency movement existed until 1968, when it merged with MR-13. This organization, named FAR (*Fuerzas Armadas Rebeles*,

or Rebel Armed Forces) was composed of various different groups and lacked cohesion. Its forces were unable to obtain a foothold in the countryside, so they moved into the cities in keeping with a principle of revolutionary warfare put forward by the Brazilian Communist Carlos Marighela. It was hoped that by pulling security forces into the urban centres, the pressure on rural insurgent groups would be reduced. The Guatemalan government responded with extreme brutality and permitted vigilante groups to operate more or less at will. Bloody clashes took place in the towns between insurgents armed with whatever weapons they could get and the better-

▲ FN 49

Guatemalan Security Forces, 1960s

The FN 49 was deployed by the security forces of Argentina, Brazil, Colombia and Venezuela. It saw considerable action during street battles with insurgents in Rio de Janeiro in the late 1960s.

Specifications

Country of Origin: Belgium	Overall Length: 1116mm (43.54in)
Date: 1949	Barrel Length: 590mm (23.23in)
Calibre: Various, including 8mm (.314in)	Muzzle Velocity: 710m/sec (2330ft/sec)
Operation: Gas	Feed/Magazine: 10-round fixed box magazine
Weight: 4.31kg (9.5lb)	Range: 500m (1640ft

▲ Madsen M45

Guatemalan Security Forces, Guatemala City, May 1967

The Guatemalan government's counter-terror campaign in the cities relied on crushing any resistance with heavy and often indiscriminate firepower. The Danish-made Madsen borrowed concepts from wartime expedient weapons such as the British Sten.

Specifications

Country of Origin: Denmark	Overall Length: 800mm (31.49in)
Date: 1945	Barrell Length: 315mm (12.40in)
Calibre: 9mm (0.35in)	Muzzel Velocity: 365m/sec (1197.5ft/sec)
Operation: Blowback	Feed/Magazine: 32-round box magazine
Weight: 3.15kg (6.94lb)	Range: 100m (328ft)

organized and more ruthless security forces. Yet despite extreme repression, the insurgency continued and in 1980 gained additional impetus.

By the mid 1990s Guatemala's economy had improved and along with it conditions for the majority of the population. With reduced cause for disaffection, a gradual move towards peace and stability resulted. Thus despite extreme measures the Guatemalan civil war was won, or at least ended, by civil reform rather than military action.

Nicaragua

Conflict in Nicaragua had been ongoing for many years when the FLSN (*Frente Sandinista de Liberacion Nacional*, or Sandinista National Liberation Front) was created in 1961. This force took its name from Augusto Sandino, who led a guerrilla force to fight US forces in Nicaragua. He was betrayed and murdered by Anastasio Somoza Garcia, who later took power in a coup. Opposition to the Somoza regime was intermittent and usually unsuccessful

Specifications

Country of Origin: USSR	Barrel Length: 415mm (16.34in)
Date: 1947	Muzzle Velocity: 600m/sec (1969ft/sec)
Calibre: 7.62mm (.3in) Soviet M1943	Feed/Magazine: 30-round detachable box
Operation: Gas	magazine
Weight: 4.3kg (9.48lb)	Range: 400m (1312ft)
Overall Length: 880mm (34.65in)	

▲ **AK-47 assault rifle**

Sandinista guerrilla forces, Managua, 1978

The Soviet Union delivered up to 100,000 AK-47s to the Sandinistas, both before and after they took power in Nicaragua. As in other theatres, the hardy AK-47 proved a superb weapon in jungle conditions.

▲ **Sa23**

Nicaraguan National Guard, June 1970

The Czech Sa23 used its trigger as a selector. A light pull fired one round; full movement initiated automatic fire.

Specifications

Country of Origin: Czechoslovakia	Overall Length: 686mm (27in)
Date: 1950	Barrell Length: 284mm (11.18in)
Calibre: 9mm (0.35in)	Muzzle Velocity: Not known
Operation: Blowback	Feed/Magazine: 24- or 40-round box magazine
Weight: 3.27kg (7.20lb)	Range: 100–200m (328–656ft)

until the foundation of the FLSN, which is usually taken as the start date for the Nicaraguan revolution. The FLSN carried out campaigns in both rural and urban areas, and worked hard to win over the people of the regions where it operated.

The FLSN organization remained small and achieved little until 1972, when the Somoza government blatantly misappropriated international relief funds after a serious earthquake. This action alienated a large segment of the population, and resulted in a rapid expansion of the FLSN as well as increased opposition through legal political channels. The government response was to increase repression.

A spectacular guerrilla success in 1978 weakened the government to the point where a coup was narrowly avoided. Insurgents were able to capture the National Palace and several hundred government officials. FLSN support increased to the point where a large-scale campaign could be launched throughout the country.

Supplied with arms from Cuba and the Soviet Union and facing demoralized government troops, the insurgents took control over the major urban areas. Despite heavy urban fighting the security forces could not dislodge the guerrillas and as a result of international pressure as well as internal collapse, the Somoza government was ousted. Here was the 'official' end of the revolution, though internal conflict continued afterwards. As with other Latin American nations, it was not armed force that decided the issue but the support or lack of it by the majority of the population.

▲ **Samonabiject Puska vz52**

Nicaraguan Security Forces, Managua, June 1979

After being replaced in Czech service by the vz58, large numbers of vz52 rifles were supplied to overseas users. The vz52 saw action in the street battles for the Nicaraguan capital, Managua.

Specifications

Country of Origin: Czechoslovakia	Overall Length: 843mm (33.2in)
Date: 1952	Barrel Length: 400mm (15.8in)
Calibre: 7.62mm (.3in) M52 or 7.62mm (.3in)	Muzzle Velocity: 710m/sec (2330ft/sec)
Soviet M1943	Feed/Magazine: 10-round detachable box
Operation: Gas	magazine
Weight: 3.11kg (6.86lb)	Range: 500m (1640ft) +

Specifications

Country of Origin: United States	Barrel Length: 508mm (20in)
Date: 1963	Muzzle Velocity: 1000m/sec (3280ft/sec)
Calibre: 5.56mm (.219in) M193	Feed/Magazine: 30-round detachable box
Operation: Gas	magazine
Weight: 2.86kg (6.3lb)	Range: 500m (1640ft) +
Overall Length: 990mm (39in)	

▲ **M16A1 assault rifle**

US Military Advisors, Panama, 1979

US forces trained and equipped 'Contra' counter-revolutionary forces in neighbouring countries after the fall of the Nicaraguan government.

Falklands War: Argentine forces
1982

Ownership of the Falkland Islands has been a subject of dispute between Britain and Argentina for many years. In 1982, the Argentine government decided to invade.

IN 1955, A MILITARY COUP replaced the democratic government of Argentina with a junta that presided over a rapid economic decline and significant urban unrest. In 1972, former president Juan Perón returned from exile to take over the reins of power but could do little to improve matters. While the countryside was relatively peaceful, the streets of major cities became battlegrounds, especially in the mid 1970s.

In 1976, a further coup created another military junta that held on to power through the usual means of intimidation and repression. Led by General Leopoldo Galtieri, the government sought some means to distract the population from internal issues and hit upon a not-uncommon solution: an external conflict.

Argentina claims the Falkland Islands under their Spanish name the Malvinas, and had been

▶ **Captured small arms**

A British soldier stacks Argentine weapons following the capture of Port Stanley by UK forces. The Argentine and British forces used virtually the same small arms, including the FN MAG, FN FAL and M1919 Browning .30-calibre machine gun (being held here).

Specifications

Country of Origin: Argentina

Date: 1960

Calibre: 7.62mm (.3in) NATO

Operation: Gas

Weight: 4.31kg (9.5lb)

Overall Length: 1053mm (41.46in)

Barrel Length: 533mm (21in)

Muzzle Velocity: 853m/sec (2800ft/sec)

Feed/Magazine: 20-round detachable box
  magazine

Range: 800m (2620ft) +

▲ **FM FAL**

10th Mechanized Infantry Brigade / 7th Regiment, Wireless Ridge, 13 June 1982

The Argentinian version of the FAL rifle was locally produced by Fabricaciones Militaires, hence the 'FM' designation. Argentine FALs were capable of fully automatic fire.

negotiating with Britain over their sovereignty for some years. The Falkland islanders themselves had voted overwhelmingly to remain British, however. Reasoning that Britain lacked the means and the will to mount an amphibious campaign in the South Atlantic, Galtieri's government decided to take the islands by force.

Tensions were running high with Chile at the time, so many of Argentina's best troops were deployed to protect against a Chilean attack. They included mountain troops who were trained for cold-environment wafare. Many of the conscripts who were sent to the islands were not similarly trained, and suffered accordingly.

The initial invasion was spearheaded by Argentine special forces, who had orders to avoid inflicting casualties if possible. It was hoped that minimal force might reduce British resolve to take back the islands. In the event, the small force of Royal Marines stationed on the island put up a spirited resistance until the situation was obviously hopeless, at which point they surrendered.

Once the islands were secured, they were garrisoned primarily with conscript troops, mostly of low quality. It was not expected that the British

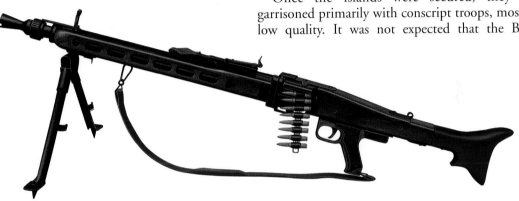

▲ Rheinmetall MG3

3rd Mechanized Infantry Brigade / 12th Regiment, Goose Green, 26 May 1982

The MG3, chambered for the same 7.62mm (.3in) ammunition as the FN FAL rifle, was the standard Argentine Army light support weapon.

Specifications

Country of Origin: West Germany	Barrel Length: 531mm (20.9in)
Date: 1966	Muzzle Velocity: 820m/sec (2690ft/sec)
Calibre: 7.62mm (.3in) NATO	Feed/Magazine: 50- or 100-round belt (50-round
Operation: Short recoil, air-cooled	belt may be contained in drum)
Weight: 11.5kg (25.35lb)	Cyclic Rate: 950–1300rpm depending on bolt
Overall Length: 1220mm (48in)	Range: 2000m (6562ft) +

Specifications

Country of Origin: Argentina	extended; 770mm (30.3in) stock folded
Date: 1960	Barrel Length: 436mm (17.1in)
Calibre: 7.62mm (.3in) NATO	Muzzle Velocity: 853m/sec (2800ft/sec)
Operation: Gas	Feed/Magazine: 20-round detachable box
Weight: 4.36kg (9.61lb)	magazine
Overall Length: 1020mm (40.15in) stock	Range: 500m (1640ft) +

▲ FM FAL (Paratroop version)

9th Infantry Brigade / 25th Infantry Regiment, Goose Green, 26 May 1982

The folding-stock version of the FAL was used by paratroops and some other formations, including the 25th Infantry, a unit similar to the US Army Rangers.

would try to recapture the Falklands, and once it was obvious that this was going to be undertaken it became problematic to reinforce the garrison by sea due to the presence of British submarines.

The Argentine garrison was strongly deployed around the capital, Port Stanley, and along the land approaches to it. Other forces were positioned at key points or held in reserve to oppose a British landing. The strength of the Argentine defence at Port Stanley made a direct assault impractical, so it was expected – correctly – that the British would land elsewhere and move on Stanley overland.

Other forces were deployed to islands in the region, such as South Georgia and Pebble Island, but these were considered peripheral to the conflict, as was the large island of West Falkland. In the final analysis, the fate of the Falkland Islands would rest upon who controlled the capital and main population centre at Port Stanley.

The Argentine infantry deployed to the islands were mostly just out of basic training and were not adequately trained for conditions on the Falklands. Nor were they up to the task of mobile warfare even if this had been practical. However, since much of the islands' terrain was impassable to vehicles and there were several obviously strong defensive positions, the conscripts were expected to be able to hold their own against even a major attack.

The key weaknesses of the Argentine forces were lack of training and the absence of mutual confidence between the officers and the enlisted men. Argentine forces were somewhat brittle; they were capable of putting up a good fight under favourable conditions, but might disintegrate when faced by setbacks.

▲ FARA 83

Under development

The FARA 83 rifle was under development as a possible replacement for the FM FAL. It is possible that some examples may have been taken to the Falklands for combat evaluation purposes.

Specifications
Country of Origin: Argentina	745mm (29.3in) stock folded
Date: 1981	Barrel Length: 452mm (17.8in)
Calibre: 5.56mm (.219in) NATO	Muzzle Velocity: 980m/sec (3215ft/sec)
Operation: Gas, rotating bolt	Feed/Magazine: 30-round detachable box
Weight: 3.95kg (8.71lb)	magazine
Overall Length: 1000mm (39.4in) stock extended;	Range: 500m (1640ft) +)

Specifications
Country of Origin: Argentina
Date: 1974
Calibre: 9mm (.35in) Parabellum
Operation: Blowback, closed bolt
Weight: 3.4kg (7.49lb)
Overall Length: 693mm (27.2in)
Barrel Length: 290mm (11.4in)
Muzzle Velocity: 400m/sec (1312ft/sec)
Feed/Magazine: 25- 32- or 40-round detachable
   box magazine
Range: 100m (328ft)

▲ FMK-3

602nd Commando, Mount Kent, 31 May 1982

The FMK-3 was developed to meet the Argentine Army's need for a close-combat weapon. It is well-balanced enough to be fired one-handed.

Falklands War: British forces
1982

It is widely accepted that 3:1 odds are needed for a successful offensive. The British could not deploy anything like enough troops to achieve this superiority.

THE BRITISH RESPONSE to the invasion of the Falkland Islands was impressively fast, but was constrained by the amount of maritime transport available. Even by converting liners and container ships to naval auxiliaries, the force that could be deployed to the Falkland Islands was severely limited.

Attempts were made to provide adequate logistical support and helicopter mobility, both of which were further reduced by air attacks on the task force as it anchored off the Falklands. Only a handful of Scorpion and Scimitar armoured vehicles, and a very limited amount of artillery, could be deployed. The Falklands campaign was obviously going to be an infantry affair.

With a landing directly at Port Stanley out of the question, San Carlos Water was chosen as the main anchorage. Lying between East and West Falkland, this location provided a fairly sheltered anchorage that could be protected against air attack by naval Harrier aircraft, warships and Rapier missile batteries landed on shore. Despite these precautions, extremely determined Argentine air attacks sank ships and reduced the resources available to the British ground forces. Perhaps most keenly felt was the loss of several Chinook transport helicopters aboard the container ship *Atlantic Conveyor*.

Air mobility

Peripheral operations by Royal Marines and special forces retook South Georgia and destroyed Argentine ground-attack aircraft based on Pebble Island, but East Falkland was a tougher proposition. Landings at Port San Carlos were more or less unopposed by ground forces, and there was no real chance of a counter-attack due to the Argentine deployments. However, the fleet was very vulnerable close inshore and suffered significant losses to air attack.

It was thus necessary to move quickly, but with few helicopters available, mobility and logistics were serious problems. The only answer was to rely on the toughness and physical fitness of the ground troops, who had to carry what they needed and march to their objectives as infantry had traditionally done. After establishing a secure beachhead the British

▲ L1A1 Self-Loading Rifle (SLR)

3 Commando Brigade / 2nd Battalion, The Parachute Regiment, Goose Green, 26 May 1982

The British version of the FN FAL, designated L1A1, was capable of semi-automatic fire only. In the British Army at that time, individual marksmanship was prized more highly than the capability to deliver suppressing fire.

Specifications

Country of Origin: United Kingdom

Date: 1954

Calibre: 7.62mm (.3in) NATO

Operation: Gas

Weight: 4.31kg (9.5lb)

Overall Length: 1055mm (41.5in)

Barrel Length: 535mm (21.1in)

Muzzle Velocity: 853m/sec (2800ft/sec)

Feed/Magazine: 20-round detachable box magazine

Range: 800m (2625ft) +

moved first against Darwin and Goose Green. The attacking force was required to march overland carrying huge loads of equipment before attacking a well-defended position. Despite being outnumbered by the defenders the paratroops given the task were able to make a successful frontal assault across a narrow isthmus and capture their objectives.

With the southern flank secured by the taking of Goose Green, British paratroops and marines advanced across the northern part of East Falkland. Their objectives were a series of small coastal settlements, after which the advance on the capital could begin in earnest. The settlements of Douglas and Teal Inlet, as well as the outer defensive positions around Port Stanley, were relatively lightly held. There was no significant counter-offensive, partly due to weather conditions and partly because the Argentine commanders knew that some British infantry were still at sea. These might be used for a direct assault if the defences around Port Stanley were weakened.

Ridge assault

Meanwhile, other British forces began pushing across the southern part of East Falkland. Both the northern and southern arms of the pincer encountered defended positions, which were usually constructed on high ground. These ridges had to be cleared by assault, supported where possible by Harriers from the Royal Navy's carrier force and the artillery, which laid down its heaviest bombardment since the end of World War II.

Between 6 and 13 June, a series of battles were fought to clear defensive positions. These were often close-quarters affairs, characterized by small-scale scrambles for positions in the tumbled rocks of the ridges. Many Argentine units fought stubbornly, though others were less determined.

One factor working in favour of the British was the fearsome reputation of the Gurkha troops who formed part of the ground force. In a close-quarters battle morale is more important than ever, and that of the Argentine conscripts was shaken by the tales they heard about Gurkha units. Some of these were spread, rather unwisely, by Argentine officers who hoped to inspire their men.

The capture of Bluff Cove on 8 June allowed a forward logistics base to be set up, which greatly eased British supply problems. Two landing ships were bombed while unloading, but it was still possible to get troops and supplies ashore.

Final battles

The final battles of the campaign were fought to clear defensive positions from the ridges above Port Stanley. On the night of 13/14 June, Wireless Ridge was taken by The Parachute Regiment while the Scots Guards assaulted Tumbledown mountain. As the Welsh Guards and Gurkhas moved up to attack the final positions at Mount William and Sapper Hill, the Argentine defence collapsed. The Argentine surrender on 14 June made an assault on Port Stanley itself unnecessary.

1st Battalion, Welsh Guards, Rifle Platoon, Rifle Section, 1982

A typical British infantry platoon of the Falklands era was made up of a platoon HQ and three rifle sections. A rifle section would include the following weapons:

2 Sterling SMG, 7 x SLR, 1 x L7A2 GPMG (plus up to 3 M72 LAW)

▲ L7A2 (FN MAG) GPMG

5th Infantry Brigade/2nd Battalion, Scots Guards, Tumbledown, 13 June 1982

The 'Gimpy' (GPMG) was an integral part of British rifle squads, providing effective and accurate automatic fire support even when heavier weapons were not available.

Specifications

Country of Origin: United Kingdom	Barrel Length: 546mm (21.5in)
Date: 1961	Muzzle Velocity: 853m/sec (2800ft/sec)
Calibre: 7.62mm (.3in) NATO	Feed/Magazine: Belt-fed
Operation: Gas, air-cooled	Cyclic Rate: 600–1000rpm
Weight: 10.15kg (22.25lb)	Range: 3000m (9842ft)
Overall Length: 1250mm (49.2in)	

◀ L2A2 HE fragmentation grenade

3 Commando Brigade/42 Commando / Royal Marines, Mount Harriet, 12 June 1982

Grenades are an effective weapon in assault operations if they can be properly placed. A lobbed grenade can drop into a position protected from direct fire.

Specifications

Country of Origin: United Kingdom	Height: 84mm (3.25in)
Date: 1960	Detonation Mechanism: Timed friction fuse
Type: Fragmentation	Filling: Composition B
Weight: .395kg (.87lb)	Lethal Radius: 10m (32.8ft)

Colombia
1960s–PRESENT

Colombia has seen more than five decades of low-intensity warfare between government forces and a variety of insurgent groups.

COLOMBIA SUFFERED PERIODS of significant unrest before the 1960s, interspersed by relatively peaceful times. Some of the causes of the current violence date back to these old disputes, but the present conflict began in the early to mid 1960s.

A number of operations were mounted by the Colombian security forces in the early 1960s, aimed at reducing the activities of insurgent groups operating throughout the country. The insurgents were pushed out of the urban centres and could only maintain bases in very remote rural areas, where they could hide their activities.

Yet by the mid 1970s a new wave of urban unrest had begun. Government countermeasures and initiatives that were intended to find a negotiated settlement calmed the situation by the early 1980s. Up until this point the conflict had been primarily political and ideological in nature, with the motivations of the insurgents varying somewhat.

Narcotic power

The situation became even more complex in the 1980s as drug barons became a potent political force in Colombia. This brought conflict with the guerrillas and with the government, which was under pressure from the USA to act against the narcotics sources.

Both the drug lords and the insurgents used terrorism and assassination to influence political decisions, with the guerrillas increasingly funded by drug money in addition to the more traditional revenue from kidnappings. By the mid 1990s the insurgents were able to carry out direct attacks on bases used by the security forces. This resulted in a withdrawal from some outlying areas.

The redeployment of security forces had some benefits, such as reduced vulnerability to attacks on small bases, but it also meant that the insurgents

could operate freely in many areas. Pro-government vigilante groups began to operate against the insurgents in some areas, using methods every bit as brutal as those of the guerrillas.

The forces deployed by the drugs cartels at times operated as something similar to rifle-armed light infantry, taking control of areas of the countryside to prevent police interference in their operations. In the urban environment, cartel gunmen found small, concealable weapons to be highly useful for security and strikes against their opponents. In addition to handguns, submachine guns were favoured, of which many came from Spanish manufacturers.

The cartels were also involved in international arms smuggling, enabling them to obtain a wide variety of weaponry for their own use, as well as selling arms for profit. Some of these weapons found their way onto the black market in Colombia despite supposedly strict gun control laws.

In recent years, the Colombian armed forces have made some progress at combating the insurgents and drug barons, but the political situation in the country remains volatile. Many of the underlying social and economic problems that caused the unrest remain. In particular, the government's anti-narcotics stance alienates segments of the population who rely on coca cultivation for their income. Since the guerrillas are willing to protect

▲ **Star Z70B**

M-19 (April 19th Movement) Insurgents, Bogota, 1985

The Star M70B was a developed version of the earlier Z-62, replacing trigger-pressure fire selection with a more conventional safe/semi/full-automatic fire selector switch.

Specifications

Country of Origin: Spain	Barrel Length: 200mm (7.87in)
Date: 1971	Muzzle Velocity: 380m/sec (1247ft/sec)
Calibre: 9mm (.35in) Parabellum	Feed/Magazine: 20-, 30-, or 40-round detachable
Operation: Blowback	box magazine
Weight: 2.87kg (6.33lb)	Range: 50m (164ft) +
Overall Length: 700mm (27.56in)	

the coca farmers from government interference, they receive support and funding that has little to do with ideology or identification with a cause; simple economic necessity drives many people into the arms of the insurgent organizations.

Urban violence

The conflict in Colombia has been characterized by urban violence, kidnapping and assassination, activities that require only small arms and a willingness to use them. Government operations against the coca plantations, and patrols aimed at finding the guerrillas' bases, have been resisted, but for the most part the conflict is fought at a low level. Although the government has achieved some successes in combating drugs gangs in recent years, the conflict is likely to continue in the same manner for some time yet.

▲ **Star Z-62**

Colombian National Police, Bogota, 1992

Experienced gained from Spanish Army service with the Z-45 resulted in Star creating an improved submachine gun in the late 1950s. This weapon entered service in 1963, as the Z-62. The Z-62 has a different layout, with the pistol grip much closer to the magazine well.

Specifications

Country of Origin: Spain	Barrel Length: 215mm (8.4in)
Date: 1963	Muzzle Velocity: 399m/sec (1312ft/sec)
Calibre: 9mm (.35in)	Feed/Magazine: 25- or 30-round detachable box
Operation: Blowback, open bolt	magazine
Weight: 3kg (6.61lb)	Range: 150–200m (492–656ft)
Overall Length: 615mm (24.2in)	

Specifications

Country of Origin: Israel	Overall Length: 730mm (28.74in)
Date: Not known	Barrell Length: 215mm (8.46in)
Calibre: 5.56mm (.219in); 7.62mm (.3in)	Muzzel Velocity: 710m/sec (2329ft/sec)
Operation: Gas, rotating bolt	Feed/Magazine: 35-round box magazine
Weight: 2.8kg (6.17lb)	Range: 300–500m (984 –1640ft)

▲ **Galil ACE 21**

Colombian National Army Special Forces Anti-Terrorist Group, Cartagena, 2004

The Galil ACE is the latest version of the Galil assault rifle. It is available with various barrel lengths for use as a support weapon, rifle or carbine.

Chapter 11

Modern Wars

Wars in the modern world are characterized
by their complexity and the predominance of urban combat,
often within an area where non-combatants are trying to go
about the business of daily life. Large-scale engagements
between national armies do happen, but confrontations
between massed armoured formations are less common than
fleeting battles between insurgents and infantry supported
by light armoured vehicles.

Often, troops are involved in 'war-like situations' rather than
straight-up warfare. They are deployed to keep the peace
rather than to fight an enemy, or to deal with an insurgency.
These priorities create ambiguities than can be exploited by
hostiles, and they require a delicate balance of restraint and
aggression if the overall mission is to be a success.

◀ **Checkpoint security**
Armed with an L7A2 general-purpose machine gun, a British Army trooper from the 3rd Battalion, the
Parachute Regiment, keeps watch as part of a vehicle checkpoint during Operation *Iraqi Freedom*, 2004.

Introduction

Warfare has always been about political outcomes rather than military victories. The side that achieves its aims will win, even if defeated in every battle.

THE TERM 'THREE-BLOCK WAR' was coined to describe a situation in which troops might be involved in humanitarian aid, peacekeeping and direct combat operations at the same time, all within a three-block radius. It reflects the complexity of many conflicts and the many missions that must be carried out in order to succeed.

Direct conflict between national armies creates a relatively straightforward situation – the goal is to defeat a clearly identifiable enemy using technology and tactics. Even here, complexities arise when combatant forces seek to limit the suffering of the enemy population. Many national governments have less regard for their own people than their enemies,

and will try to hide their facilities among innocents. Positioning command posts and arms factories beside hospitals and schools may limit the willingness of a hostile force to attack them.

Much of this complexity is inadvertent, however. It is very rare to encounter a theatre of conflict where there are absolutely no civilians, so military forces must take care only to engage properly identified targets. This situation of course allows hostiles to hide among the innocent population in order to gather information or approach their targets, but while making war without regard to the suffering of innocents might be simpler, it is also horrific and politically costly.

▲ **Sniper security**

A US Army sniper team scan for enemy activity during a foot patrol near Forward Operating Base Mizan, Afghanistan, 2009. The sniper is armed with a Barrett M82 'Light' .50-calibre anti-materiel rifle. The soldier with binoculars carries an M4 carbine slung from his shoulder. In the background (left) appears to be an abandoned Soviet-made PKM light machine gun.

▲ **Classic Soviet LMG**
Armed with an RPK light machine gun, an Iraqi army soldier from 5th Iraqi Army Division undergoes training in Kirkush Military Training Base, Iraq, 2011.

Operations are particularly difficult where a peacekeeping force is involved in a complex conflict featuring many factions, including irregular forces who might not wear uniforms or identifying insignia. Today's friendlies might be tomorrow's hostiles, and even without the prospect of treachery it can be hard to tell one group apart from another – especially if deliberate deception is employed.

The problem in many cases is not so much dealing with enemy combatants as identifying them and finding their whereabouts. Combatants may conceal themselves in remote mountain bases or fade back into the general population to avoid detection. In either case, once contact is lost it is very difficult to regain, a fact that permits hostiles to make traditional hit-and-run attacks against targets of their choosing.

Modern wars are, for the most part, won in the hearts and minds of the people and, to some extent, their political leadership. Military success plays a part in the outcome, of course, but the overall mission is political. It is not enough to keep on killing guerrillas; if the population is hostile then more will appear. The people must be won over or at least dissuaded from supporting the insurgents. This means that troops must work with the locals, talk to them, and win their acceptance – perhaps even friendship. Such cannot be done from behind tank armour or a strike jet's cockpit.

The close contact required by foot and light vehicle patrolling, and by operating checkpoints and guarding aid stations, exposes troops to attack with basic weapons. Similarly, when attacking a remote insurgent base it is usually infantry that have to take the brunt of the fighting; other arms cannot always be brought to bear.

Modern ground troops are supported by a wealth of technological equipment: remote-controlled drones, GPS-guided artillery shells and all-but-impervious main battle tanks (MBTs). Yet they still must engage hostiles, clear enemy positions and secure key areas in the same manner as infantry of all eras. Infantry weapons are still, arguably, the most important of military tools. It is the soldier on the ground who makes the shoot/don't shoot decision, and success or failure in the overall mission will be influenced greatly by the combined weight of those decisions.

Former Yugoslavia
1990s

Traditionally referred to as the 'powder-keg of Europe', the Balkans once again ignited into warfare in the early 1990s.

The presence of many different ethnic, religious and political groupings has always made the Balkans a potentially unstable region. In the early years of the twentieth century, national boundaries were redrawn on many occasions. From this complex situation emerged the Kingdom of Yugoslavia, which was invaded by the Axis powers in World War II. After liberation, Yugoslavia became the Socialist Federal Republic of Yugoslavia (SFRY).

Yugoslavia at this time comprised several states, including the republics of Serbia, Croatia and Bosnia-Herzegovina. Within each of these states lived a mix of Christians and Muslims, and most states had significant populations whose ethnic origins differed from the state as a whole. Bosnia, for example, was home to large populations of Serbs and Croats, who were more inclined towards loyalty to Serbia or Croatia than to their ostensible homeland in Bosnia.

Despite this internal complexity, Yugoslavia was a prosperous nation in the post-war years and enjoyed solid economic growth. Although having a

Communist government, Yugoslavia was not aligned with the Soviet Union and received support from the West to ensure that it did not become so. Changes in the East–West political situation caused this support to be reduced, and Yugoslavia's economy suffered accordingly.

With international debt increasing and the economy declining fast, the national government granted the member republics greater control over their affairs, encouraging a general move towards independence. Autonomous regions, such as Kosovo in Serbia, were created, which caused resentment in some quarters. Disagreements between the various member states of Yugoslavia caused endless political wrangling, which came violently to a head at the end of the 1980s.

It is hard to pinpoint a precise moment when the breakup of Yugoslavia began, but the announcement of secession from Croatia by Croatian Serbs saw the beginning of armed conflict. Croatia was at that time moving towards independence, and its constitution

▲ **Vz58**

Bosnian Irregulars, Sarajevo, May 1994

The Czech-made Vz58 resembles an AK-47 and uses the same ammunition, but it is a separately developed gas-operated design.

Specifications

Country of Origin: Czechoslovakia
Date: 1958
Calibre: 7.62mm (.3in) Soviet M1943
Operation: Gas, falling breech-block
Weight: 2.91kg (6.42lb)
Overall Length: 845mm (33.3in)

Barrel Length: 390mm (15.4in)
Muzzle Velocity: 705m/sec (2313ft/sec)
Feed/Magazine: 30-round detachable box
  magazine
Range: 400m (1312ft)

seemed to be treating Serbs as second-class citizens. This was unacceptable to Croatian Serbs, who had the support of many Yugoslavian Army officers.

Serb domination

Much of the army's officer class were ethnic Serbs, who were naturally sympathetic to their cousins in Croatia. The Federal Army had taken steps to disarm Croatian forces during the run-up to independence, which gave the Serbs a major advantage. Both sides lacked significant armament at the beginning of the conflict, but the Croatian Serbs were supplied by sympathetic Federal Army officers. The emerging state of Croatia, on the other hand, had to obtain weapons through international channels, often negotiating embargo conditions. Serb forces generally had access to equipment from the former Yugoslav

army, and were well equipped with military weapons. These included Zastava assault rifles, which were derived from the AK series. One notable difference was that the Zastava rifles did not use chrome lining in the barrel, which made them less resistant to corrosion. However, they were correspondingly more accurate and proved both robust and reliable in combat situations.

Other factions were badly affected by the arms embargo and were forced to buy weapons on the black market or from criminal groups within their own society. These weapons tended to be suited to urban criminality rather than military combat, and included a range of handguns and submachine guns which were mainly of Eastern European origin.

The emerging conflict was particularly unpleasant, with accusations of atrocities and massacres levelled

▶ Agram 2000

Croatian Irregulars / Croatian War of Independence, 1995

Despite its highly modern appearance, the Agram 2000 was developed from the Beretta Modello 12, which dates back to the late 1950s.

Specifications

Country of Origin: Croatia	Barrel Length: 200mm (7.8in)
Date: 1990	Muzzle Velocity: Not known
Calibre: 9mm (.35in) Parabellum	Feed/Magazine: 15-, 22- or 32-round detachable
Operation: Blowback	box magazine
Weight: 1.8kg (3.96lb)	Range: 100m (328ft)
Overall Length: 482mm (18.9in)	

▶ CZ85 pistol

Serbian Irregulars, Srebrenica, February 1995

The Czech-made CZ85 pistol is an updated version of the CZ75, differing mainly in having an ambidextrous safety and slide stop.

Specifications

Country of Origin: Czechoslovakia	Barrel Length: 120mm (4.7in)
Date: 1986	Muzzle Velocity: 370m/sec (1214ft/sec)
Calibre: 9mm (.35in) Parabellum	Feed/Magazine: 16-round detachable box
Operation: Blowback	magazine
Weight: 1kg (2.2lb)	Range: 40m (131ft)
Overall Length: 206mm (8.1in)	

against both sides; many Croatian leaders were later convicted of war crimes. Attacks on civilians were employed both as a military gambit to weaken the enemy's resolve and also in an effort to remove unwanted ethnic groups from Croatian territory. Croatia was also attacked from outside, notably by Serbian forces, throughout five years of war.

Border clashes

Soon after fighting broke out in Croatia came the declaration of independence by Slovenia. The subsequent clash with the Yugoslavian federal forces became known as the Ten-Day War. This was a fairly minor conflict, with few casualties. Federal Yugoslavian troops generally took up positions on the borders of the republic of Slovenia, and primarily confined themselves to containment operations. After some skirmishing a ceasefire was agreed and eventually the federal forces pulled out, essentially confirming Slovenian independence.

The fate of Bosnia was a particular bone of contention between the various former Yugoslavian factions. After an initial period of heavy fighting, which was marked by atrocities and the murder of surrendered enemy personnel, UN peacekeeping forces attempted to create safe areas within the conflict zone, beginning a long and difficult deployment where their hands were often tied by rules of engagement that, for example, allowed hostiles to walk away unhindered after throwing a

▶ CZ99 pistol

Federal Armoured Forces, Slovenian Border, June 1991

Unrelated to Czech 'CZ' pistols, the Zastava CZ99 was produced to meet the needs of the Yugoslavian military and passed into the hands of various forces.

Specifications

Country of Origin: Yugoslavia	Overall Length: 190mm (7.4in)
Date: 1990	Barrel Length: 108mm (4.25in)
Calibre: 9mm (.35in) Parabellum,	Muzzle Velocity: 300–457m/sec (985–1500ft/sec)
10.16mm (.4in) / 40 S&W	Feed/Magazine: 15- (9mm/.35in) or 10/12-round
Operation: Single- or double-action	(10.16mm/.4in) detachable magazine
Weight: 1.145kg (2.5lb)	Range: 40m (131ft)

Specifications

Country of Origin: Czechoslovakia	Barrel Length: 115mm (4.5in)
Date: 1960	Muzzle Velocity: 320m/sec (1050ft/sec)
Calibre: 7.65mm (.301in)	Feed/Magazine: 10- or 20-round detachable
Operation: Blowback, closed bolt	box magazine
Weight: 1.28kg (2.8lb)	Range: 25m (82ft)
Overall Length: 517mm (20.3in)	

▲ M84 submachine gun (Vz61 Skorpion)

Serbian Forces, Sarajevo, April 1995

A license-built version of the Czech Vz61 Skorpion, the M84 was adopted by Yugoslavian forces as a personal defence weapon for vehicle crews.

grenade at UN troops or the people they were deployed to protect.

From 1992 onwards, the conflict spread to Bosnia-Herzegovina. Again, various factions were involved but overall the conflict pitted Serbs against Bosnian and Croat forces. The Serbs were in general well equipped, with support from both Serbia and Serbian sympathisers within the federal armed forces. The latter gradually fragmented, with most heavy equipment and stocks of ammunition ending up in Serb hands.

Early in the conflict, Serbian forces attempted to capture Sarajevo, capital of Bosnia. Although they were able to penetrate the city and took control of some key points, the numerous but poorly equipped defenders were able to prevent the city's fall. The

Specifications

Country of Origin: Yugoslavia

Date: 1968

Calibre: 7.62mm (.3in)

Operation: Gas (rotating bolt)

Weight: 3.70kg (8.16lb)

Overall Length: 875mm (34.4in)

Barrell Length: 415mm (16.33in)

Muzzle Velocity: 720m/sec (2362ft/sec)

Feed/Magazine: 30-round detachable box
      magazine

Range: 410m (1345ft)

▲ **Zastava M70**

Serbian Forces, Sarajevo, March 1993

Fitted with a telescopic sight, the M70 assault rifle was adequate as a sniping weapon in a medium-range urban context, when fired from tall buildings along the streets of Sarajevo.

Specifications

Country of Origin: Yugoslavia

Date: 1972

Calibre: 7.62mm (.3in)

Operation: Gas, rotating bolt

Weight: 5.5kg (12.12lb)

Overall Length: 1025mm (40.35in)

Barrell Length: 542mm (21.33in)

Muzzel Velocity: 745m/sec (2444ft/sec)

Feed/Magazine: 30- or 40-round box magazines
      or 75-round drums

Range: 400m (1312ft)

▲ **Zastava M72**

Slovenian Provisional Forces, Ljubljana, June 1991

A light support version of the M70 rifle, the M72 served with the Yugoslavian armed forces and was thus obtained by most successor forces.

▲ **Balkans battle**
Unidentified irregulars move warily through a street somewhere in the former Yugoslavia, armed with Zastava assault rifles.

ensuing battle for the city remains the longest siege of a capital city in modern times. Sarajevo was more or less entirely cut off by Serbian positions in the surrounding hills.

With no means of reply to shelling by Serb artillery, located in fortified firebases, the people of Sarajevo and the defenders were forced to live under constant fire, which was directed at civilian targets as well as military ones. Snipers in tall buildings deliberately attacked civilians as part of a campaign to wear down the defenders.

Despite their advantages in heavy weapons, Serb forces were still unable to take complete possession of the city, although they dominated some areas. Assaults intended to increase Serbian control resulted in street fighting, with blocks changing hands in bitter close-range firefights. The Bosnians managed to get hold of enough small arms to mount a defence

against these attacks, though they lacked the large-scale military capability required to break out or force a supply corridor through the siege lines.

UN aid

UN aid was brought into Sarajevo via the airport, a hazardous business that required the deployment of peacekeeping troops to protect the aid shipments and the airport itself. The UN involvement gradually expanded into air strikes on Serbian artillery and later logistics assets, with the combined effect of easing the pressure on the Bosnian forces to the point at which they could begin to take offensive action.

This conflict, which became known as the Bosnian War, was ended by a negotiated ceasefire in 1995. Increasing Bosnian success in the field, coupled with threats of additional UN airstrikes, contributed to a willingness to bring the war to a close. The siege of

Sarajevo was lifted by Serb withdrawal rather than a relief operation.

Much of the conflict in the former Yugoslavia was fought by paramilitaries and militias, many of whom regarded civilians as legitimate targets. Although heavy weapons and artillery were available and were used liberally, much of the fighting was expressed by small-arms engagements between personnel armed with much the same equipment on both sides.

The UN embargo on arms shipments to Yugoslavia affected the Serb forces less than other factions, as they had extensive access to the armouries of the Federal Army. Most other factions were forced to obtain whatever weaponry they could by smuggling, black market sales or scrounging from battlefields.

Most of this weaponry was Eastern European in origin, i.e. heavily influenced by Soviet equipment. Assault rifles were ubiquitous, but in urban combat around towns, villages and the suburbs of major cities, submachine guns proved to be an effective close-range weapon.

▶ PM-63

Kosovan Irregulars, Kosovo, March 1992

The PM-63 uses a slide that is integral with the breech-block, rather like an automatic pistol. Accurate automatic fire would not be possible with the PM-63, with so much reciprocating weight moving around.

Specifications

Country of Origin: Poland	Barrel Length: 152mm (6in)
Date: 1964	Muzzle Velocity: 320m/sec (1050ft/sec)
Calibre: 9mm (.35in) Makarov	Feed/Magazine: 15- or 25-round detachable box
Operation: Blowback	magazine
Weight: 1.6kg (3.53lb)	Range: 100–150m (328–492ft)
Overall Length: 583mm (23in)	

Specifications

Country of Origin: FR Yugoslavia	Overall Length: 540mm (21.25in)
Date: Not known	Barrell Length: 254mm (10.0in)
Calibre: 7.62mm (.3in)	Muzzel Velocity: 678 m/sec (2224 ft/sec)
Operation: Gas-operated, rotating bolt	Feed/Magazine: 30-round detachable box
Weight: 3.5kg (7.72lb)	magazine
	Range: 200m (656ft)

▲ Zastava M92

Croatian Armed Forces, post-Conflict

The M92 was developed from the M85, itself a copy of the Soviet AKSU-74. The weapon is chambered for 7.62x39mm, the M85 for 5.56x45mm.

Wars in the Caucasus

1994–PRESENT

The breakup of the Soviet Union exposed old tensions and created new ones, creating a volatile situation on Russia's southern flank.

WITH THE DISSOLUTION of the Soviet Union, most of its former territories entered into treaties with Russia defining their new relationship. Chechnya was a notable exception, and after some internal conflict a government emerged which was committed to full independence from Russia. Moscow made a military response, but this was rapidly withdrawn.

After many years of relying on the venerable AK series, Russian forces began to move towards a new generation of more sophisticated weapons influenced by concepts developed elsewhere. Many of these weapons were chambered for 'Western' calibres and are compatible with a variety of rail-mounted accessories, increasing their attractiveness to international buyers. Although these weapons proved themselves effective, the move away from AK-series rifles was slowed by the sheer numbers of Kalashnikov-based weapons available. Despite its longevity, the AK series remains effective, and serves to arm second-line units or else are sold on the open market, ensuring that they will be available for a long time to come.

Chechnya

Chechnya soon began to suffer economic problems in addition to repeated coup attempts and outright civil war. Economic difficulties were exacerbated by the exodus of thousands of non-ethnic Chechens,

▲ **Ammo belt**

An Azeri soldier adjusts a light machine-gun's ammo belt during the Nagorno-Karabakh border conflict, 1992.

▶ **PSM pistol**

Russian Peacekeeping Forces, South Ossetia, January 2008

The PSM fires a weak, small-calibre round but has the advantage of being very small and light, and thus easy to carry.

Specifications

Country of Origin: USSR	Barrel Length: 85mm (3.35in)
Date: 1973	Muzzle Velocity: 315m/sec (1033ft/sec)
Calibre: 5.45mm (.215in) Soviet Pistol	Feed/Magazine: 8-round detachable box
Operation: Blowback	magazine
Weight: .46kg (1.01lb)	Range: 40m (131ft)
Overall Length: 160mm (6.3in)	

many of whom had been experts and skilled workers in key industries. Russian forces became increasingly involved in Chechen infighting, first as covert support for the government's opponents and later more directly. In December 1994 the decision was taken to enter Chechnya and oust the pro-independence government.

The Russian offensive began with air strikes that demolished the Chechen air force, but this success was offset by political difficulties in a complex ethnic situation. Many officials within Russia, and large numbers of Russian Army officers, opposed the conflict. Some of the units detailed for the invasion were at low readiness and struggled even to move to the border. Although the Russian Army enjoyed air superiority and vastly better equipment, the conscript

forces it fielded were ill-trained and unenthusiastic, which permitted the Chechens to launch hit-and-run raids on demoralized troops. Nevertheless, the advance towards the Chechen capital of Grozny could not be halted and soon Russian forces encircled the city.

Initial attempts to push into the city were repulsed with heavy Russian losses, despite major artillery and air support and the use of armoured forces. Instead the Russians were forced to grind their way through the increasingly ruined city street by street, finally achieving what appeared as victory in March 1995.

The weapons used by both sides in this bitter street fighting were much the same Soviet-era assault rifles and other infantry weapons. The AK series of rifles were designed to be used by poorly trained conscripts

▶ **PMM pistol**

Kchevki Tank Group, Tskhinvali, August 2008

The PMM (or Makarov) was the standard issue sidearm to Soviet-era forces. The huge numbers manufactured ensured that it remained in use for many years afterwards.

Specifications

Country of Origin: USSR/Russia	Overall Length: 165mm (6.49in)
Date: 1952	Barrell Length: 93.5mm (3.68in)
Calibre: 9mm (.35in)	Muzzle Velocity: 430m/sec (1410ft/sec)
Operation: Double action	Feed/Magazine: 12-round box magazine
Weight: .76kg (1.67lb)	Range: 50m (164ft)

Specifications

Country of Origin: Russia	Barrel Length: 405mm (15.9in)
Date: 1994	Muzzle Velocity: 900m/sec (2953ft/sec)
Calibre: 5.45mm (.215in)	Feed/Magazine: 30- or 45-round AK-74-
Operation: Gas	compatible box magazine; 60-round casket
Weight: 3.85kg (8.49lb)	magazine
Overall Length: 943mm (37.1in)	Range: 400m (1312ft)

▲ **AN-94 assault rifle**

Russian Army / 19th Motorized Rifle Division, Tskhinvali, August 2008

Designed as the successor to the Soviet era AK-74, the AN-94 is a much more complex weapon capable of firing two-round bursts at an extremely high rate of fire, or fire at full automatic on a lower rate.

and militia, and indeed they were in this conflict. At close quarters in urban terrain, firepower and reliability counted for more than long-range accuracy, and here the AK assault rifle excelled.

Having taken Grozny, Russian forces were able to gain ground in the country, pushing the Chechens back into increasingly remote areas. The war became a guerrilla conflict, crossing the line into terrorism through hostage-taking and attacks on civilian targets. Despite some successful counter-attacks and sympathetic insurgency in Russia and elsewhere, Chechen forces were gradually defeated in the field. However, Grozny was twice retaken by the Chechens,

who took advantage of Russian weakness there as troops were massed for operations elsewhere.

A ceasefire was followed by a formal peace treaty in November 1996, but tensions still existed between Russia and its former territory. A general deterioration in the internal security situation in Chechnya led to open combat between the Chechen government forces and various militias. After numerous incidents involving Russian personnel, a second invasion was launched.

Russian intervention began with an air campaign in late 1999, followed by a ground invasion. The Russian advance was methodical and well supported

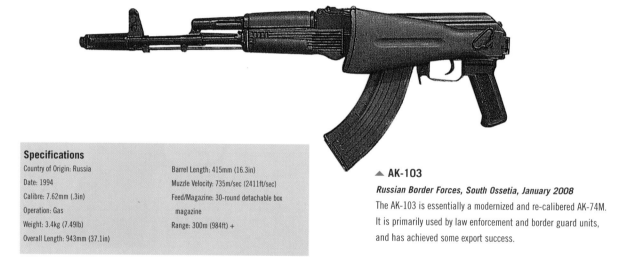

Specifications

Country of Origin: Russia	Barrel Length: 415mm (16.3in)
Date: 1994	Muzzle Velocity: 735m/sec (2411ft/sec)
Calibre: 7.62mm (.3in)	Feed/Magazine: 30-round detachable box
Operation: Gas	magazine
Weight: 3.4kg (7.49lb)	Range: 300m (984ft) +
Overall Length: 943mm (37.1in)	

▲ **AK-103**

Russian Border Forces, South Ossetia, January 2008
The AK-103 is essentially a modernized and re-calibered AK-74M. It is primarily used by law enforcement and border guard units, and has achieved some export success.

Specifications

Country of Origin: Russia	Barrell Length: 415mm (16.3in)
Date: 1990s	Muzzel Velocity: 900m/sec (2,953 ft/sec)
Calibre: 5.45mm (.21in)	Feed/Magazine: 30-round detachable box
Operation: Gas	magazine
Weight: 3.8kg (8.38lb)	Range: 500m (1640ft)
Overall Length: 943mm (37.1in)	

▲ **AK-107**

Russian Army / 20th Motorized Rifle Division, Abkhazia, August 2008
The AK-107 was developed as a cheaper alternative to the AN-94. It is capable of full- or semi automatic fire as well as three-round bursts.

by both artillery and strike aircraft, reaching Grozny by mid October. Other forces drove on major cities in Chechnya, meeting resistance mainly from bands of militia fighters equipped with small arms only. Direct Russian rule over Chechnya was established in May 2000, with a gradual move towards autonomy.

South Ossetia

Elsewhere, the breakup of the Soviet Union created other problems. Conflict in South Ossetia during 1991–92 and Abkhazia in 1992–93 left parts of these regions in separatist hands, and other areas controlled by pro-Russian factions.

During August 2008, Georgia attempted to regain control of South Ossetia, launching an offensive into the region that initially met with success. Georgian forces attacked Tskhinvali, clashing with local forces and also Russian peacekeepers stationed there. The Georgians reached the city centre, but could not hold it in the face of determined resistance

Russia responded to the incursion by sending its own forces into South Ossetia and launching airstrikes against the Georgian advance. Georgian and Russian armoured forces clashed at times, though Russian air power prevented Georgian tanks from having much effect on the conflict. Much of the

▲ AK-200

Under development

The AK-200 is the latest Russian assault rifle, developed from the AK-74. It reflects modern preferences for accessory rails and advanced materials, allowing the attachment of modular equipment, including advanced optical sight combinations, laser illuminators, flashlights, vertical foregrips, bipods and grenade launchers.

Specifications

Country of Origin: Russia
Date: 2010
Calibre: 5.56mm (0.21in)
Operation: Gas, rotating bolt
Weight: 3.8 kg (8.38 lb)
Overall Length: 943mm (37.1in)

Barrell Length: 415mm (16.3in)
Muzzle Velocity: 900m/sec (2953ft/sec)
Feed/Magazine: 30-round detachable box
  magazine
Range: 500m (1640ft)

Specifications

Country of Origin: Russia
Date: Early 1990s
Calibre: 7.62mm (.3in)
Operation: Gas, rotating bolt
Weight: 4.68kg (10.3lb)
Overall Length: 1225mm (48.2in)

Barrell Length: 560mm (22.2in)
Muzzel Velocity: 830m/sec (2,723ft/sec)
Feed/Magazine: 10-round detachable box
  magazine
Range: 800m (2624ft)

▲ SVD-S Dragunov sniper rifle

76th Pskov Air Assault Division, Abkhazia, August 2008

The SVD-S is a modified version of the proven SVD sniper rifle. It is intended for airborne troops and has a folding stock.

ground fighting was urban combat between Georgian infantry and local irregulars. Ossetian forces inflicted casualties on Georgian vehicles in close-range ambushes with RPG-7 anti-tank weapons.

Russian operations were hampered by the need to funnel reinforcements through a narrow route, but gradually the balance of forces came to favour Russia. Despite counter-attacks, the Russians were able to drive Georgian forces out of Tskhinvali and, ultimately, from South Ossetia. Russian forces then pushed into Georgia, advancing on the city of Gori. After heavy fighting the Georgians retreated and the city was taken.

The conflict came to an end with a ceasefire that was followed by a Russian withdrawal from the occupied territories.

Specifications

Country of Origin: Russia
Date: 1999
Calibre: 7.62mm (.3in)
Operation: Gas
Weight: 8.7kg (19.18lb)
Overall Length: 1155mm (45.47in)

Barrell Length: 640mm (25.19in)
Muzzle Velocity: 825m/sec (2706ft/sec)
Feed/Magazine: 100- and 200-round belt fed
 magazine
Range: 1500m (4921ft)

▲ 'Pecheneg' Kalashnikov infantry machine gun
Russian Army / 19th Motorized Rifle Division, Tskhinvali, August 2008
The Pecheneg is a development of the PKM machine gun, chambered for 7.62x54mm. It does not have a quick-change barrel and is aimed at the squad support weapon niche rather than the general-purpose machine gun role.

Iraqi Army and insurgent weapons
2003–PRESENT

The 1991 Gulf War was limited by its UN remit to removing Iraqi forces from Kuwait. The 2003 invasion was a wholly different prospect, launched with the goal of regime change in Iraq.

AT THE END OF THE 1991 GULF WAR there was a significant 'on to Baghdad' sentiment among the Coalition forces that had driven the Iraqi Army from Kuwait. Many people forecast that there would be another Gulf War in the near future, suggesting that the dictator Saddam Hussein could be toppled while he was weak, or else a far more costly war would be required in the future.

Despite internal uprisings, the Saddam regime managed to survive its catastrophic defeat in 1991, and brutally put down all attempts at resistance. By 2003 the Iraqi forces had rebuilt their strength and were, at least on paper, formidable. However, the equipment fielded by this impressively large army was outdated. Armed with Soviet-era weaponry for the most part, the Iraqi Army was a generation or more behind the international forces it faced in 2003.

Internally, too, the Iraqi military was weak. The regular army was composed largely of ill-trained conscripts, many of whom were opposed to the regime. Few were active supporters. The officer class was more loyal, but the Iraqi Army as a whole was neither skilled nor motivated. Indeed, concerns about its loyalty were among the reasons for the original formation of the Republican Guard.

The Republican Guard was a political force as much as a military one, intended to counterbalance the army's power. Loyal to the Saddam regime, it received the best equipment and had far higher morale than the purely military formations. Small arms and light support weapons used by both formations were the same, being Soviet-era weaponry well suited to use in harsh desert conditions by conscript troops.

Under the codename Operation *Iraqi Freedom*, the United States and the United Kingdom led the invasion of Iraq in March 2003. British forces aimed for Iraq's second city of Basra, while the US military drove on Baghdad itself. Led by armoured forces, the advance on Baghdad was rapid. However, attacks against the logistics 'tail' that followed the 'teeth' formations demonstrated that a significant will to resist existed.

Many Iraqi Army formations disintegrated under air strikes or armoured assault, or surrendered at the first opportunity. Yet there were increasing numbers of irregulars in civilian clothes, some of whom were army personnel in disguise. These insurgents attacked whatever targets they could, then attempted to disappear into the civilian population. Coalition forces were hampered by a desire to avoid civilian casualties, which required great restraint even under

fire. The policy paid off to a great extent; most ordinary Iraqis hated the brutal Saddam regime and simply stayed out of the way of the fighting. Despite exhortations to rise up and defend the homeland, Saddam's people mostly stood aside as the Coalition demolished what army units tried to stand and fight.

Despite determined resistance here and there, the Iraqi Army could not hope to prevent the fall of Basra and Baghdad, and soon afterwards the rest of the country was in Coalition hands. This victory marked the end of the conflict against the Saddam Hussein regime, but a difficult period lay ahead. Coalition forces found themselves drawn into conflict with all manner of opponents.

Some of these enemies were die-hard supporters of Saddam Hussein and his Ba'ath party. Others were anti-Western Jihadists from Iraq and other countries, who had come to join the conflict as a means to strike at their ideological enemies. Militias loyal to various political and religious figures also clashed in the power vacuum created by the collapse of the dictatorship. Not all of these groups were exclusively opposed to the Coalition. Some fought one another, or took on all-comers for control of a key city or region. In the midst of this chaotic and dangerous situation the Coalition forces attempted to restore order, to hand control to local authorities, and to avoid inflaming the situation by over-reaction.

Once the formal ground campaign was over, and success had apparently been achieved, the Coalition

Specifications	
Country of Origin: USSR	Barrel Length: 400mm (15.8in)
Date: 1974	Muzzle Velocity: 900m/sec (2952ft/sec)
Calibre: 5.45mm (.215in) M74	Feed/Magazine: 30-round detachable box
Operation: Gas	magazine
Weight: 3.6kg (7.94lb)	Range: 300m (984ft)
Overall Length: 943mm (37.1in)	

▲ **AK-74**

Fedayeen Saddam, Baghdad, April 2003

The AK-74 is primarily distinguishable from its predecessor AKM/AK-47 by the long groove in the stock and the indentation above the magazine well, as well as its smaller-calibre round.

forces went over to a 'peacekeeping' role, though their enemies did not. Advanced weaponry and heavily armoured tanks were only so much use when trying to maintain law and order in a densely populated city, and foot patrols put Coalition soldiers in a position where any insurgent with a weapon had a chance to cause casualties.

Thus the war to depose Saddam Hussein was largely fought by aircraft, missiles and armoured vehicles, but the fight to control Iraq fell upon the infantry. Highly skilled and well equipped Coalition soldiers had the advantage, man for man, in a firefight, but the insurgents were on home ground and could hide among innocents. With no shortage of weaponry available after the disbandment of the Iraqi Army, the insurgency after the fall of Iraq proved more of a threat than the organized resistance of the Iraqi Army.

▲ **PKM**

Iraqi Army / Republican Guard / Baghdad Division, Kut, April 2003

A contemporary of the US M60, the PKM machinegun is a robust and effective weapon which has achieved good export sales.

Specifications

Country of Origin: USSR	Barrel Length: 658mm (25.9in)
Date: 1969	Muzzle Velocity: 800m/sec (2600ft/sec)
Calibre: 7.62mm (.3in) M1943	Feed/Magazine: Belt-fed (belts contained in
Operation: Gas, air-cooled	boxes)
Weight: 9kg (19.84lb)	Cyclic Rate: 710rpm
Overall Length: 1160mm (45.67in)	Range: 2000m (6560ft) +

▲ **RPG-7**

Iraqi Insurgents, Fallujah, December 2004

Although the RPG-7 is limited in its effectiveness against main battle tanks, it posed a significant threat to lighter vehicles and to buildings used as Coalition bases.

Specifications

Country of Origin: USSR	Overall Length: 950mm (37.4in)
Date: 1961	Muzzle Velocity: 115m/sec (377ft/sec)
Calibre: 40mm (1.57in)	Feed/Magazine: Single-shot, muzzle-loaded
Operation: Rocket motor	Range: c.920m (3018ft)
Weight: 7kg (15lb)	

Iraq and Afghanistan: Sniper weapons and tactics

2000–PRESENT

Marksmanship is of course a key skill for the sniper, but there is more to sniping than hitting the target.

WHILE MOST INFANTRY TACTICS revolve around volume of fire, suppressing an enemy force as other elements move into a better position, sniping is entirely the opposite. A sniper may only fire one shot in an entire engagement. Yet man for man snipers are among the most influential of combat assets.

A sniper must obviously be a good shot, and must be able to hit targets reliably at extreme ranges. This skill necessitates an ability to predict the target's movements, account for wind and bullet drop, estimate the effects of humidity and temperature, and a host of other factors. Just as important, a sniper must be able to get into a good position and remain there undetected. He also needs to be able to escape from an enemy search party if necessary.

Observation and stealth skills are of paramount importance to the sniper, as well as an understanding of human behaviour. It is often possible to predict where an enemy will stop by observing local conditions, allowing a shot to be set up in advance.

Furthermore, when hunting enemy snipers or gunmen, by looking for good places to shoot from, the sniper may be able to figure out where a hostile might hide himself.

A sniper might only take one shot at a target, so that shot must count. He might ignore an ordinary enemy soldier or gunman in the hope that a higher-value target may present himself. By refraining from shooting the first target that appears he gives himself the chance to make a greater difference to the course of the campaign.

High-value target

Eliminating an officer or effective leader can have serious effects on enemy combat capabilities. Communications personnel and specialists are also high-value targets. Snipers are trained to choose a target that will have a significant effect rather than simply hoping to inflict a casualty, though morale can be seriously impaired by general sniper attacks.

▲ **Dragunov SVD**

Taliban Guerrillas, Helmand Province, April 2008

A number of Dragunov rifles were captured by Afghan fighters during the Russian occupation, and have since been used against Western forces.

Specifications

Country of Origin: USSR	Barrel Length: 610mm (24in)
Date: 1963	Muzzle Velocity: 828m/sec (2720ft/sec)
Calibre: 7.62mm (.3in) Soviet	Feed/Magazine: 10-round detachable box
Operation: Gas	magazine
Weight: 4.31kg (9.5lb)	Range: 1000m (3280ft)
Overall Length: 1225mm (48.2in)	

Snipers are also reconnaissance assets, reporting on what they observe or calling in artillery and air support on valuable targets. Here, too, their keen observation skills allow them to gather information or direct fire better than the typical infantry soldier. An enemy unit that does not know it is being observed may be surprised by an air strike or bombardment, suffering more serious casualties.

Teamwork

Snipers rarely work alone. The usual practice is to create two- or three-man teams, often with an experienced sniper educating a less-experienced one in the process. A sniper can only observe in one direction at a time, so having a companion to provide security is useful. A spotter can also report the results of a shot, which may occur out of the sniper's field of

▲ M14 Enhanced Battle Rifle (EBR)

US Army / 10th Mountain Division, Afghanistan, May 2010

Developed directly from the M14 sniper rifle, progenitor of the M21 sniper rifle, the M14 EBR is issued to US Army designated marksmen and US special forces.

Specifications

Country of Origin: United States	Overall Length: 889mm (35in)
Date: 2001	Barrell Length: 457mm (18in)
Calibre: 7.62mm (.3in) NATO	Muzzle Velocity: 975.4m/sec(3200ft/sec)
Operation: Gas, rotating bolt	Feed/Magazine: 10- or 20-round detachable box
Weight: 5.1kg (11.24lb)	magazine
	Range: 800m (2624ft) +

▲ M39 Marksman rifle

US Marine Corps / 2nd Marine Expeditionary Brigade, An Nasiriyah, Iraq, March 2003

Also derived from the M14, the M39 was produced to meet the needs of US Marine Corps marksmen and explosive ordnance disposal teams working in urban areas.

Specifications

Country of Origin: United States	Barrel Length: 560mm (22in)
Date: 2008	Muzzle Velocity: 865m/sec (2837ft/sec)
Calibre: 7.62mm (.3in) NATO	Feed/Magazine: 20-round detachable box
Operation: Gas, rotating bolt	magazine
Weight: 7.5kg (16.5lb)	Range: 780m (2559ft)
Overall Length: 1120mm (44.2in)	

vision, and can direct the sniper onto new targets as they appear.

Snipers in Iraq and Afghanistan have typically made use of fairly large-calibre rifles (7.62mm/.300 being common), which have excellent ballistic properties over long range but are relatively easy to carry. Very large calibre 'anti-materiel rifles' are primarily intended for use against hard targets such as communications equipment and vehicles, but can also be used for extremely long-range sniping. They are very bulky, however, and difficult to transport for a sniper team operating on foot in the mountains of Afghanistan.

Snipers are sometimes deployed in support of an infantry operation, targeting enemy assets such as machine-gun crews and officers with precision fire to facilitate an infantry advance. They are also used as defensive assets. For example, it is not uncommon for a convoy to drop off a sniper team en route to carry out its mission. The sniper team can then observe a road and prevent hostiles from planting explosives or setting up an ambush. The team is then picked up as the convoy returns, or by other assets.

In urban combat such as that encountered in Iraq, snipers are invaluable. Their precision helps reduce the chances of collateral casualties whilst enabling

▲ M110 Semi-Automatic Sniper System

US Army /121st Infantry Regiment, Khowst, Afghanistan, September 2009

The M110 was developed to meet US Army requirements, and is being adopted by the Marine Corps to replace the M39.

Specifications

Country of Origin: United States
Date: 2008
Calibre: 7.62mm (.3in) NATO
Operation: Gas, rotating bolt
Weight: 6.94kg (15.3lb)
Overall Length: 1029mm (40.5in)

Barrel Length: 508mm (20in)
Muzzle Velocity: 783m/sec (2570ft/sec)
Feed/Magazine: 10- or 20-round detachable box magazine
Range: 800m (2625ft)

▲ McMillan TAC-50

Canadian Army / Princess Patricia's Canadian Light Infantry, Shah-I-Kot Valley, March 2002

Firing extremely powerful ammunition adapted from a heavy machine gun round, the TAC-50 was used to make what was then the world's longest confirmed kill in March 2002. Master Corporal Arron Perry killed an enemy combatant from 2310m (7579ft) and Corporal Rob Furlong killed an enemy combatant at a distance of 2430m (7972ft) in the same month.

Specifications

Country of Origin: United States
Date: 2000
Calibre: 12.7mm (.5in)
Operation: Manually-operated rotary bolt action
Weight: 11.8kg (26lb)
Overall Length: 1448mm (57in)

Barrel Length: 736mm (29in)
Muzzle Velocity: 823m/sec (2700ft/sec)
Feed/Magazine: 5-round detachable box magazine
Range: 1600m (5249ft)

friendly forces to eliminate hostiles located in an inaccessible area, such as on a rooftop. By the time infantry got to the enemy location through the streets, the hostiles would be long gone. A sniper's bullet can get there a lot quicker, and will not be ambushed en route.

In more open terrain such as the desert, or when shooting from one area of high ground to another in Afghanistan's mountains, snipers can pick off hostiles which might be difficult targets for personnel armed with small-calibre assault rifles. Guerrillas concealed among the rocks above a road in Afghanistan are a hard target for troops armed with assault rifles, but a sniper or designated marksman may be able to deal with them. A designated marksman is not a sniper as such, but uses a similar weapon with a high degree of skill. He is part of an infantry force, and takes difficult or long-range shots when necessary.

Specifications

Country of Origin: United States	Barrel Length: 736mm (29in)
Date: 1987	Muzzle Velocity: 853m/sec (2800ft/sec)
Calibre: 12.7mm (.5in)	Feed/Magazine: 5-round detachable box
Operation: Bolt action	magazine
Weight: 9.53kg (21lb)	Range: 1000m (3280ft) +
Overall Length: 1346mm (53in)	

▲ **Harris M87R**

US Navy Seals, Afghanistan, March 2011

The M87R is used for some US special forces missions. It is too bulky for rapid assault movements, but has a variety of applications as a support weapon.

Specifications

Country of Origin: United Kingdom	Barrel Length: 692mm (27.2in)
Date: 2006	Muzzle Velocity: Not known
Calibre: 12.7mm (.5in)	Feed/Magazine: 5- or 10-round detachable box
Operation: Gas	magazine
Weight: 12.2kg (27lb)	Range: 1500m (4921ft)
Overall Length: 1369mm (53.9in)	

▲ **Accuracy International AS50**

British Army Special Forces, Afghanistan

The AS50 is the largest-calibre rifle produced by Accuracy International. It can deliver explosive or incendiary rounds over extreme distances. The rifle is highly transportable and lightweight. It can be disassembled in under three minutes and serviced without tools.

Iraq and Afghanistan: Occupation and counter-insurgency
2001–PRESENT

Despite the vast technological resources available, modern conflicts are often won or lost at the squad level. 'Boots on the ground' have never been more important.

THE OVERTHROW OF SADDAM HUSSEIN'S REGIME in Iraq was not by any means an easy task, but at least there were obvious targets to aim for. The Coalition forces were opposed initially by formal units that could be located and attacked by conventional means; air power, tanks and artillery were highly effective in destroying the Republican Guard and the Iraqi Army.

Even during the Coalition advance towards Baghdad, irregular forces harassed logistics convoys and units attempting to secure ground that had been taken. Although the major formations of the Iraqi military were in disarray, a challenge was still mounted by various insurgency groups.

Some of these irregulars were army personnel cut off from their units and still determined to carry out their orders to defend the nation, but the majority did not belong to the army, at least, not any more.

Army personnel who wanted to continue the fight joined groups of insurgents who lacked heavy weapons, but retained the will to fight. Others came from political or religious groups, some from outside Iraq. Coordination among the insurgents was rare, but their activities were still a distraction and a nuisance for Coalition forces trying to demolish Saddam's regime. These fighters inflicted the occasional real setback, but for the most part were unable to greatly affect the outcome of the campaign at the military level.

Fighting insurgency
After the fall of Baghdad and the end of the war as such, the insurgency did not end. Indeed, it became more complex as groups fought for control of regions and cities. At times some groups entered into ceasefires or cooperation agreements with the

Specifications
Country of Origin: United States
Date: 2009
Calibre: 7.62mm (.3in) SCAR-H,
  5.56mm (.219in) SCAR-L
Operation: Gas, rotating bolt
Weight: 3.58kg (7.9lb) SCAR-H;
3.29kg (7.3lb) SCAR-L

Overall Length: Various, depending on variant
Barrel Length: 400mm (16in) SCAR-H; 351mm
  (13.8in) SCAR-L
Muzzle Velocity: 870m/sec (2870ft/sec)
Feed/Magazine: 20-round box magazine
  (SCAR-H) or STANAG box magazine (SCAR-L)
Range: 600m (1968ft)

▲ **FN SCAR**
US Navy SEALs, Afghanistan, April 2009
The SCAR was developed to meet the requirements of US special forces personnel. The SCAR-L is chambered for 5.56mm (.219in) ammunition; the SCAR-H uses 7.62mm (.3in) rounds. It is a lightweight and portable support weapon with a sniper capability.

Coalition, while others in the same area began a new campaign of violence. The political situation changed constantly, making it hard to keep track of which groups were at any time friendly, neutral, suspect or outright hostile.

Dealing with the insurgency in Iraq was a frustrating business. 'Friendly' locals might turn hostile for no immediately obvious reason, and often local groups would change allegiance. For example, control of the city of Fallujah was handed over to a locally raised and led security force, which soon afterward disbanded and gave its weapons to anti-

Coalition insurgents. US troops were thus forced to fight for the city all over again, an occurrence made even more bitter by the betrayal of trust that brought it about.

Against this backdrop of sudden political shifts, ambushes and attacks with mortars and RPGs against their bases, the Coalition forces struggled to win over the Iraqi people and accomplish their goals. Much of their work was of reconstruction; getting the power back on and clean water flowing to homes in the cities, bringing humanitarian aid and medical assistance to those worst affected by the war.

▲ **M16A4 assault rifle**

US Marine Corps / 2nd Marine Division, Al Anbar, Iraq, April 2006
The M16A4, used by the US Marine Corps, is capable of taking a range of accessories, including foregrips, scopes and laser sights.

Specifications

Country of Origin: United States
Date: 1957
Calibre: 5.56mm (0.219in) NATO
Operation: Gas, rotating bolt
Weight: 3.58kg (7.9lb)
Overall Length: 1003mm (39.5in)
Barrell Length: 508mm (20in)
Muzzle Velocity: 948m/sec (3110ft/sec)
Feed/Magazine: 30-round detachable box magazine
Range: 800m (2624ft)

Specifications

Country of Origin: United States
Date: 1969
Calibre: 40mm (1.57in)
Operation: Breech-loaded
Weight: 1.63kg (3.5lb) loaded
Overall Length (M203 grenade launcher): 380mm (15in)
Barrel Length: 305mm (12in)
Muzzle Velocity: 75m/sec (245ft/sec)
Feed/Magazine: Single shot
Range: 400m (1312ft)

▲ **M16 with M203 grenade launcher**

US Army / 4th Infantry Division, Laghman Province, Afghanistan, March 2011
The M203 grenade launcher can deliver a range of ordnance at greater distances than a solider can throw a hand grenade. It is to be replaced in service with the M320 grenade launcher.

▶ **Loophole**

A US soldier aims his M4 carbine through a loop hole in a wall during a firefight with insurgents in Iraq, 2005. Compact and hardy, the M4 has proved an excellent weapon in urban warfare.

Interfering in these tasks was one way the insurgents hoped to discredit the Coalition, so simply pulling out of a dangerous area was not always a solution.

It was here that the key work of the Coalition was done. Fighting the insurgents was a necessary task, as was defending personnel and installations, but any insurgent killed or detained might be replaced by another. By returning the cities of Iraq to something as close to normal as possible, Coalition forces took away many of the factors that fed insurgent recruitment. Operating in the community, and a potentially hostile one at that, required patience and restraint, coupled with watchfulness and a streetwise cunning that allowed Coalition troops to predict insurgent activity. For example, the sudden disappearance of local children from the street would often indicate that an ambush was in preparation.

Different approaches were tried, depending upon the circumstances. Where possible, Coalition forces cooperated with local leaders and tried to allow the local police or friendly militias to keep order. This would make their presence seem less intrusive and helped support the gradual handover of control to Iraqi authorities.

However, when attacked, or when control of an area was lost, Coalition forces had to respond with precise but overwhelming force.

▲ **Colt M4 carbine**

US Army / 82nd Airborne Division, Fallujah, January 2004

The M4 carbine is fitted with picatinny rails under the barrel and atop the receiver, enabling the use of various accessories. Swapping accessories is a simple matter.

Specifications

Country of Origin: United States	Barrel Length: 368mm (14.5in)
Date: 1997	Muzzle Velocity: 884m/sec (2900ft/sec)
Calibre: 5.56mm (.219in) NATO	Feed/Magazine: 30-round detachable box
Operation: Gas	magazine or other STANAG magazines
Weight: 2.88kg (6.36lb)	Range: 400m (1312ft)
Overall Length: 838mm (33in)	

Despite bold attempts to make a quantum leap in small arms technology in recent years, US forces were armed for the most part with a developed version of the venerable M16 family. However, this M16A4 and M4 carbine are significantly improved over their predecessors. Capable of taking a range of accessories using standardised rail systems, the M4 in particular has shown itself to be a versatile and effective combat weapon. Light and easily manoeuvred for urban combat, its telescopic stock can be quickly tailored to a specific user and accessories can be swapped for different missions.

On the other hand, events in Afghanistan and Iraq showed that some weapons were due for upgrade or replacement. Many of the M249 SAWs in use are now over 20 years old and are becoming worn out. These weapons remain effective, but the specific examples in use are showing their age.

Armoured vehicles proved useful in supporting raids, securing static checkpoints and dealing with insurgents in strong defensive positions, but the burden fell mainly upon infantry, who operated on foot or from lightly protected vehicles. At times, almost any movement within some cities was prone to attacks by snipers and RPG-armed gunmen. This made even routine movements such as resupply or

personnel transfers problematic in the extreme. The British found the 'multiple' to be a useful combat force. Essentially a half platoon, the multiple provided enough sets of eyes and sufficient firepower to be effective in close urban terrain without becoming unwieldy or requiring manpower that was often simply not available. At times, quite sizeable forces were committed to an operation, but counter-insurgency work is a manpower-intensive activity and often small units had to cover a wide area for lack of enough men to do the job properly.

Both the British and US forces faced grim battles for cities such as Fallujah and Basra, dealing with uprisings and insurgent attacks whilst remaining

US INFANTRY SQUAD, 2006		
Unit	Equipment	Men
Squad leader	1 x M4 carbine	1
Medic	1 x M4 carbine	1
Fireteam 1	1 x M249 LMG (SAW) 2 x M16 or M4 rifles 1 x M16/M203 grenade launcher	4
Fireteam 2	1 x M249 LMG (SAW) 2 x M16 or M4 rifles 1 x M16/M203 grenade launcher	4

US Infantry Squad, 2006

A US Army infantry squad consists of 9–13 soldiers led by a staff sergeant. Each squad is composed of at least two fire teams. Each fire team consists of four men, led by a corporal. A fire team is made up of two riflemen (one being the team leader), a grenadier and an automatic rifleman, armed with an M249 LMG. Sometimes a squad can be enhanced with advanced marksmen depending on the mission requirements.

Leader (1 x M4 carbine)   **Medic (1 x M4 carbine)**

Fireteam 1 (1 x M249 SAW, 2 x M4 carbine, 1 x M16/M203 grenade launcher)

Fireteam 2 (1 x M249 SAW, 2 x M4 carbine, 1 x M16/M203 grenade launcher)

mindful of the surrounding population. Most combat in this environment was at close quarters and multiple levels, with gunmen on rooftops and upstairs windows as well as at street level. The RPG-7 was used liberally against buildings and personnel as well as vehicles.

While a tank or infantry combat vehicle would likely survive even multiple hits, the Land Rovers and Humvees used by infantry formations were very vulnerable. The best response to an RPG ambush was rapid and accurate return fire, hopefully eliminating the operator or forcing him to take cover before firing, or at least to take a hurried shot rather than aiming carefully. More open roads had their own hazards, ranging from ambushes to roadside bombs. The logistical apparatus required to keep the Coalition forces in fighting condition, plus that required for reconstruction, was an inviting target for the insurgents. Detecting and removing Improvised Explosive Devices (IEDs) was a vital task for Coalition forces, who used a range of methods and technologies, including specialized bomb disposal equipment, alongside more traditional bomb-defusing skills. Powerful rifles were used by some Explosive Ordnance Disposal (EOD) personnel to destroy IEDs from a safe distance.

IEDs were also a major threat in Afghanistan, though some characteristics of the campaign were quite different. The invasion of Afghanistan came about as a result of the same world events as the Iraq campaign, notably the 11 September 2001 terrorist attacks on the USA, and here, too, there was an initial military campaign aimed at regime change followed by a lengthy insurgency.

Afghanistan

In 2001, at the time of the invasion, Afghanistan was under the control of the fundamentalist Islamic

▲ **Squad assault**
A US Marine squad manoeuvres during the fighting for the town of Fallujah, 2004. While one machinegun team gives covering fire with their M240 LMG, another machine-gun team dashes across open ground to etsablish a new position.

Taliban, which openly sponsored terrorism against the West. After years of Soviet occupation and internal turmoil, Afghanistan was not in a position to offer significant opposition to the initial campaign, which deposed the Taliban and established an interim government, followed by democratic elections.

The new government of Afghanistan was supported by an international coalition, which protected the capital, Kabul, and the immediate area. However, much of the country remained beyond effective government control. Various factions, many

of them tribal in nature, controlled parts of Afghanistan's provinces. Among these factions were guerrillas loyal to the ousted Taliban, or at least its fundamentalist ideals.

The invasion of Afghanistan was followed by an attempt to locate and apprehend the leaders of the al-Qaeda terrorist organization, notably Osama bin Laden. While this was eventually accomplished, it was a slow process. So, too, was the loosening of the insurgents' grip on the provinces. As in Iraq, the support of the population for the new government

▲ M60E3 GPMG

US Navy SEALs, Afghanistan, March 2011

The E3 version of the M60 was adopted by the US Marine Corps. It is still used by some special operations units, but has generally been replaced by the M240.

Specifications

Country of Origin: United States

Date: 1994

Calibre: 7.62mm (.3in) NATO

Operation: Gas, air-cooled

Weight: 8.61kg (18.98lb)

Overall Length: 1067mm (42in)

Barrel Length: 560mm (22.04in)

Muzzle Velocity: 860m/sec (2821ft/sec)

Feed/Magazine: Belt-fed

Cyclic Rate: 550rpm

Range: 1100m (3609ft) +

▲ M240 general-purpose machine gun

US Marine Corps / 2nd Marine Division, Al Anbar, Iraq, April 2006

The M240 was originally adopted by the US military as a vehicular weapon, but eventually supplanted the M60 in the general-purpose machinegun role.

Specifications

Country of Origin: Belgium/United States

Date: 1977

Calibre: 7.62mm (.3in) NATO

Operation: Gas, open bolt

Weight: 11.79kg (26lb)

Overall Length: 1263mm (49.7in)

Barrel Length: 630mm (24.8in)

Muzzle Velocity: 853m/sec (2800ft/sec)

Feed/Magazine: Belt-fed

Cyclic Rate: 650–1000rpm

Range: 800m (2625ft)

largely depended upon proving that the government could defeat the guerrillas and protect its people.

Infiltration and guerrilla tactics

While the Taliban were generally pushed out of the major cities, they were able to infiltrate back in to carry out attacks. They were also able to take control of many provincial towns and villages, supporting their activities with funds and supplies extorted from those who would not give them willingly. Breaking the hold of the Taliban on any given town was not an immense problem, but keeping them out was a different matter.

The Afghan people have been fighting guerrilla wars against various invaders for most of their history, sometimes with the very same weapons their ancestors used. Taliban fighters were encountered armed with weapons taken from the Russian or earlier invasions, such as Lee-Enfield rifles and even weapons from before the twentieth century. They have in some cases used the same ambush points above the few passes though Afghanistan's mountains that their predecessors did.

Dealing with such skilled guerrilla fighters was a matter of breaking their power in any given region and helping the local population gain the strength and confidence to prevent the Taliban from coming back. More importantly, the locals had to be convinced that it was in their interests to do so. This meant a 'boots on the ground' presence, patrols, and the creation of local security and police forces. The security/police units were at times infiltrated by Taliban fighters who thus gained training and knowledge of their enemies' methods before gong 'over the wall' to return to their comrades. Some went so far as to attack their supposed allies before fleeing.

Despite such frustrations, the task of nation-building lies at the heart of defeating any insurgency. The enemy's ability to fight must also be weakened, which meant taking the war to the insurgents. Thus alongside operations to win over and strengthen the local population, the Coalition launched attacks on Taliban strongholds in remote areas. Many of these strongholds lay in steep mountain valleys, which reduced the opportunities for using artillery and armour, except with the new generation of precision munitions available.

GPS- and laser-guided shells and bombs permitted strikes in areas previously immune to such attacks, and huge penetrator bombs threatened apparently impregnable cave and tunnel strongholds. However, success required that the Taliban be confronted in the countryside and the mountains, and defeated on the ground.

Over the years there has been a steady move towards smaller-calibre weapons. 7.62x51mm battle rifles gave way to 5.56x45mm assault rifles. For the most part, experience has shown this to be the right

▲ **M249 Squad Automatic Weapon (SAW)**

US Army / 82nd Airborne Division, Fallujah, January 2004

The M249 is a squad-level support weapon, and is often used in assault tactics. It can take rifle magazines in addition to the more usual linked belt.

Specifications

Country of Origin: United States	Barrel Length: 521mm (21in)
Date: 1982	Muzzle Velocity: 915m/sec (3000ft/sec)
Calibre: 5.56mm (.219in) NATO	Feed/Magazine: 30-round STANAG magazine or
Operation: Gas, open bolt	200-round belt
Weight: 7.5kg (17lb)	Cyclic Rate: 750–1000rpm
Overall Length: 1041mm (41in)	Range: 910m (2985ft)

▶ **Overwatch mission**

Armed with an Accuracy International L96 sniper rifle, a British Royal Marine sniper team return enemy fire in Lakari Bazaar, Afghanistan, July 2009. The rifle stock and barrel has been covered with tape to stop light reflections giving away their position.

choice. A smaller-calibre weapon can be just as lethal at most likely combat ranges as a heavier calibre, and is accurate to a distance far beyond that at which the average soldier can hit anything.

Most modern combat takes place at fairly short ranges, where firepower is more important than accuracy. Thus most assault rifles are effective out to 300–400m (984–1312ft), which is more than enough in most cases. But when ambushed by Taliban riflemen hidden among rocks several hundred metres away and above the road, troops equipped with weapons such as the M4 or M16 may find that their weapons lack the accurate range. Marksmanship training at such ranges may also be lacking.

Thus the 'designated marksman rifle' proved itself invaluable in Afghanistan. A larger calibre weapon

with a greater accurate range, in the hands of a soldier trained almost to sniper standards, permits precision return fire against an ambush while other soldiers use automatic suppressive fire. Larger-calibre weapons are also useful when firing across a valley at hostiles on the far side.

However, the majority of troops deployed to Afghanistan were still equipped with 5.56mm (.219in) assault rifles, and these performed satisfactorily in most engagements. The firepower

▲ **Diemaco C8**

Canadian Army / Princess Patricia's Canadian Light Infantry, Paktia Province, Afghanistan, March 2002

The C8 is a Canadian-made version of the M4 carbine. The Canadian equivalent to the M16 is designated C7.

Specifications

Country of Origin: Canada	Barrel Length: 508mm (20in)
Date: 1994	Muzzle Velocity: 900m/sec (3030ft/sec)
Calibre: 5.56mm (.219in) NATO	Feed/Magazine: Various 30-round STANAG
Operation: Gas, rotating bolt	magazines
Weight: 3.3kg (7.3lb) unloaded	Range: 400m (1312ft)
Overall Length: 1006mm (39.6in)	

Specifications

Country of Origin: United Kingdom

Date: 1985

Calibre: 5.56mm (.219in) NATO

Operation: Gas

Weight: 3.71kg (8.1lb)

Overall Length: 709mm (27.9in)

Barrel Length: 442mm (17.4in)

Muzzle Velocity: 940m/sec (3084ft/sec)

Feed/Magazine: 30-round detachable
  box magazine

Range: 300m (984ft)

▲ L22 carbine

British Army / 7th Armoured Brigade, Afghanistan, July 2011

The L22 is an shortened version of the L85 assault rifle. It is used by some British vehicle crews and other personnel needing a very compact weapon.

Specifications

Country of Origin: United Kingdom

Date: 1997

Calibre: 7.62mm (.3in) / .300 Winchester
  Magnum, 8.58mm (.338in) / .338 Lapua
  Magnum

Operation: Bolt action

Weight: 6.8kg (15lb)

Overall Length: 1300mm (51in)

Barrel Length: 686mm (27in)

Muzzle Velocity: c.850m/sec (2788ft/sec)

Feed/Magazine: 5-round detachable box
  magazine

Range: 1100m (3609ft) .300 Winchester; 1500m
  (4921ft) .338

▲ L115A3 / AWM

British Army / Household Cavalry, Helmand Province, Afghanistan, November 2009

The world record for the longest sniper kill – actually two kills in rapid succession – was established by British corporal Craig Harrison at 2475m (8119ft) using the L115A3 rifle.

▲ L129A1 sharpshooter rifle

British Army / 16 Air Assault Brigade, Helmand Province, Afghanistan, March 2011

The L129A1 was procured to meet an urgent need for longer-range capability within an infantry force. A semi-automatic weapon, it offers greater firepower than a bolt-action sniper rifle such as the L96.

Specifications

Country of Origin: United Kingdom

Date: 2010

Calibre: 7.62mm (.3in) NATO

Operation: Gas, semi-automatic

Weight: 4.5kg (9.92lb)

Overall Length: 990mm (38.9in)

Barrel Length: 406mm (16in)

Muzzle Velocity: Not known

Feed/Magazine: 20-round detachable box
  magazine

Range: 800m (2625ft)

offered by a small squad of infantrymen equipped with assault rifles, squad support weapons and perhaps a general-purpose machine gun is impressive. When outnumbered and defending a checkpoint or forward base, this degree of firepower can be the decider between defeat and victory – or at least holding on long enough for help to arrive.

The use of under-barrel grenade launchers, which give an infantry squad a measure of indirect area fire capability, have also added greatly to infantry capabilities. A skilled grenadier can drop a 40mm (1.57in) grenade among a group of hostiles, even if they are behind cover. He can then switch back to using his rifle, ensuring that his grenade-launching capability does not rob the squad of a rifle. For a small unit, even just one rifle is a significant asset.

▲ Heckler & Koch HK416

German Army / German Mechanized Infantry Brigade 41, Kunduz Province, Afghanistan, May 2009

Based on the US M4 Carbine, the HK416 uses a gas piston system derived from the G36 rifle. It has four picatinny rails for a range of accessories. The weapon is also used by the US military and Norwegian armed forces.

Specifications

Country of Origin: Germany	Barrell Length: 228mm (9.0in)
Date: 2005	Muzzle Velocity: Varies by barrel length and type
Calibre: 5.56mm (0.21in)	of round used
Operation: Gas, rotating bolt	Feed/Magazine: 20-, 30-round STANAG magazine
Weight: 2.950kg (6.50lb)	or 100-round Beta C-Mag box magazine
Overall Length: 690mm (27.2in)	Range: 365m (1200ft)

Specifications

Country of Origin: Germany	Overall Length: 1030mm (40.6in)
Date: 2005	Barrel Length: 482mm (19in)
Calibre: 5.56mm (.219in) NATO	Muzzle Velocity: 920m/sec (3018ft/sec)
Operation: Gas, rotating bolt	Feed/Magazine: Disintegrating link belt
Weight: 8.15kg (17.97lb)	Cycle Rate: 850rpm
	Range: c.1000m (3280ft)

▲ Heckler & Koch MG4

German Army / German Airborne Brigade 26, Kunduz Province, Afghanistan, July 2009

The MG4 was developed in the 1990s as a squad support weapon. It has a folding stock, which greatly shortens the weapon when moving in and out of vehicles or helicopters. It can be fired with the stock folded.

▲ **Khaybar KH 2002**

Islamic Jihadists, Iraq, post 2004

Developed from the M16 by way of a Chinese assault rifle, the Iranian Khaybar may have found its way into the hands of Islamic fighters resisting the Coalition occupation, despite efforts to prevent arms smuggling in the region.

Specifications

Country of Origin: Iran	Barrel Length: Not known
Date: 2004	Muzzle Velocity: 900–950m/sec
Calibre: 5.56mm (.219in)	(2952–3116ft/sec)
Operation: Gas, rotating bolt	Feed/Magazine: Various STANAG magazines
Weight: 3.7kg (8.15lb)	Range: 450m (1476ft)
Overall Length: 730mm (28.7in)	

Tensions in East Asia

1980–PRESENT

Tensions in the Far East are a consequence of both age-old rivalries as well as unresolved issues from the Cold War.

MANY OF THE CONFLICTS that exist today in Asia are historic in origin, and often it is difficult to find a root cause of a current war. This in turn makes it hard to find lasting solutions, as there are rivalries and enmities in the region going back decades or even centuries.

World War II and the Chinese Civil War (which began before 1939 and ended in 1949) had very significant effects upon the region. Not only was Western colonial influence greatly reduced in East Asia but the rise of a Communist state in China added a new ideological conflict to an already bubbling pot. The clash of Communism versus democracy was, as we have seen, a key factor in the Vietnam War and the Korean Conflict. The latter resulted largely from the arbitrary partition of Korea at the end of World War II. The north of the country was occupied by Soviet troops and became a Communist state, while the south was pro-Western, with large numbers of American and other Allied troops present.

After attempts to reunify the country by negotiation and open warfare failed, an armed standoff began which continues to this day. Matters are complicated by disputes over ownership of islands off the Korean coast. Any nation is of course entitled to position forces in its sovereign territory, but the presence of forces on islands close to the border has been cited as a threat and a provocation at times.

Open conflict between North and South Korea has not occurred since the 1950s, but both Koreas today maintain strong military forces; incidents are not uncommon. North Korea obtained much of its military technology from China and the Soviet

Union, and uses a military system common in 'Communist bloc' countries. Weaponry tends to be fairly low-tech and is recognizably derived from Russian equipment or Chinese copies of it.

South Korean military equipment tends to be heavily influenced by Western designs, and is usually compatible with items like M16 magazines and standard optical sights. Gear tends to be more high-tech than Northern equivalents, and is interoperable with the equipment issued to US forces that would

almost certainly assist South Korea in repelling a renewed invasion from the North.

Taiwan also faces the possibility of invasion. At the end of the Chinese Civil War the defeated Nationalists retreated to what is now Taiwan, establishing the Republic of China. The mainland became dominated by the People's Republic of China. Both, as their names suggest, assert that they are the legitimate government of all China. Taiwanese (i.e. Republic of China) equipment is Western

▲ Norinco Type 86S

People's Liberation Army (PRC), mid-1980s

Despite its appearance, the Type 86S has many of its internal workings in common with the AK assault rifle series. It was not adopted for general service.

Specifications

Country of Origin: China	Overall Length: 667mm (26.25in)
Date: 1980	Barrel Length: 438mm (17.2in)
Calibre: 7.62mm (.3in)	Muzzle Velocity: 710m/sec (2429ft/sec)
Operation: Gas	Feed/Magazine: 30-round box magazine
Weight: 3.59kg (7.91lb)	Range: 300m (984ft)

Specifications

Country of Origin: China	Barrel Length: 445mm (17.5in)
Date: 1977	Muzzle Velocity: 720m/sec (2362ft/sec)
Calibre: 7.62mm (.3in)	Feed/Magazine: 30-round detachable box or
Operation: Gas, rotating bolt	75-round drum magazine
Weight: 3.4kg (7.5lb)	Cyclic Rate: c.650rpm
Overall Length: 955mm (37.6in)	Range: 500m (1640ft)

▲ Type 81

People's Liberation Army (PRC), early 1990s

Clearly derived from the AK series, the Type 81 was produced in assault rifle and light machinegun configurations. It can feed from a 75-round drum or a standard rifle magazine.

influenced and sometimes derived from US designs, while the arms and equipment of the People's Republic of China (PRC) is heavily influenced by Soviet/Russian designs. Much of the PRC's early military equipment was directly copied from Soviet arms, although relations between these two Communist nations cooled in the latter half of the twentieth century.

The PRC is a major force in world affairs, and is closing the technological gap between its equipment and that of more advanced nations. Modern Chinese weapons may still show Soviet-era influences, but they are becoming more refined as China gains experience in developing new military systems.

The Chinese military still emphasizes huge available manpower over technological excellence. Equipping such a large force necessitates designs produced with an eye to their cost and ease of maintenance, so many Chinese weapon systems have traditionally been simple and robust.

Specifications

Country of Origin: China

Date: 1997

Calibre: 5.8mm (.228in) DBP87

Operation: Gas, rotating bolt

Weight: 3.25kg (7.2lb)

Overall Length: 745mm (29.3in) rifle

Barrel Length: 463mm (18.2in)

Muzzle Velocity: 930m/sec (3050ft/sec)

Feed/Magazine: 30-round box or 75-round drum
  magazine

Range: 400m (1312ft)

▲ **QBZ-95**

People's Liberation Army (PRC), 1995

Chinese designers produced an entirely new family of weapons built around a specially developed cartridge. Rifle, carbine and light machine gun versions exist.

Specifications

Country of Origin: China

Date: 2003

Calibre: 5.8mm (.228in) DBP87,
  5.56mm (.219in) NATO

Operation: Gas-operated, rotating bolt

Weight: 3.5kg (7.71lb)

Overall Length: 960mm (37.79in) stock extended;
  710mm (27.95in) stock folded

Barrel Length: Not known

Muzzle Velocity: 930m/sec (3050ft/sec)

Feed/Magazine: 30-round detachable box
  magazine

Range: 400m (1312ft)

▲ **QBZ-03**

People's Liberation Army (PRC), 2005

Disappointment with the QBZ-95 caused Chinese designers to return to a more conventional weapon derived from the Type 81. The standard-issue rifle can launch rifle grenades without requiring an adapter.

It is inconceivable that Taiwan could launch an invasion of mainland China; its forces would simply be swallowed up by the vast numbers facing them. Were tensions to boil over, an invasion of Taiwan by the PRC would pit the relatively high-tech forces of Taiwan against overwhelming numbers. The main defence of Taiwan is its island location and the force-multiplying effect of defending a shoreline. It is possible that Chinese troops could be prevented from getting ashore in sufficient numbers to overpower the defenders, at least long enough for overseas assistance to arrive.

Taiwan has links with the West and would probably receive rapid assistance. However, it is never good strategy to reinforce defeat, so the Taiwanese forces' priority would be to demonstrate that they possessed both the means and the will to defend their island unilaterally. The possession of well-equipped armed forces makes a statement to the world that this capability exists.

▲ Type 65

Republic of China Division (Taiwan) Armed Forces, 1985

Heavily influenced by the US M16 family, the Type 65 was introduced in the 1970s and evolved through updated variants into the T65K2.

Specifications

Country of Origin: Taiwan	Overall Length: 990mm (38.9in)
Date: 1976	Barrel Length:508mm (20in)
Calibre: 5.56mm (.219in) NATO	Muzzle Velocity: 990m/sec (2530ft/sec)
Operation: Gas	Feed/Magazine: Various STANAG magazines
Weight: 3.31kg (7.29lb)	Range: 500m (1640ft) +

▶ Daewoo K1

South Korean Armed Forces, 1990

The K1 assault rifle was developed to meet a South Korean need to replace ageing M3 submachine guns and other US weapons then in service. Because of this lineage, it is sometimes designated as a submachine gun, although it fires rifle ammunition.

Specifications

Country of Origin: South Korea	Overall Length: 838mm (32.99in)
Date: 1981	Barrel Length: 263mm (10.35in)
Calibre: 5.56mm (.219in) NATO	Muzzle Velocity: 820m/sec (2690ft/sec)
Operation: Gas, rotating bolt	Feed/Magazine: Various STANAG magazines
Weight: 2.87kg (6.32lb)	Range: 250m (820ft)

▲ **INSAS squad automatic rifle**

Indian Army / 2nd Rajputana Rifles, Kargil District, Kashmir, 1999

Based on a developed version of the AK-47 action, the INSAS (Indian National Small Arms System) rifle is gas-operated and capable of semi- or fully-automatic fire in addition to three-round bursts. The support version of the INSAS assault rifle differs mainly in its heavier barrel, which has different rifling to improve long-range performance. The INSAS saw combat during the 1999 Kargil War with Pakistan, where the rifle had some reliability problems in the very cold climate.

Specifications

Country of Origin: India	Overall Length: 960mm (37.8in)
Date: 1998	Barrel Length:464mm (18.3in)
Calibre: 5.56mm (.219in) NATO	Muzzle Velocity: 900m/sec (2953ft/sec)
Operation: Gas	Feed/Magazine: 20- or 30-round detachable box
Weight: 4.25kg (9.4lb)	magazine
	Range: 800m (2625ft) +

South-East Asia
1980–PRESENT

South-East Asia has a long history of tension and conflict involving both states and stateless organizations striving for nationhood or independence.

THE WITHDRAWAL OF COLONIAL POWERS after World War II and the rise of Communism only added to existing tensions in South-East Asia. The region includes some of the world's most powerful economies and some of the poorest regions on the planet, so it is perhaps inevitable that conflicts frequently arise.

Some of these conflicts are based on economic factors. For example, large numbers of ships pass through the Straits of Malacca between Indonesia and Peninsular Malaysia. In this narrow waterway operate bands of pirates who use helicopters and small boats to attack vulnerable vessels. Despite the best efforts of the world's navies and local law enforcement agencies, these pirates are able to withdraw to villages along the nearby coasts and islands and hide when they are not active.

There is nothing political about the actions of these pirates, except where they exert influence over local government officers. However, in other areas of South-East Asia there are political conflicts. One such

saw the emergence of the world's newest sovereign state, the Democratic Republic of Timor-Leste, better known as East Timor.

This state had its origins in a declaration of independence made when the Portuguese withdrew from their colonies in the region. Independence was forestalled by an invasion from Indonesia, resulting in bloody fighting. A guerrilla war went on through the 1980s and 1990s, until international pressure caused the withdrawal of Indonesian forces and permitted East Timor to finally assert its independence.

Other conflicts in South-East Asia are internal, such as that in Myanmar (Burma). An extremely poor country despite good natural resources, Myanmar suffers from a highly corrupt government. A military coup placed a junta in power in 1962, and although elections were implemented, the exclusion of other political parties made this nothing more than a public relations gesture.

Opposition to the government was dealt with using heavy-handed methods, and racist policies were implemented against groups not recognized by the government as true citizens of Burma. These actions led to a major uprising and coup in 1988, at which time the nation adopted its new name. Internal conflict continued, however, with details hard to come by outside the country. Accusations have been made of forced labour projects and ongoing campaigns to oppress or eradicate groups disliked by the government.

Internal conflicts of this sort are normally fought by infantry and light vehicles, with air support and artillery playing a fairly minor supporting role. There is a fine line between attempting to reassert the

government's control over its sovereign territory and terrorizing the populace into submission, and with few details of operations or clashes available to outside agencies it is hard to establish the true nature of Myanmar's internal troubles.

Despite the support of China for the North Vietnamese in their conflicts with France and the United States, Vietnam and China clashed at the end of the 1970s. The war arose as a result of Vietnamese incursions into Cambodia and the occupation of the Spratly Islands, which China had claimed as its own territory. The Sino-Vietnamese war took the form of a raid in massive force rather than a campaign of

▲ SR-88

Singapore Armed Forces, 1987

Developed from the SAR-80, the SAR-88 achieved good sales to armed forces throughout the region. It can take an M203 under-barrel grenade launcher.

Specifications

Country of Origin: Singapore	Barrel Length: 460mm (18.1in)
Date: 1984	Muzzle Velocity: Not known
Calibre: 5.56mm (.219in) NATO	Feed/Magazine: 30-round detachable box
Operation: Gas, rotating bolt	magazine
Weight: 3.68kg (8.11lb)	Range: 800m (2625ft)
Overall Length: 960mm (37.7in)	

Specifications

Country of Origin: Singapore	Barrel Length: 460mm (18.1in)
Date: 1990	Muzzle Velocity: Not known
Calibre: 5.56mm (.219in) NATO	Feed/Magazine: 30-round detachable box
Operation: Gas, rotating bolt	magazine
Weight: 3.68kg (8.11lb)	Range: 800m (2625ft)
Overall Length: 960mm (37.7in)	

▲ SR-88A

Singapore Armed Forces, 1990

An updated SR-88 using lighter materials, the SR-88A is also available in a short 'carbine' configuration for use by airmobile troops and vehicle crews. Its magazine catch will accept a regular M16 magazine and a C-mag, which is also used in M16 rifles.

conquest. Chinese forces captured some objectives and destroyed infrastructure before retiring. The conflict then simmered on in the form of border skirmishes until 1989, when Vietnam granted the political concessions China wanted. Notably, this included a withdrawal from Cambodia.

Some parts of South-East Asia have seen relatively little conflict in recent years. Singapore, for example, is a highly prosperous island nation with a healthy arms industry. Singaporean weapons are equivalent to many Western systems and can often interchange

accessories and magazines with them. Many of these weapons are exported, creating an alternative to the traditional Western/Russian/Chinese choice facing many importers.

Until fairly recently, a nation seeking weapons had to make a choice between Western and Communist suppliers. Today, however, the range of high-quality weapons on offer has been greatly increased. This is not solely due to the expansion of South-East Asian arms manufacturing, but it has been a significant factor.

▲ SAR 21

Singapore Armed Forces / 2004

The SAR-21 was the world's first assault rifle to incorporate a laser sighting aid as standard fit, inside the carrying handle. Carbine and light support versions are also manufactured.

Specifications

Country of Origin: Singapore	Barrel Length: 508mm (20in)
Date: 1999	Muzzle Velocity: 970m/sec (3182ft/sec)
Calibre: 5.56mm (.219in) NATO	Feed/Magazine: 30-round box magazine;
Operation: Gas, rotating bolt	plastic or STANAG magazines
Weight: 3.82kg (8.42lb)	Range: 460m (1509ft)
Overall Length: 805mm (31.7in)	

Specifications

Country of Origin: Indonesia	Overall Length: 990mm (38.97in)
Date: 2005	Barrell Length: 740mm (29.13in)
Calibre: 5.56mm (0.219in) NATO	Muzzle Velocity: 710m/sec (2329ft/sec)
Operation: Gas, rotating bolt	Feed/Magazine: Various STANAG magazines
Weight: 3.4kg (7.49lb)	Range: 500m (1640ft)

▲ Pindad SS2

Indonesian Armed Forces, 2007

The Pindad SS2 is derived from the FN FNC rifle. It is actually a weapon family, with carbine, rifle and 'para-sniper' versions all based on a common receiver. It can also be fitted with an SPG-1A underbarrel grenade launcher, as illustrated.

Chapter 12

Peacekeeping, Counter-terrorism & Law Enforcement

There have been few 'gentlemen's wars' in history, where the military situation remained uncomplicated by humanitarian or social factors. Increasingly, modern military operations must switch between warfighting and lower-intensity conflict in which troops are expected to maintain law and order, enforce a ceasefire or deal with insurgents amid the mass of ordinary people who need to get on with their lives. Conversely, law enforcement agencies may have to deal with heavily armed opposition from stateless groups such as terrorist organizations or drugs cartels. Whilst military backup may be available on call, often it is law enforcement personnel who are on the frontline.

◀ **Riot control**
Venezuelan National guardsmen fire shotguns at protesters to keep apart militant supporters of President Hugo Chávez and opposition marchers who were protesting against the government's military takeover of the city police force, Caracas, November 2002.

Introduction

The line between dealing with criminal activity and military opposition is a fine one. Some criminal organizations are armed with military equipment, while many governments consider paramilitary insurgent groups to be civilian criminals rather than enemy combatants.

WHERE MILITARY FORCES are deployed in an 'aid to civil power' context they have some law enforcement rights, but are usually there to back up the police rather than to replace them. If martial law has been declared then the situation is different, but under normal circumstances the military is present to assist and support the normal law enforcement process. Captured members of paramilitary organizations are tried in the courts and prosecuted for the same offences as anyone else might be – murder, weapons possession and so forth. Unless special legislation is in place then the regular legal system must be followed. Military personnel deployed in aid to the civil power are also bound by rules of

engagement. Where an enemy combatant would be a legitimate target in a war zone, troops assisting police are normally expected to arrest a suspect rather than simply open fire. They may, of course, use their weapons if fired upon, or to protect innocents, but potential hostiles are usually considered criminal suspects rather than enemy combatants until they give clear indication of their intentions.

Peacekeeping forces are in a similar position. They must often operate among a hostile or potentially hostile population, attempting to enforce a ceasefire or international mandate that local political groups do not want. Peacekeepers are, by their presence, targets for hostile groups, but are forced to remain

▲ **Indonesian peacekeepers**
Indonesian Army soldiers board an aircraft at Mombasa, Kenya, to take a flight to Elizabethville, Congo, as part of United Nations peacekeeping operations, 1960. They are armed with M3 submachine guns with flash hider attachments.

▲ **Taking cover**
A wounded British soldier mans a L4 Bren light machine gun on the Ulster/Republic of Ireland border during a patrol, 1977.

within the rules of engagement. These may prevent them from taking pre-emptive action to protect themselves, or force them to remain inactive while snipers fire over their positions at the innocents they are supposed to be protecting.

Combating terrorism

There are philosophical questions about the status of insurgents and guerrillas, i.e., whether they are criminals or enemy combatants, and the situation is often little clearer with terrorists. Any armed group that uses fear to obtain its political, religious or social ends can legitimately be labelled a terrorist organization. Terrorists are criminals under law, but can also be subject to military action. For example, in the situation where a terrorist training camp or weapons cache is identified, it might be raided by law enforcement personnel, or military means might be used to eliminate it.

The latter is more likely if the facility is overseas and beyond the reach of domestic law enforcement agencies. For the most part, domestic counter-terrorism work is the function of specially trained paramilitary law enforcement agencies. These units are equipped with military hardware and very highly trained, but are part of the civilian law enforcement

process. They are not optimized to fight foreign troops but to deal with relatively small terrorist groups or heavily armed criminals. Thus the fight against terrorism involves both military and law enforcement assets.

Urban concerns

Counter-terrorism units and law enforcement agencies generally operate in the urban environment, where innocent people may be close by. Precision is extremely important in this context, and for this reason semi-automatic weapons are often favoured over fully-automatic ones. Combat, if it occurs, is generally at short range and often inside buildings. Even sniping is rarely conducted at ranges greater than 100–200 metres (300–600 feet). One key consideration is over-penetration; law enforcement officers cannot afford to have a shot pass through the target and injure someone else, or a missed shot go through a wall and hit an innocent bystander.

Against these concerns must be balanced the need for a quick 'stop' of the target. Officers are often outnumbered and may have to shoot in order to prevent a hostile from endangering civilians. Lethality is less of a consideration than the ability to immediately disable a criminal or terrorist.

Northern Ireland: British forces
1968–98

The 'Troubles' in Northern Ireland involved several paramilitary organizations as well as the Royal Ulster Constabulary and the British Army.

THE POLITICAL SITUATION in Northern Ireland has always been complex, with Catholic/Protestant religious divides usually but not always paralleling political beliefs. The question of whether Northern Ireland should remain part of the United Kingdom or join Eire provided motivation for some groups involved in the conflict, but others had a different agenda only loosely connected with the political fate of the region.

Opinions differ as to when the Troubles began. There has always been some level of political agitation and sectarian violence in Northern Ireland due to the region's history. However, in the mid 1960s a move towards increased violence began. In August 1969, British troops were deployed to Northern Ireland to assist the civil authorities in maintaining order. This move was prompted by

severe rioting which had caused several deaths. The army, however, was unable to prevent an escalation of violence, and the next few years were very difficult for the people of Belfast in particular.

Several paramilitary organizations emerged before or during the Troubles. Loyalist groups such as the Ulster Volunteer Force (UVF) targeted the Catholic community while the Irish Republican Army (IRA) attacked Protestants and the British Army. Both, of course, claimed only to be protecting their own people from aggression. The IRA fragmented in 1969 into the Official IRA, which was primarily concerned with political activity, and the Provisional IRA, which was committed to direct action. Like other paramilitaries in Northern Ireland, the IRA was declared an illegal organization by the government, but was not recognized as a hostile military force. Therefore, the British Army was officially aiding the civil power against criminal groups composed of British citizens. Its powers were limited to supporting the police rather than fighting a war against the IRA.

Peacekeeping role

For three decades British Army units rotated through Northern Ireland, deploying to Belfast and the surrounding area. Troops manned checkpoints and patrolled the streets, supported police operations and worked as peacekeepers rather than combat troops. Some major operations were mounted. In 1972, large areas of Belfast and Derry were barricaded by local people to prevent road access, and had become 'no-go areas' for the authorities. At the end of July, the army mounted Operation *Motorman*, sending thousands of troops into the no-go areas, along with armoured engineering vehicles to dismantle the barricades. Such overwhelming force was used that the IRA did not try to resist the operation.

Some British Army bases were in a state of virtual siege at times. Resupply by helicopter was the only way that some areas could be manned, due to the number of roadside bombs, ambushes or sniper

▲ **Counter-sniper action**
Armed with an SLR fitted with a sniper scope, a British soldier watches out for enemy activity somewhere in Belfast, 1978.

Specifications

Country of Origin: United Kingdom

Date: 1956

Calibre: 9mm (.35in) Parabellum

Operation: Blowback

Weight: 2.7kg (5.9lb) empty

Overall Length: 686mm (27in) stock extended;
481mm (18.9in) stock folded

Barrel Length: 196mm (7.7in)

Muzzle Velocity: 395m/sec (1295ft/sec)

Feed/Magazine: 34-round detachable box
magazine

Range: 200m (656ft)

▲ Sterling L2A3

British Army / Royal Engineers, Derry, July 1972

The A3 variant of the Sterling submachine gun was adopted by the British Army in
1956. It was the last Sterling model to go into general service.

▲ Heckler & Koch HK53

British Army / 14 Intelligence Company, Northern Ireland October, 1979

The HK 53 was favoured by SAS intelligence operatives for its increased firepower
compared to a conventional 9mm submachine gun.

Specifications

Country of Origin: Germany

Date: 1975

Calibre: 5.56mm (.219in) NATO

Operation: Blowback

Weight: 2.54kg (5.6lb)

Overall Length: 680mm (26.8in)

Barrel Length: 225mm (8.85in)

Muzzle Velocity: 400m/sec (1312ft/sec)

Feed/Magazine: 25- or 30-round detachable box
magazine

Range: 400m (1312ft)

attacks on ground convoys. Parts of Country Antrim were known as 'Bandit Country' by British troops due to the level of support for the IRA there. Operations in this area were very hazardous.

SLR in action

The L1A1 self-loading rifle (SLR) was not ideally suited to operations in a urban environment. Long and heavy, it was designed for engagements at a considerable distance rather than quick movement through urban terrain. However, it did offer good stopping power on a hit. In the rural environment, or when operating from a 'hide' created in a building, the accuracy of the L1A1 made it highly effective. With it, any soldier could disable a vehicle in use by paramilitary gunmen and could engage and suppress a distant sniper who might be immune to return fire from smaller-calibre weapons. This was particularly useful when on patrol in rural areas controlled by the paramilitaries.

Special forces role

British special forces personnel were deployed to Northern Ireland at various times, operating against the paramilitaries in a covert manner. For the most part their duties were intelligence-gathering and surveillance, though they undertook a range of other missions. Special forces personnel made a number of arrests of IRA suspects, approaching the target in a covert manner and striking swiftly, or hunting enemy personnel in the countryside. They were also instrumental in defending Loughgall police station in 1987. Having obtained information that the IRA intended to attack the station, a detachment of the Special Air Service (SAS) troopers laid an ambush. A

group of IRA personnel, using a stolen digger to carry a large bomb, were ambushed whilst approaching the police station. Eight IRA members were killed.

Usually, clashes between the paramilitaries and the army were relatively small-scale affairs. British units learned to make highly effective use of cover whilst on patrol, and evolved excellent urban counter-sniper techniques. The goal was always to arrest anyone attacking the police, army or civilians, but troops were permitted to open fire when necessary. The army took a steady stream of casualties over the years, but was able to keep the situation in Northern Ireland under control while a political solution was sought.

Specifications

Country of Origin: United Kingdom
Date: 1958
Calibre: 7.62mm (.3in) NATO
Operation: Gas, self-loading
Weight: 4.31kg (9.5lb)
Overall Length: 1090mm (43in)

Barrel Length: 535mm (21.1in)
Muzzle Velocity: 853m/sec (2800ft/sec)
Feed/Magazine: 20-round detachable box magazine
Range: 800m (2625ft) +

▲ **L1A1 self-loading rifle**
British Army / 2nd Battalion, The Parachute Regiment, Belfast, September 1979
Its powerful round could be a two-edged sword; on the one hand it permitted troops to tackle a sniper hiding behind a typical brick wall, but equally it posed a significant hazard to anyone within a large radius on a ricochet or missed shot.

Specifications

Country of Origin: United Kingdom
Date: 1970
Calibre: 7.62mm (.3in) NATO
Operation: Bolt action
Weight: 4.42kg (9.7lb)
Overall Length: 1180mm (46.4in)

Barrel Length: 700mm (27in)
Muzzle Velocity: 744m/sec (2441ft/sec)
Feed/Magazine: 10-round detachable box magazine
Range: 500m (1640ft)

▲ **Enfield Enforcer**
Royal Ulster Constabulary, Belfast, October 1986
The Enforcer was developed for law-enforcement use from the L42A1 sniper rifle, itself derived from the Lee-Enfield Mk 3.

Irish Republican Army (IRA)

1968–PRESENT

The term 'IRA' is most commonly associated with the Provisional IRA, but there have in fact been several organizations using the same name.

THE IRISH REPUBLICAN ARMY (IRA) was formed in the early twentieth century, passing through several incarnations before splitting in 1969 into the Official IRA (OIRA) and the Provisional IRA (PIRA). The latter conducted an armed struggle against the Royal Ulster Constabulary (RUC), British Army and Loyalist paramilitaries and is commonly known as 'The IRA'. Political agreements ended the armed struggle, though some splinter groups of the PIRA still continue to advocate violence and claim the IRA name as their own.

From 1969 until the conflict was declared to be over in 2005, the PIRA carried out a mostly urban guerrilla campaign, intermixed with acts of terrorism. The campaign was largely conducted in Northern Ireland, but attacks were made on the British mainland. Bombs were a favoured weapon, and were used with some sophistication. For example, at times a second bomb would be planted near a suitable point for a command post. When the British Army arrived to deal with the first bomb, their deployment might make the command team susceptible to attack with the second device.

Direct action was also taken against police and army patrols and bases, including mortar and sniper attacks. The weapons used in these attacks were initially of World War II vintage, though some more modern equipment was available. Libya supplied significant quantities of arms at the end of the 1970s and early 1980s, including numbers of RPG-7 launchers and AK-47 assault rifles.

The IRA also obtained weapons from various other sources, including Browning pistols, Heckler & Koch rifles, AR-18 Armalite and M16 automatic rifles from North America. Some were stolen from the military and police, some bought on the black market and secretly shipped into the country, often through the Republic of Ireland. Many of these were basic infantry weapons, but more advanced equipment was also available. Rumours that the IRA had obtained one or more US-made Barrett M82 anti-materiel rifles caused grave concern among the security forces.

Small arms were used to attack the security services of course, but were also used to control and/or intimidate the local population.

▲ **Armalite AR-18**

Provisional IRA / Belfast Brigade, Belfast, August 1980

Essentially an upgraded AR-15, the AR-18 was not adopted for military service but was obtained in quantity by the IRA, with whom it became closely associated.

Specifications

Country of Origin: United States

Date: 1966

Calibre: 5.56mm (.219in) M109

Operation: Gas

Weight: 3.04kg (6.7lb)

Overall Length: 965mm (38in)

Barrel Length: 463mm (18.25in)

Muzzle Velocity: 990m/sec (2530ft/sec)

Feed/Magazine: 20-round detachable box
    magazine

Range: 500m (1640ft) +

▶ Browning High Power

Provisional IRA / Belfast Brigade, Belfast, January 1970

The Browning High-Power was produced in vast numbers for the British Army and became readily available on the black market after World War II.

Specifications

Country of Origin: Belgium/United States

Date: 1935

Calibre: 9mm (.35in) Parabellum

Operation: Short recoil

Weight: .99kg (2.19lb)

Overall Length: 197mm (7.75in)

Barrel Length: 118mm (4.65in)

Muzzle Velocity: 335m/sec (1100ft/sec)

Feed/Magazine: 13-round detachable box
 magazine

Range: 30m (98ft)

▲ RPG-7D

Provisional IRA / Belfast Brigade, Belfast, June 1997

RPG-7s supplied by Libya were used to attack Army and Royal Ulster Constabulary armoured vehicles. Not all such attacks were successful.

Specifications

Country of Origin: USSR

Date: 1961

Calibre: 40mm (1.57in)

Operation: Rocket motor

Weight: 7kg (15lb)

Overall Length: 950mm (37.4in)

Muzzle Velocity: 115m/sec (377ft/sec)

Feed/Magazine: Single-shot, muzzle-loaded

Range: c.920m (3018ft)

International peacekeeping
1980–PRESENT

Peacekeeping forces have been deployed by the United Nations more than 60 times since World War II. There have also been numerous non-UN peacekeeping operations.

PEACEKEEPING IS A RATHER DIFFERENT prospect to warfighting, though troops may find themselves in a deadly combat situation at any time. In many ways, peacekeeping can be more stressful for the personnel involved than open warfare. Peacekeeping operations are invariably of lengthy duration, and personnel are expected to deal with a range of challenges and threats on a constant basis. Peacekeepers are also forced to remain within strict rules of engagement which may prevent them from taking combat actions that their instincts tell them are right.

Peacekeepers are often forced to confront the aftermath of conflict and the human suffering that results from it. They may at times find themselves trying to support a peace process that none of the warring factions seems to want, and may be responsible for the lives of aid workers or innocent non-combatants as well as their own safety. This is a difficult enough prospect at the best of times, but in an environment where it is hard to tell hostiles from innocents it can be a virtually impossible task.

Showing restraint

Peacekeeping forces are supposedly not expected to have to fight. Their role is to support the move towards a lasting peace by verifying compliance with treaties and other agreements, by observing the fairness of elections, and by providing an 'armed presence' to deter interference with aid work or reconstruction. However, even if the political leadership and the majority of members of the opposing groups genuinely want peace, there will usually be some who want to keep fighting and who see the peacekeepers as legitimate targets.

Peacekeeping, correctly defined, takes place after all parties have decided that they want or are willing to accept an end to the conflict. Peacekeepers are thus deployed with mutual consent of combatants. Operations where peace must be imposed upon one or more of the combatants might more properly be defined as 'peace enforcement'. Yet these activities generally fall under the popular conception of peacekeeping.

Most peacekeeping operations are undertaken after a UN resolution, and frequently under the direct control of the UN itself. The personnel involved are contributed by national forces, however; the UN has no armed forces of its own. It has been suggested that a UN army could and perhaps should be raised, but so far this idea has not been implemented.

Operating under UN control, and alongside forces contributed by other nations, can be a serious challenge. Equipment may not be interoperable; ammunition calibres vary and troops may not even speak the same language. Trust and good joint working practices must also be built during the deployment and until they are, efficiency suffers. Efficiency is also a problem due to the way the UN operates. A consensus is needed in order to make many decisions, and this can take time. Peacekeeping operations can thus be cumbersome and slow to react to local conditions.

Somalia

Some peacekeeping operations have been notable successes, although often only after a lengthy period. Others, such as peacekeeping efforts in Somalia, have influenced the situation but not resolved it. The Somali Civil War, which began in 1991, has seen various attempts to intervene under UN and non-UN command, but conflict continues. Intervention in Somalia resulted in the origin of the term 'Mogadishu Line', named for the capital of Somalia. The Mogadishu Line is the point where peacekeeping ends and troops are instead involved in open conflict.

◀ MAB PA-15

Finnish Contingent / EUFOR Althea, Bosnia, December 2004

The French-developed MAB-PA-15 was not adopted by the French armed forces, but was taken up by the Finnish Army and some police forces.

Specifications	
Country of Origin: France	Barrel Length: 114mm (4.5in)
Date: 1975	Muzzle Velocity: 330m/sec (1100ft/sec)
Calibre: 9mm (.35in) Parabellum	Feed/Magazine: 15-round detachable box
Operation: Delayed blowback	magazine
Weight: 1.07kg (2.36lb)	Range: 40m (131ft)
Overall Length: 203mm (8in)	

UN peacekeepers were deployed to Somalia in 1992 mainly to support humanitarian relief operations, but became involved in combat against various local factions. Intense fighting in Mogadishu and casualties elsewhere caused the UN to withdraw its peacekeeping forces. There was, in truth, no peace to keep in Somalia at that time. The conflict, with all its associated suffering and damage to the stability of the region, went on unimpeded.

Later interventions in Somalia included strikes by US forces against some factions, but this was connected with efforts against the al-Qaeda terrorist organization and was not a peacekeeping measure. An African Union force deployed to Somalia in 2008 in support of a new coalition government's attempts to create peace and stability. This measure met with fierce opposition from some factions in the civil war, who saw the peacekeepers as intruders in their homeland.

Many peacekeeping troops come from developing nations rather than the world's major powers. The reason is not least due to the fact that the UN pays a subsidy for troops deployed as peacekeepers, which helps less-developed nations support their military establishment and allows their forces to gain operational experience.

Specifications

Country of Origin: West Germany	Barrel Length: 450mm (17.71in)
Date: 1959	Muzzle Velocity: 800m/sec (2625ft/sec)
Calibre: 7.62mm (.3in) NATO	Feed/Magazine: 20-round detachable box
Operation: Delayed blowback	magazine
Weight: 4.4kg (9.7lb)	Range: 500m (1640ft) +
Overall Length: 1025mm (40.35in)	

▲ **Heckler & Koch G3**

RUF Insurgents, Sierra Leone, July 2000

The HK G3 has been widely exported, in several variants. The G3SG/1 'sharpshooter' version is essentially the same weapon with a scope and a modified stock.

▲ **Heckler & Koch G41**

German Special Forces, Counter-terrorism Operations, post-1987

The G41 was to have replaced the G3 in German Army service, but proved too expensive. A few examples found their way into the hands of special forces units. Others appeared on the open market.

Specifications

Country of Origin: West Germany	Barrel Length: 450mm (17.7in)
Date: 1987	Muzzle Velocity: 920m/sec (3018ft/sec) SS109
Calibre: 5.56mm (.219in) NATO	cartridge; 950m/sec (3117ft/sec) M193
Operation: Roller-delayed blowback	cartridge
Weight: 4.1kg (9.04lb)	Feed/Magazine: Various STANAG magazines
Overall Length: 997mm (39.3in)	Range: 100–400m (328–1312ft)

The equipment requirements for peacekeeping are different to warfighting, to some extent. Peacekeepers generally only need personal small arms and light support weapons as they are unlikely to be engaged by major enemy forces. Such equipment is inexpensive, and in many cases outdated weapons will suffice. A peacekeeping force needs patience, training and diligence more than state-of-the-art military technology, and these human factors can be supplied by any nation.

Most of the time peacekeepers are policemen, security guards, observers and advisors. Their weapons are a deterrent rather than their main asset. However, when local factions turn on the peacekeepers, the possession of effective weapons and the training to use them becomes essential to survival.

▲ FAMAS F1

French Army / 8th Marine Infantry Parachute Regiment, 'The Red Line', Chad, January 1984

The FAMAS F1 was adopted in 1978 by the French Army. It suffered from a number of defects and was followed by the improved G1 version.

Specifications

Country of Origin: France	Overall Length: 757mm (29.8in)
Date: 1978	Barrel Length: 488mm (19.2in)
Calibre: 5.56mm (.219in) NATO	Muzzle Velocity: 960m/sec (3100ft/sec)
Operation: Gas	Feed/Magazine: 25-round box magazine
Weight: 3.61kg (7.96lb)	Range: 300m (984ft)

Specifications

Country of Origin: Austria	Barrel Length: 508mm (20in)
Date: 1980	Muzzle Velocity: 970m/sec (3182ft/sec)
Calibre: 9mm (.35in) Parabellum,	Feed/Magazine: 25-, 32-round (9mm/.35in) or
5.56mm (.219in) NATO	30-, 42-round (5.56mm/.219in) detachable
Operation: Gas, rotating bolt	box magazine
Weight: 3.6kg (7.9lb)	Range: 2700m (8858ft)
Overall Length: 790mm (31.1in)	

▲ Steyr-Mannlicher AUG

Austrian Contingent / EUFOR Althea, Bosnia, January 2010

The AUG uses a two-stage trigger to select semi-automatic or full-automatic fire. Some models have a blocking projection that prevents the trigger from being moved far enough for full-automatic operation when in position.

Heckler & Koch support weapons
1960s–Present

Heckler & Koch created a family of closely related support weapons capable of meeting the needs of law enforcement, counter-terrorist units or military formations.

GENERAL-PURPOSE MACHINE GUNS (GPMGs) generally use a fairly heavy rifle calibre round; typically 7.62mm (0.3in). They are usually belt-fed, firing from an open bolt. This means that the bolt starts the firing cycle in the rear position, running forward to chamber a round before firing takes place. The open-bolt system reduces accuracy somewhat, but GPMGs are not precision weapons. They are intended to put a lot of rounds into a general area. Operating from an open bolt improves cooling, which is an asset during sustained fire

GPMGs are heavy and ammunition belts are cumbersome. Lighter automatic weapons, fed from a box or drum and firing an intermediate assault rifle cartridge, are more mobile and thus easily integrated into a rifle squad. Using a light support weapon derived from an assault rifle has the additional advantages that ammunition can be shared and troops can be quickly trained to operate and maintain a similar weapon to the standard service rifle.

In the early 1960s, Heckler & Koch began producing a light support weapon derived from the G3 rifle. Designated the HK21, this weapon was somewhere between the light support and GPMG categories. The gun was belt-fed, firing 7.62x51mm ammunition, but this was fed from underneath, like a rifle, rather than from the side in more typical machine-gun style. The HK21 also fired from a closed bolt, meaning that the bolt began the firing cycle locked in the forward position. This improved accuracy but reduced sustained-fire capability due to greater heating.

The HK21's unusual feed system enabled it to be fitted with a magazine adapter, converting it from belt to magazine feed. It therefore allowed the use of rifle magazines, turning the weapon into a heavy rifle. Large-capacity drum magazines were also produced, giving an infantry squad effective fire support

▶ **H&K stalwart**
US Navy SEALs have employed the highly effective Heckler & Koch MP5 submachine gun on operations. The weapon is also used by FBI Hostage Rescue Teams, the British SAS, and dozens of other countries around the world.

capability without impairing the mobility of the soldiers using the weapon.

From this weapon, a range of variants appeared. A numerical system was used to describe them, giving rise to model numbers. The first digit indicated the weapon's type or intended use, which was largely dictated by feed mechanism. The HK21's '2' indicated belt feed and an intended role as a GPMG. A '1' indicated a magazine-fed light machine gun. The second digit was used to indicate calibre, with a '1' indicating 7.62x51mm NATO and a '3' indicating 5.56x45mm NATO.

A few examples were produced in 7.62x39mm Soviet calibre, which was designated by a '2'. Thus an H&K22 would be a belt-fed GPMG chambered for 7.62mm Soviet. However, this chambering was not produced in significant numbers.

The designation system is confused by the fact that conversion from belt to magazine feed is a simple matter of using an adapter, and similarly most weapons in the family can be converted from one calibre to another by changing the barrel. All recent models have a quick-change barrel, to facilitate sustained fire, so in theory a member of this weapon

▲ Heckler & Koch HK11

Hellenic Army (Land Forces of Greece), 1980

The 7.62mm (.3in) HK11 is basically an assault rifle with a bipod. It is instantly familiar to anyone trained on the G3 assault rifle.

Specifications

Country of Origin: West Germany	Barrel Length: 450mm (17.72in)
Date: 1970	Muzzle Velocity: 800m/sec (2625ft/sec)
Calibre: 7.62mm (.3in) NATO	Feed/Magazine: 20-round detachable box or 80-
Operation: Delayed blowback, selective fire	round drum magazine
Weight: 8.15kg (17.97lb)	Range: 1000m (3280ft) +
Overall Length: 1030mm (40.55in)	

▲ Heckler & Koch HK13

Unknown

The HK13 is accurate enough to be used for precision fire, using semi-automatic or three-round burst mode. This is attractive to law-enforcement or counter-terrorism units.

Specifications

Country of Origin: West Germany	Overall Length: 1030mm (40.55in)
Date: 1972	Barrel Length: 450mm (17.72in)
Calibre: 5.56mm (.219in) NATO	Muzzle Velocity: 925m/sec (3035ft/sec)
Operation: Roller-locked delayed blowback,	Feed/Magazine: 20- or 30-round detachable box
air-cooled	magazine or belt-fed
Weight: 8kg (17.64lb)	Range: 1000m (3280ft) +

family can be converted to any other designation in a matter of moments.

In practice, they are all the same weapon, built around the same delayed-blowback action, and the designation is simply a way of determining the configuration of the weapon. Some models also have an 'E' designation, which indicates an export model with a longer receiver. The accuracy and lightness of these weapons, and the three-round burst capability

of later examples, make them popular with law enforcement and special operations units, as well as the regular armed forces of many nations. The optional vertical foregrip facilitates 'assault' firing and, combined with a large-capacity drum magazine, gives the individual soldier high firepower without weighing all that much more than a standard rifle.

▲ HK21

Royal Malaysia Police (RMP), Pasukan Gerakan Khas (Counter-terrorism Police Squad), 2000

The light machine gun member of the family, the HK21 can carry the belt in a metal container, which fixes to the feed mechanism. It can also take loose belts.

Specifications

Country of Origin: West Germany	Overall Length: 1021mm (40.2in)
Date: 1970	Barrel Length: 450mm (17.72in)
Calibre: 7.62mm (.3in) NATO	Muzzle Velocity: 800m/sec (2625ft/sec)
Operation: Delayed blowback	Feed/Magazine: Belt-fed
Weight: 7.92kg (17.46lb)	Range: 2000m (6560ft)

▲ HK23

Turkish Gendarmerie, 2005

Chambered for 7.62mm (.3in) ammunition, the HK23 is at the 'light' end of the machine-gun spectrum, in terms both of weight and sustained-fire capability. The trade-off between mobility and firepower is always a difficult one.

Specifications

Country of Origin: West Germany	Barrel Length: 450mm (17.71in)
Date: 1981	Muzzle Velocity: 925m/sec (3035ft/sec)
Calibre: 5.56mm (.219in) NATO	Feed/Magazine: 20- or 30-round box magazine,
Operation: Delayed blowback	100-round drum magazine or 50- or
Weight: 8.7kg (19.18lb) on bipod	100-round belt
Overall Length: 1030mm (40.5in)	Range: 1000m (3280ft) +

Peacekeeping forces specialist weapons

1990–PRESENT

Precision rifles give peacekeeping and security forces the ability to deal with snipers and other threats without endangering non-combatants.

THE PRESENCE OF PEACEKEEPING FORCES often forces insurgent groups to adopt a different style of warfare. Rather than launching direct attacks, they might resort to long-range sniping or harassing fire. The planting of IEDs is also a common tactic. Both avoid the need to come into direct contact with peacekeepers, which might trigger a response in force that the insurgents cannot deal with.

Bombs and sniper bullets are also deniable, in that it is hard to prove who launched the attack. This suits the agenda of some groups, who wish to continue their war while still benefiting from overseas aid provided by the same nations that sent the peacekeepers. Proof that a group has broken a ceasefire or attacked either peacekeeping forces or the people they are protecting might result in aid being withdrawn or exclusion from negotiations aimed at ending the conflict.

Thus it is not uncommon for combatant groups to act friendly or at least avoid obvious hostile actions when close to overseas observers or peacekeepers, and instead try to strike from a distance when the opportunity presents itself. Peacekeepers are often bound by strict rules of engagement that permit only a very precise response against personnel undertaking immediately hostile actions.

Sniper rifles are among the few weapon systems that are precise enough to deal with these threats. Most sniping weapons use a fairly heavy cartridge such as 7.62x51mm or .308. By definition, any hostile who is close enough to shoot is within range of a sniper's return fire. His muzzle flash may give away his location, or thermal sensors might be used to find him, at which point an almost certainly more

▲ **PGM Hecate II**

French Commandement des Opérations Spéciales (COS), Afghanistan, 2001

In addition to sniping work, the Hecate II is used by Explosive Ordnance Disposal (EOD) personnel to deal with unexploded bombs and shells, using high-explosive ammunition.

Specifications

Country of Origin: France	Barrel Length: 700mm (27.6in)
Date: 1993	Muzzle Velocity: 825m/sec (2707ft/sec)
Calibre: 12.7mm (.5in) .50 BMG	Feed/Magazine: 7-round detachable box
Operation: Bolt action	magazine
Weight: 13.8kg (30.42lb)	Range: 2000m (6560ft) +
Overall Length: 1380mm (54.3in)	

skilled marksman will undertake to eliminate him. A single shot poses minimal hazard to non-combatants, although some hostiles will shoot from populous areas in the hope that the security forces will be reluctant to return fire.

Sniper weapons also give security forces the reach to eliminate bomb-planters who may be fairly distant, or enemy personnel on a rooftop separated by several streets. Even very strict rules of engagement will not be violated by a single shot aimed at a gunman who is firing his weapon or a hostile in the act of planting an IED. His heavily-armed but not actively hostile companions may not be legitimate targets under certain rules of engagement, which

would make engagement with less precise weapons or automatic fire problematic, but a sniper would still be able to take his shot with legal confidence.

Very heavy rifles such as 12.7mm (.5in) and even 14.5mm (.57in) weapons now available, have tremendously long effective ranges and are sometimes used to tackle difficult targets at extreme distance. Their massive projectiles give an excellent chance of a one-shot kill, which is necessary at such ranges. A second chance is unlikely once the target realizes he is under fire and moves or takes cover. However, these weapons are not really intended for personnel targets.

Extremely heavy rifles are termed 'anti-materiel rifles' and are descended from the anti-tank rifles of

▲ Heckler & Koch MSG90

US Hostage Rescue Team (HRT) / FBI, Quantico, Virginia, 2000

The MSG90 was produced as a cheaper alternative to the PSG-1 sniping rifle, which is favoured by many police forces. Although lighter, it is robust and extremely accurate.

Specifications

Country of Origin: Germany	Barrel Length: 600mm (23.6in)
Date: 1997	Muzzle Velocity: 815m/sec (2675ft/sec)
Calibre: 7.62mm (.3in) NATO	Feed/Magazine: 5- or 20-round detachable box
Operation: Roller-delayed blowback	magazine
Weight: 6.4kg (14.1lb)	Range: 600m (1968ft)
Overall Length: 1165mm (45.8in)	

Specifications

Country of Origin: West Germany	Overall Length: 905mm (35.63in)
Date: 1982	Barrel Length: 650mm (25.59in)
Calibre: 7.62mm (.3in) /.300 Winchester	Muzzle Velocity: c.800m/sec (2624ft/sec)
Magnum	Feed/Magazine: 6-round detachable box
Operation: Gas	magazine
Weight: 8.31kg (18.32lb)	Range: 1000m (3280ft) +

▲ Walther WA2000

German Bundespolizei (BPOL), 1986

One of the finest and, not coincidentally, expensive sniping weapons ever created, the WA2000 is better suited to law-enforcement use and security work than the rigours of general military use.

the early to mid-twentieth century. These weapons can use explosive or armour-piercing ammunition and are intended primarily for attacking equipment. A well-placed .50-calibre rifle round will disable a vehicle by smashing the engine block, enabling the occupants to be arrested or prevented from driving a truck bomb into their target.

Communications equipment is another key target for sniping attack. Disrupting communications can degrade an enemy force's capabilities far more than eliminating one member of the formation, though long-range sniping has also been used to take out a known insurgent or terrorist leader, which can have a similarly debilitating effect on enemy operations.

Heavy rifles are also used to deal with explosive devices, which may be too dangerous to approach. A heavy-calibre round can break up an explosive device and render it harmless, or may cause it to explode prematurely while personnel are kept at a safe distance. In order to make use of these weapons' long ranges, advanced sighting aids are employed. Even something as basic as a telescopic sight is a precision optical instrument, toughened to survive not only the rigours of field operations but also the recoil of the weapon it is mounted on, without going out of alignment. Low-light and thermal sights allow observation and shooting even in darkness, enabling the sniper to protect an area round the clock.

▲ **Gepard M6**

Indian Army special forces, 2000

The M6 fires an extremely powerful 14.5mm (.57in) round, whose accuracy is questionable beyond about 1000m (3280ft). It is highly effective as an anti-materiel weapon, but is not useful for very long-range sniping.

Specifications

Country of Origin: Hungary	Overall Length: 1125mm (44.29in)
Date: 1995	Barrel Length: 730mm (28.7in)
Calibre: 14.5mm (.57in)	Muzzle Velocity: 780m/sec (2559ft/sec)
Operation: Semi-automatic	Feed/Magazine: 5-round magazine
Weight: 11.4kg (25.1lb)	Range: 600–1000m (1968–3280ft)

Specifications

Country of Origin: Austria	Overall Length: 1370mm (54in)
Date: 2004	Barrel Length: 833mm (33in)
Calibre: 12.7mm (.5in) / .50 BMG	Muzzle Velocity: Not known
Operation: Bolt action	Feed/Magazine: Single shot
Weight: 12.4kg (28.5lb)	Range: 1500m (4921ft)

▲ **Steyr HS .50**

Iranian military, 2007

The HS .50 is a bolt-action, single-shot weapon available in .50 calibre and also in .460. The HS .50 M1 is an upgraded version fed from a five-round magazine.

Special operations handguns
1970–PRESENT

Handguns are normally carried as a backup weapon, but in some cases they can give special operations personnel an additional capability.

TRADITIONALLY, REGULAR INFANTRY personnel did not carry sidearms in addition to their individual weapons. Handguns might be issued for security duties, but for the most part they were carried by personnel whose main function was not direct combat with the enemy, and who thus did not need or could not carry a rifle. Handguns have traditionally been associated with officers, rear-echelon personnel, vehicle crews, specialists and possibly medics.

There has been a move in some quarters towards providing infantrymen with a backup weapon, but this is by no means prevalent. Even without considering the cost, troops are already carrying enough weight and the majority will never need a handgun. It is fairly rare for rifles or other longarms to jam or malfunction, and on most of those occasions a soldier can take cover and clear his weapon, or obtain a replacement from a casualty.

For special operations personnel, the situation is a little different. Handguns might at times be the only weapons they can carry, for example when concealed firearms are necessary. At other times, a handgun provides an emergency backup or close-range weapon that can be deployed quickly.

Close quarters

Handguns are easy to use at close quarters or in a confined space, but that is about the limit of their advantages. They lack stopping power, possibly requiring several shots to halt a charging hostile, and do not carry much ammunition. They are also inaccurate beyond a short distance, even if the user is a skilled marksman. However, for a small team involved in an intense fight, the ability to swap to another weapon when ammunition runs out or a longarm malfunctions can be vital.

A soldier who is able to draw his handgun is still in the fight even if his capabilities are limited. A soldier whose only weapon has been dropped or is otherwise out of commission deprives the team of a significant proportion of its firepower. Thus handguns are

▲ **S&W Model 39 'Hush Puppy'**
US Navy SEALs, 1980
Developed from the general-issue Model 39, the 'Hush Puppy' was used primarily to eliminate guard dogs. It featured a slide lock to reduce the mechanical noise of a shot.

Specifications

Country of Origin: United States
Date: 1967
Calibre: 9mm (.35in) Parabellum
Operation: Recoil, locked-breech
Weight: .96kg (2.1lb)
Overall Length: 323mm (12.75in)

Barrel Length: 101mm (3.9in)
Muzzle Velocity: 274m/sec (900ft/sec)
Feed/Magazine: 8-round detachable box
     magazine
Range: 30m (98ft)

routinely carried as backup weapons by special operations personnel. Most are fairly standard weapons, though usually of high quality. Some are more specialist pieces.

Handguns with either a fixed or detachable suppressor are a useful tool for eliminating sentries or guard dogs without alerting other hostiles, and have been a staple of special operations armament for decades. A suppressor does not completely eliminate the sound of a weapon, but it makes it likely that a gunshot will not be noticed or recognized over other background noise.

A range of high-end pistols have been produced for special operations use. In many cases, these firearms have emerged via input at the design stage by experienced users, whose expertise was valuable to a project not specifically aimed at creating a special forces weapon. Other projects have produced weapons that have no possible civilian use, and whose capabilities are unlikely to be required even by regular military personnel.

Examples of the pure special forces weapon are specialist underwater pistols. Both the USA and Russia produced successful underwater weapons for

▶ Heckler & Koch P11

German Navy / Kampfschwimmer ('Combat Swimmers'), Operation Enduring Freedom, 2002

Developed from an earlier underwater weapon, the P11 uses a five-shot barrel cluster. The less bulky Russian equivalent weapon has four barrels but is broadly similar.

Specifications

Country of Origin: West Germany	Barrel Length: N/A
Date: 1976	Muzzle Velocity: N/A
Calibre: 7.6mm (.3in)	Feed/Magazine: 5 rounds in disposable barrel
Operation: Electric-actuated	cluster
Weight: 1.2kg (2.7lb) loaded	Range: 30m (98ft) in air; 10–15m
Overall Length: 200mm (7.87in)	(33–49ft) underwater

▲ Heckler & Koch VP70

Portuguese National Republican Guard, 1990

The VP70 was the world's first polymer-framed handgun. It could deliver three-round bursts at 2200rpm, and could be fitted with a stock to create a carbine-like weapon.

Specifications

Country of Origin: West Germany	Overall Length: 204mm (8in)
Date: 1970	Barrel Length: 116mm (4.6in)
Calibre: 9mm (.35in) Parabellum	Muzzle Velocity: 350m/sec (1148ft/sec)
Operation: Blowback	Feed/Magazine: 18-round box magazine
Weight: .82kg (1.8lb)	Range: 40m (131ft)

use by special forces divers. These are not conventional handguns; they shoot a metal dart rather than a standard bullet, Firing is electrically initiated rather than using the mechanical initiation of a primer.

These weapons use a 'pepperbox' configuration – a cluster of pre-loaded barrels which, when empty, is swapped for another rather than being reloaded in the field. Underwater weapons of this sort are limited in their applications. They do work in air, but accurate range is very short and they are inefficient compared to a standard firearm. Thus they are issued only for specialist applications.

Special operations units tend to use the best weapons they can obtain – which is often a matter of personal preference. They are often permitted to choose their own weapons, either from an approved list or at will. Cost factors that would preclude a given weapon from being issued in the thousands to combat troops will not prevent an elite operator from carrying one.

The precise balance of size, magazine capacity, accuracy, calibre and other factors favoured by any one individual can vary somewhat, but certain weapons have emerged as favourites either due to a single essential feature or, more commonly, simply because they are very good handguns. Perhaps the most vital factor for any special operations weapon is reliability – with so few personnel in a team, weapons must function when they are needed. An otherwise excellent but temperamental weapon is simply not an option.

▶ Heckler & Koch SOCOM Mk23

Royal Malaysia Police (RMP), 2000

Developed to meet the needs of special forces personnel, the SOCOM Mk 23 is supremely rugged and reliable. Its subsonic .45-calibre round offers good stopping power and is suitable for use with a silencer.

Specifications

Country of Origin: Germany/United States	Barrell Length: 150mm (5.9in)
Date: 1996	Muzzel Velocity: 260m/sec (850ft/sec)
Calibre: 11.43mm (.45in)	Feed/Magazine: 12-round detachable box
Operation: Short recoil	magazine
Weight: 1.1kg (2.42lb)	Range: 25m (82.02ft)
Overall Length: 245mm (9.64in)	

◀ FN Five-Seven

French Groupe d'Intervention de la Gendarmerie Nationale (GIGN), 2005

Sharing a specially developed 5.7mm (.22in) round with the P90 carbine, the Five-Seven offers similar ballistic performance to a 9mm (.35in) but is more accurate due to the flatter trajectory of its high-velocity round.

Specifications

Country of Origin: Belgium	Barrell Length: 122mm (4.8in)
Date: 1998	Muzzel Velocity: 625m/sec (2050ft/sec)
Calibre: 5.7mm (.22in)	Feed/Magazine: 20-round detachable box
Operation: Delayed blowback	magazine
Weight: .744kg (1.64lb)	Range: 50m (164ft)
Overall Length: 208mm (8.18in)	

Law enforcement shotguns

1980–PRESENT

Shotguns have limited utility in a military combat situation, but are highly useful in security and law enforcement operations.

SHOTGUNS ARE SMOOTHBORE WEAPONS designed to deliver a group of projectiles rather than a single bullet. The size of the shot used can vary considerably; heavy buckshot offers good knockdown power whilst lighter birdshot increases the chance of a hit. For combat applications, heavy shot is generally used, though lighter shot may be substituted when needed, perhaps on occasions where causing superficial wounds and pain are preferable to disabling or killing hostiles.

Shot is not aerodynamic and loses velocity quickly due to friction from the air. Heavier shot remains dangerous out to a greater distance, but even so the lethal range of a shotgun is strictly limited. This is one reason why shotguns are not normally carried by combat personnel.

The spread of shot is controlled by the 'choke' of the weapon, which is either a fixed or variable narrowing of the bore. For combat applications a fairly tight choke is desirable, ensuring a close shot pattern. More dispersed shot patterns reduce the chances of 'stopping' the target (i.e. stopping him doing whatever it is he intends), which is often more important than lethality. Highly dispersed shot may also pose a hazard to bystanders.

Shot does not penetrate well. This limitation makes shotguns ineffective weapons for shooting through light cover, but at the same time it reduces the hazard to innocents who may be on the other side of a thin urban wall. This lack of penetration actually contributes to stopping power – a high-velocity bullet may tear right through a non-critical part of a human

▲ **Riot squad**
Armed with riot shields and shotguns, Venezuelan police clash with protesters in Caracas, November 2002.

being, taking much of its energy with it. A shotgun dumps all of its energy into the target. Light body armour might prevent the shot from entering the body, but the impact will still cause injury.

Shotguns are popular longarms for law enforcement and security personnel for these and other reasons. They are effective but do not cause much property damage or risk hitting a secondary target after overpenetration. Just as importantly, they are intimidating in a way that a handgun simply is not; criminals who might try their luck against a police officer armed with a semi-automatic pistol will often give up without a fight in the face of a shotgun.

In a military context, shotguns are sometimes used as counter-ambush weapons. They enable scouts or point men to return fire rapidly into a general area,

hopefully forcing ambushers to take cover. In this application, the weapon's lack of precision is an asset; the aim is to get as much lead moving towards suspected ambush positions as possible rather than hitting an individual target.

Shotguns can also be used to breach locked doors or deliver specialist ammunition. Some specialist rounds are gimmicky or of marginal use, such as mixed heavy and light shot loads. Others are extremely effective. These include solid ball or 'slug' rounds, which consist of a single extremely heavy projectile. Range is still limited, but a slug round has immense stopping power and will penetrate much of the cover found in the urban environment.

Other specialist ammunition includes gas delivery shells, which can penetrate a door before discharging

Specifications

Country of Origin: United States

Date: 1972

Gauge/Calibre: 12-gauge

Operation: Forced gas blowback, selective fire

Weight: 7.3kg (16.09lb)

Overall Length: 991mm (39.01in)

Barrel Length: 457mm (17.99in)

Muzzle Velocity: 350m/sec (1100 ft/sec)

Feed/Magazine: 7-round detachable box or 20-
    round drum magazine

Range: 100m (328ft)

▲ Atchisson assault shotgun
Unknown

The first full-automatic shotgun to be produced, the Atchisson assault shotgun was constructed largely from parts of other weapons. The trigger group came from a Browning M1918 and the forearm and stock from an M16.

▲ Franchi SPAS-12
Indonesian Komando Pasukan Katak (Kopaska), East Timor, 1990

The SPAS-12 can be set for pump-action or semi-automatic use, enabling the use of specialist ammunition between shots with standard shells. Indonesian security forces used the shotgun in fighting rebels in East Timor.

Specifications

Country of Origin: Italy

Date: 1979

Gauge/Calibre: 12-gauge

Operation: Pump action/gas

Weight: 4.2kg (9.26lb)

Overall Length: 930mm (36.6in)

Barrel Length: 460mm (18.11in)

Muzzle Velocity: Variable

Feed/Magazine: 7-round integral tubular
    magazine

Range: 100m (328ft)

tear gas into a room, and 'beanbag' ammunition, consisting of shot contained in a soft bag. Designed to stun and knock down a target whilst being far less lethal than penetrating shot, beanbag ammunition can be used to make an arrest under conditions where lethal force would otherwise be necessary.

By far the most common use of shotguns in law enforcement is for combat with standard ammunition, or to deter potential hostiles by the shotgun's visual threat. Most shotguns used by police departments and security personnel are simple, robust pump-action weapons. These have the advantage of an extremely rugged action and the ability to eject a misfired cartridge and chamber the

next by manually working the action. Some pump-action shotguns have a magazine cut-off, which allows a specialist shell to be loaded directly into the breech and fired, followed by normal shot if necessary.

The main drawbacks with pump-action shotguns are that they are slow to load and fire. Shells must be manually loaded into the internal magazine one at a time, and firing rate is slowed by the need to work the action between shots, a process that also takes the weapon off target. Thus many law enforcement agencies use semi-automatic shotguns for hostage-rescue and other high-threat units. A semi-automatic shotgun may still be slow to load, but once ready it

Specifications

Country of Origin: Italy	Barrel Length: 450mm (17.71in)
Date: 1985	Muzzle Velocity: Variable, depending on type of
Gauge/Calibre: 12-gauge	ammunition
Operation: Pump action / gas	Feed/Magazine: 10-round detachable box
Weight: 3.9kg (8.5lb) or 4.1kg (9lb)	magazine
Overall Length: 980mm (38.58in)	Range: 100m (328ft)

▲ Franchi SPAS-15

Serbian Land Forces / Special Brigade, 2008

Magazine feed makes the SPAS-15 much quicker to load than most combat shotguns. It can be switched to pump-action mode to make use of low-pressure less-lethal rounds.

▲ Benelli M4 Super 90

Royal Malaysian Customs (RMC), Straits of Melaka, 2005

The semi-automatic M4 is favoured by US Marine Corps security teams, and by numerous special police units such as SWAT and counter-terrorist teams throughout the world.

Specifications

Country of Origin: Italy	Barrel Length: 470mm (18.50in)
Date: 1998	Muzzle Velocity: Variable
Gauge/Calibre: 12-gauge	Feed/Magazine: 6-round under-barrel integral
Operation: Gas, semi-automatic	tubular magazine
Weight: 3.8kg (8.37lb)	Range: 100m (328ft)
Overall Length: 1010mm (39.76in)	

can deliver several rapid shots, which is usually enough to disable any opponent.

Where even more firepower is desirable, a number of full-automatic shotgun designs exist. These are military weapons for the most part, designed for base security or urban combat applications. Usually fed from a drum or box magazine, automatic shotguns are bulky and heavy but offer massive firepower at short range, albeit with ferocious recoil that can make these weapons difficult to handle for some personnel.

Like rifles and submachine guns, combat shotguns can often take a range of accessories and modifications to increase their utility. Advanced sights are common, along with laser pointers and tactical flashlights. Some weapons offer the choice of a fixed or folding stock, and in cases the latter can be configured as an elbow hook rather than a stock, facilitating one-handed shooting. However, firing any shotgun one-handed is inadvisable for all but the most substantial people.

Specifications

Country of Origin: South Korea	Barrel Length: 460mm (18.11in)
Date: 1992	Muzzle Velocity: 400m/sec (1300ft/sec)
Gauge/Calibre: 12-gauge	Feed/Magazine: 10-round box or 20-round drum
Operation: Gas	detachable magazine
Weight: 5.5kg (12.12lb)	Range: 200m (656ft)
Overall Length: 960mm (37.79in)	

▲ USAS-12

Korean National Police Agency (KNPA), 2000

Heavily influenced by the Atchisson assault shotgun, the USAS-12 achieved respectable sales to various military and security users in East Asia.

▲ AA-12

Unknown

The AA-12 can deliver normal shot or a range of specialist ammunition including high-explosive and fragmentation rounds designed to detonate in the air, showering the target with small projectiles.

Specifications

Country of Origin: United States	Barrel Length: 330mm (13in)
Date: 2005	Muzzle Velocity: 350m/sec (1100ft/sec)
Gauge/Calibre: 12-gauge	Feed/Magazine: 8-round detachable box or
Operation: Forced gas blowback, selective fire	20- or 32-round drum magazine
Weight: 5.7kg (12.6lb)	Range: 200m (656ft) FRAG-12 ammunition
Overall Length: 966mm (38in)	

Law enforcement and counter-terrorism
1980–PRESENT

A range of light automatic weapons are available to personnel who require a high-firepower weapon but cannot carry a full-sized rifle.

WITHIN THE MILITARY there are many personnel who may be expected to go into harm's way, but whose main duties do not include direct combat with the enemy. Yet vehicle crews, artillerymen, logistics personnel, specialists such as communications operators, combat pioneers and many officers still have need of an effective weapon.

Many of these personnel cannot make proper use of a rifle while encumbered by their equipment, or when within a vehicle. Others cannot carry the weight of a rifle and ammunition along with their specialist equipment. One solution to this problem is to issue a pistol, but handguns are at best marginally effective. A more potent weapon is desirable.

Submachine guns and carbines have at times been issued to these personnel, and are also used by security troops who are likely to operate in the confined spaces of a base or naval vessel. Engagement ranges for these troops tend to be short, making volume of fire more important than accurate range. Pistol-calibre ammunition is also lighter than an equivalent number of rifle rounds, reducing the load on a soldier.

In a law enforcement and security context, submachine guns or carbines are excellent weapons. Most law-enforcement personnel, even those operating in a paramilitary environment such as hostage rescue or counter-terrorism, tend to engage at short ranges where submachine guns are effective.

Bodyguards

Bodyguards also find light, high-firepower weapons useful. If the threat is fairly distant, the most effective response is likely to be to move the principal

Specifications

Country of Origin: United States	Barrel Length: 267mm (10.5in)
Date: late 1980s	Muzzle Velocity: 396m/sec (1300ft/sec)
Calibre: 9mm (.35in) Parabellum	Feed/Magazine: 32-round detachable box
Operation: Blowback, closed bolt	magazine
Weight: 2.6kg (5.75lb)	Range: 300m (984ft)
Overall Length: 730mm (28.9in)	

▲ **Colt 9mm SMG**
US Drug Enforcement Administration (DEA), 1995

Colt's 9mm submachine gun/carbine is rather bulky for a weapon of its calibre, but its weight does reduce felt recoil to almost nothing.

Specifications

Country of Origin: West Germany

Date: 1966

Calibre: 9mm (.35in)

Operation: Delayed blowback

Weight: 3.08kg (6.8lb)

Overall Length: 700mm (27.6in)

Barrel Length: 225mm (8.9in)

Muzzle Velocity: 285m/sec (935ft/sec)

Feed/Magazine: 15-, 30- or 32- round detachable
  box magazine

Range: 200m (656ft)

▲ Heckler & Koch MP5

German Bundespolizei (Federal Police), 1995

The H&K MP5 achieved huge market success, with a vast range of specialist variants produced. Accurate and compact, this personal defence weapon has proved very popular with special forces and law enforcement agencies around the world.

▲ FN P90

Belgian Special Forces Group (SFG), Gulf War, 1991

The FN P90 personal defence weapon uses the same cartridge as the Five-Seven Pistol. The gun has a novel loading system whereby rounds are carried in a clear plastic cartridge situated at a right-angle to the barrel. Ejection is via the hollow grip.

Specifications

Country of Origin: Belgium	Barrel Length: 263mm (7.75in)
Date: 1990	Muzzle Velocity: 850m/sec (2800ft/sec)
Calibre: 5.7mm (.22in) FN	Feed/Magazine: 50-round detachable box
Operation: Blowback	magazine
Weight: 2.8kg (6.17lb)	Range: 200m (656ft) +
Overall Length: 400mm (15.75in)	

quickly to cover or out of the threat zone. Shooting the attackers is only a priority if the threat is at close range. The ability to respond with overwhelming firepower is of paramount importance under such circumstances.

Thus for many years the submachine gun fulfilled an intermediate role between handguns and rifles. Submachine guns generally (but not always) use a pistol-calibre round but, possessing as they do a longer barrel than a handgun, have a greater effective range and higher accuracy. Various types of submachine guns have emerged over the years,

ranging from large, almost rifle-like weapons down to overgrown pistols.

Personal defence weapons

In recent years the term 'personal defence weapon', or PDW, has emerged. This name to some extent refers to a role rather than a specific type of weapon. Most PDWs are identifiable as submachine guns; they are light, pistol-calibre automatic weapons. However, a number of different approaches have been taken to the PDW concept. Some are extremely small, representing an attempt to cram submachine gun firepower into something little larger than a pistol. Others are definitely longarms, but again offer unusually high firepower for their size. This, more than anything else defines a PDW. It is a weapon intended for self-defence rather than full-scale combat, providing a heavy punch in a small package. Some PDWs use specially developed advanced ammunition, while others are chambered for existing calibres.

PDWs are in many ways ideal weapons for law enforcement personnel, as their small size makes them easy to manoeuvre inside buildings or vehicles. A short, light weapon can be brought on target quickly when moving through a cluttered area, and a high rate of fire enables hostiles to be quickly disabled before they can pose a threat to innocents or law enforcement personnel.

One approach to the PDW concept is demonstrated by the Colt 9mm (.35in) submachine gun. This is a version of the M4 carbine converted to 9mm calibre and is rather large for a submachine gun, being more of a 9mm carbine. However, it is

smaller and lighter than a rifle, yet can be used by anyone familiar with the M16 or M4 rifle with minimal conversion training. This weapon would be severely limited on the battlefield, but is well suited for security or emergency self-defence use. It is favoured by some law enforcement agencies, whose agents may have to face opposition armed with automatic weapons.

Weapons such as the FN P90 carbine are similarly sized but very different in approach. Using a 5.7mm (.22in) round in common with the Five-Seven pistol, the P90 was designed to pack as much firepower as possible into a small weapon. Its ammunition was designed to give superior performance against body armour to existing 9mm rounds, and is carried in a 50-round cassette. Although it was developed specifically as a PDW, most users of the P90 treat it as an offensive rather than defensive arm, issuing it as main armament rather than an emergency weapon for personnel less likely to engage in combat.

At the other end of the scale are weapons such as the Russian-made PP2000. This is a very small

▲ **Colt SMG**

Firing 9mm Parabellum rounds, the Colt submachine gun closely resembles the M16 assault rifle in shape and appearance. It has proved popular with special forces and law enforcement agencies.

weapon, not much larger than a typical pistol. It is chambered for standard 9mm ammunition, but also capable of using an armour-piercing round. Its intended users were those who might need more firepower than a handgun, but could not necessarily carry assault rifles or full-sized submachine guns.

Somewhere between these two extremes lie most typical PDWs. Some are versions of existing submachine guns, usually made as small as possible, while others are custom designed for the role. While certainly effective, these weapons face the same challenges that traditional submachine guns have

▲ Heckler & Koch MP7
Austrian EKO Cobra (Einsatzkommando Cobra), 2003

Like some other purpose-designed PDWs, the MP7 was built around custom ammunition, giving enhanced penetrative capabilities over standard submachine gun calibres.

Specifications

Country of Origin: Germany	Barrel Length: 180mm (7.1in)
Date: 2001	Muzzle Velocity: c.725m/sec (2379ft/sec)
Calibre: 4.6mm (.18in)	Feed/Magazine: 20-, 30-, 40-round detachable
Operation: Gas, short-stroke piston, rotating bolt	box magazine
Weight: 1.9kg (4.19lb) without magazine	Range: 200m (656ft)
Overall Length: 638mm (25.1in)	

Specifications

Country of Origin: Germany	Overall Length: 690mm (27.2in)
Date: 1999	Barrel Length: 200mm (7.9in)
Calibre: 11.4mm (.45in) / 45 ACP, 10.16mm	Muzzle Velocity: Not known
(.4in) .40 S&W, 9mm (.35in) Parabellum	Feed/Magazine: 25- or 30-round detachable box
Operation: Blowback, closed bolt	magazine
Weight: 2.3kg (5lb)	Range: 100m (328ft)

▲ Heckler & Koch UMP (Universal Machine Pistol)
US Customs and Border Protection, 2005

Aimed mainly at the law enforcement marketplace, the Universal Machine Pistol (UMP) was made available in a range of powerful calibres, including .45 ACP and .40, with a 9mm version following soon afterward.

since the invention of the assault rifle. With small, lightweight rifles available, the light automatic weapon niche has been squeezed, and many PDW designs do not offer sufficiently great advantages over a carbine version of an existing assault rifle.

Yet although the gap between handguns and assault rifles has shrunk, it does still exist. The larger submachine guns and carbine-type PDWs may face competition from weapons like the M4 carbine, but the smaller ones do seem to have a promising future.

A weapon that can be carried in a hip or shoulder holster but which can deliver automatic fire and perhaps even defeat body armour offers capabilities that no other weapon can deliver.

Thus while the larger PDWs have joined the assault rifle/submachine gun marketplace and may or may not prosper, it is likely that the smaller ones will find continued favour with law enforcement and special operations personnel, bodyguards, and possibly other non-infantry military personnel.

▶ Steyr TMP

Gruppo di Intervento Speciale, Italy, 2003

The Steyr Tactical Machine Pistol is primarily a defensive weapon. The foregrip helps reduce muzzle climb when delivering automatic fire. Both Austrian police and anti-terrorist units have adopted the TMP.

Specifications

Country of Origin: Austria	Barrel Length: 130mm (5.1in)
Date: 2000	Muzzle Velocity: 380m/sec (1247ft/sec)
Calibre: 9mm (.35in) Parabellum	Feed/Magazine: 15- or 30-round detachable box
Operation: Short recoil, rotating barrel	magazine
Weight: 1.3kg (2.9lb)	Range: 100m (328ft)
Overall Length: 282mm (11.1in)	

▲ CZW 438 M9

Unknown

The CZW 438 was originally chambered for 4.38x30mm ammunition. The M9 variant uses vastly more common 9x19mm rounds, but shares almost all components with the original weapon.

Specifications

Country of Origin: Czech Republic	Barrel Length: 220mm (8.66in)
Date: 2002	Muzzle Velocity: Not known
Calibre: 9mm (.35in) Parabellum	Feed/Magazine: 15- or 30-round detachable box
Operation: Lever-delayed blowback	magazine
Weight: 2.7kg (5.95lb)	Range: 200m (656ft)
Overall Length: 690mm (27.1in)	

The World's Assault Rifle: AK-47

MODEL	7.62mm AK-47 ASSAULT RIFLE	7.62mm AKM ASSAULT RIFLE
Calibre	7.62 x 39mm M43 rimless	7.62 x 39mm M43 rimless
Operation	Gas-operation	Gas-operation
Length	9870mm (32.25in)	878mm (34.56in)
Weight	4.3kg (9.4lb)	3.85kg (8.4lb)
Barrel	R415mm (16.33m), four grooves, right hand	415mm (16.33in), four grooves, right hand
Magazine	Detachable 30-round box magazine	Detachable 30-round box magazine
Rate of fire	775rpm	600rpm
Muzzle velocity	71 0mps (2329fps)	71 0mps (2329fps)
Maximum range	800m (2624.6ft)	1000m (3280ft)

MODEL	7.62mm AK-74 ASSAULT RIFLE	5.45mm AK-107 ASSAULT RIFLE
Calibre	5.45 x 39mm M74 rimless	5.45 x 39mm M74 rimless
Operation	Gas-operation	Gas-operation, counter-recoil system
Length	943mm (37.1 in)	695mm (27.3in)
Weight	3.4kg (7.54b)	3.6kg (7.2lb)
Barrel	415mm (16.33m), four grooves, right hand	415mm (16.33m), four grooves, right hand
Magazine	Detachable 30-round box magazine	Detachable 30-round box magazine
Rate of fire	600rpm	850-900rpm
Muzzle velocity	900mps (2952fps)	840mps (2755fps)
Maximum range	1000m (3280ft)	1000m (3280ft)

MODEL	AN-94 AKABAN	7.62mm RPK LIGHT MACHINE GUN
Calibre	5.45 x 39mm M74 rimless	7.62 x 39mm M43 rimless
Operation	Gas-operation	Gas-operation
Length	943mm (37.1 in) stock extended; 728mm (28.6in) stockfolded	1040mm (40.9in)
Weight	3.85kg (8.47lb)	5kg (11.02lb) with bipod
Barrel	405mm (15.9in), four grooves, right hand	590mm (23.22in), four grooves, right hand
Magazine	Detachable 30-round box magazine	Detachable 30- or 40-round box magazine, 75-round drum
Rate of fire	1800 and 600rpm variable	600rpm
Muzzle velocity	n/a	735mps (2411 fps)
Maximum range	n/a	1200m (3937ft)

MODEL	5.45mm RPK LIGHT MACHINE GUN	7.62mm SVD SNIPER RIFLE
Calibre	5.45 x 39mm M74 rimless	7.62 x 54R
Operation	Gas-operation	Gas-operation, semi-automatic
Length	1060mm (41.73in)	1220mm (48.03in)
Weight	5.64kg (12.431 b) with bipod	4.3kg (9.471b), empty with PSO-1 magazine
Barrel	590mm (23.22m), four grooves, right hand	545mm (21.4in), four grooves, right hand
Magazine	Detachable 30-, 40- or 45-round box magazine	Detachable 10-round box magazine
Rate of fire	850rpm	N/A
Muzzle velocity	925mps (3034fps)	830mps (2723fps)
Maximum range	1000m (3280ft)	1300m (4265ft)

MODEL	YUGOSLAVIAN 7.62mm MODEL 64 ASSAULT RIFLE	REPUBLIC OF SOUTH AFRICA 5.56mm VEKTOR R4
Calibre	5.45 x 39mm M74 rimless	5.45 x 45mm
Operation	Gas-operation	Gas-operation
Length	1040mm (40.9in)	1005mm (39.56in) butt extended; 740mm (29.13in) butt folded
Weight	3.9kg (8.5lb)	4.3kg (9.4lb) without magazine
Barrel	500mm (19.68m), four grooves, right hand	460mm (18.11 in), six grooves, right hand
Magazine	Detachable 30-round box magazine	Detachable 35-round box magazine
Rate of fire	775rpm	675rpm
Muzzle velocity	730mps (2395fps)	980mps (3215fps)
Maximum range	1000m (3280ft)	1000m (3280ft)

MODEL	CHINESE 7.62mm TYPE 56 ASSAULT RIFLE	FINNISH 7.62mm MODEL 62 VALMET ASSAULT RIFLE
Calibre	7.62 x 39mm M43 rimless	7.62 x 39mm M43 rimless
Operation	Gas-operation	Gas-operation
Length	870mm (34.25in)	915mm (36in)
Weight	4.45kg (9.81b)	4.0kg (8.8lb)
Barrel	415mm (16.33in), four grooves, right hand	420mm (16.53in), four grooves, right hand
Magazine	Detachable 30-round box magazine	Detachable 30-round box magazine
Rate of fire	775rpm	750rpm
Muzzle velocity	720mps (2362fps)	710mps(2329fps)
Maximum range	800m (2624ft)	1000m (3280ft)

MODEL	FINNISH 7.62mm MODEL 78 VALMET LIGHT MACHINE GUN	7.62mm AK-103 ASSAULT RIFLE
Calibre	7.62 x 51 mm NATO rimless, 7.62 x 39mm M43, 5.56 x 45mm NATO	7.62 x 39mm M43 rimless
Operation	Gas-operation	Gas-operation
Length	1060mm (4173in)	943mm (37.12in) butt extended; 700mm (27.5in) butt folded
Weight	4.7kg (10.361b)	3.4kg (7.4lb)
Barrel	550mm (21.65in), four grooves, right hand	415mm (16.33in), four grooves, right hand
Magazine	Detachable 15- or 30-round box magazine	Detachable 30-round box magazine
Rate of fire	750rpm	775rpm
Muzzle velocity	720mps (2362fps) for M43 round	715mps (2345fps)
Maximum range	1000m (3280ft)	1000m (3280ft)

MODEL	5.45mm AKSU-74 SUBMACHINE GUN	5.56mm GALIL ARM
Calibre	5.45 x 39mm M74 rimless	5.56 x 45mm rimless
Operation	Gas-operation	Gas-operation
Length	675mm (26.57in) butt extended; 420mm (16.53in) butt folded	979mm (38.5in) butt extended; 742mm (29.2in) butt folded
Weight	2.7kg (5.9lb)	4.35kg (9.5lb)
Barrel	200mm (7.8in), four grooves, right hand	460mm (18.11 in), six grooves, right hand
Magazine	Detachable 30-round box magazine	Detachable 12-, 25-, 35-, 50-round box magazine
Rate of fire	800rpm	650rpm
Muzzle velocity	735mps (2411 fps)	980mps (3215fps)
Maximum range	500m (1640ft)	1000m (3280ft)

MODEL	POLISH 5.56mm KA-90 TANTAL ASSAULT RIFLE	POLISH 5.56mm KA-91 ONYX SUBMACHINE GUN
Calibre	5.56 x 45mm rimless	5.56 x 45mm rimless
Operation	Gas-operation	Gas-operation
Length	943mm (37.12in) butt extended; 742mm (29.21 in) butt folded	720mm (28.34in) butt extended; 519mm (20.43in) butt folded
Weight	3.4kg (7.49lb)	2.9kg (6.3lb)
Barrel	423mm (16.65in), four grooves, right hand	207mm (8.14in), four grooves, right hand
Magazine	Detachable 30-round box magazine	Detachable 30-round box magazine
Rate of fire	700rpm	700rpm
Muzzle velocity	900mps (2952fps)	71 0mps (2329fps)
Maximum range	800m (2624ft)	400m (1312ft)

MODEL	HUNGARIAN 5.56mm NGM ASSAULT RIFLE	ROMANIAN S.45mm KA-90 AI-74 ASSAULT RIFLE
Calibre	5.56 x 45mm rimless	5.45 x 39mm M74
Operation	Gas-operation	Gas-operation
Length	979mm (38.54in) butt extended; 742mm (29.21 in) butt folded	940mm (37in)
Weight	4.35kg (9.5lb)	3.4kg (7.491b)
Barrel	460mm (18.11 in), six grooves, right hand	415mm (16.33in), four grooves, right hand
Magazine	Detachable 12-, 25-, 35- or 50-round box magazine	Detachable 30-round box magazine
Rate of fire	650rpm	700rpm
Muzzle velocity	980mps (3215fps)	880mps (2887fps)
Maximum range	800m (2624ft)	800m (2624ft)

Glossary

Bolt

The part of a firearm which usually contains the firing pin or striker and which closes the breech ready for firing.

Blowback

Operating system in which the bolt is not locked to the breech, thus it is consequently pushed back by breech pressure on firing and cycles the gun.

Breech

The rear of the gun barrel.

Breech-block

Another method of closing the breech which generally involves a substantial rectangular block rather than a cylindrical bolt.

Carbine

A shortened rifle for specific assault roles.

Chamber

The section at the end of the barrel which receives and seats the cartridge ready for firing.

Closed bolt

A mechanical system in which the bolt is closed up to the cartridge before the trigger is pulled. This allows greater stability through reducing the forward motion of parts on firing.

Delayed blowback

A delay mechanically imposed on a blowback system to allow pressures in the breech to drop to safe levels before breech opening.

Double action

Relates to pistols which can be fired both by cocking the hammer and then pulling the trigger, and by a single long pull on the trigger which performs both cocking and firing actions.

Gas operation

Operating system in which a gun is cycled by gas being bled off from the barrel and used against a piston or the bolt to drive the bolt backwards and cycle the gun for the next round.

GPMG

Abbreviation for General Purpose Machine Gun. A versatile light machine gun intended to perform a range of different roles.

HMG

Abbreviation for heavy machine gun.

LMG

Abbreviation for light machine gun.

Locking

Describes the various methods by which the bolt or breech block is locked behind the chamber ready for firing.

Long recoil

A method of recoil operation in which the barrel and bolt recoil for a length greater than that of the entire cartridge, during which extraction and loading are performed.

Muzzle brake

A muzzle attachment which diverts muzzle blast sideways and thus reduces overall recoil.

Open bolt

A mechanical system in which the bolt is kept at a distance from the cartridge before the trigger is pulled. This allows for better cooling of the weapon between shots.

Receiver

The body of the weapon which contains the gun's main operating parts.

Recoil
The rearward force generated by the explosive power of a projectile being fired.

Recoil operated
Operating system in which the gun is cycled by the recoil-propelled force of both barrel and bolt when the weapon is fired. Both components recoil together for a certain distance before the barrel stops and the bolt continues backwards to perform reloading and rechambering.

Self-loading
Operating system in which one pull of the trigger allows the gun to fires and reload in a single action.

Shaped charge
An anti-armour charge designed to concentrate the effect of an explosive warhead by focusing a cone of superheated gas on a critical point on the target.

Short recoil
A compressed version of recoil operation in which the barrel and bolt move back less than the length of the cartridge before the bolt detaches and continues backwards to perform reloading and rechambering.

SMG
Abbreviation for submachine gun.

Further Reading

Books:

Chant, Chris. *Small Arms.* Silverdale Books, 2003.

Dougherty, Martin J. *Small Arms: From the Civil War to the Present.* Barnes & Noble, 2005.

Dougherty, Martin J. *Small Arms Visual Encyclopedia.* Amber Books Ltd, 2011.

Philip, Craig. *The World's Great Small Arms.* Barnes & Noble, 2002.

Stronge, Charles. *Sniper in Action.* Amber Books Ltd, 2010.

Zaloga, Stephen J. and Leland S. Ness. *Red Army Handbook, 1939–1945.* Sutton Publishing Ltd, 1998.

Useful web sites:

http://www.bayonetstrength.150m.com/
Offers a detailed breakdown of unit organisation from battalion level and below for every major combatant nation in World War II. Also includes a section on small arms of the period.

http://www.historyofwar.org/index.html
A detailed, wide-ranging general guide to warfare, weapons and battles, with a comprehensive section on World War I and World War II.

Index

Page numbers in *italics* refer to illustrations and tables.